THE PUZZLE POST

PUZZLE FUN!

The Ultimate Brainbending Workout

ARCTURUS

1 MINUTE NUMBER CRUNCH

Beginner								Answer
75	x 2	– 72	÷ 3	+ 18	3/4 of this	x 4	÷ 11	

Intermediate								Answer
7	Cubed	+ 7	+ 10%	x 0.4	x 2	x 0.75	+ 169	

Advanced								Answer
784	9/14 of this	+ 7/18 of this	350% of this	– 1294	75% of this	8/3 of this	÷ 1/4	

Did You Know?:
Six planets in our solar system rotate in the same direction as the Sun (anticlockwise when viewed from above the Sun's north pole), but Venus and Uranus have retrograde rotation: in other words, they move in a clockwise direction.

HIGH-SPEED CROSSWORD

Across
1 Delay
4 Mel of baseball fame
7 "___ Maria"
8 Bank offering
9 In good shape
12 Scary snake
14 Solid ___ rock: 2 wds.
15 Otherwise
16 "Welcome Back, Kotter" star
18 Was sweet (on)
20 Oil of ___
21 Lennon's lady
22 "West Side Story" song
25 Exact revenge: 2 wds.
27 Like some country roads
29 "Scram!"
32 Miles per hour, e.g.
33 Prepared
35 Stick (to)
38 Each: 2 wds.
39 Even score
40 Unthankful person
42 "To ___ is human ..."
43 Coloring fluid
44 "Winnie-the-Pooh" baby
45 "Casablanca" pianist
46 2,000 lb.

Down
1 Texas city on the Rio Grande
2 Toyota model
3 Meets up: 2 wds.
4 Black gold
5 Arduous journey
6 "Gone With the Wind" plantation
9 Not doing well emotionally: 2 wds.
10 Bartender on "The Love Boat"
11 Roberts of "That '70s Show"
13 Golf peg
17 Small hole
19 Computer info
23 Guys
24 "... lived happily ___ after"
26 Robert ___: 2 wds.
27 Give a speech
28 Low point
30 "Same here!": 3 wds.
31 Use, as a computer: 2 wds.
34 Listening organ
36 Clears
37 Irish singing great
41 Beauty

CODEWORD CONUNDRUM

A B C D E F G H I J K L M
N O P Q R S T U V W X Y Z

Reference Box

1	2	3	4	5 P	6	7	8	9	10	11	12	13
14	15	16	17	18	19 E	20	21	22	23	24	25	26
					A							

DOUBLE FUN SUDOKU

TASTY TEASER

		6			3		1	
		9		6	4	5		
1	7	4				6	2	3
		3			5		7	
7			9		1			2
	4		6			8		
4	8	2				7	9	1
		7	2	8		3		
	9				5			

BRAIN BUSTER

		4	9					7
3		6					1	
	5		1			4	8	
	8			2				
2								4
			7			9		
	8	9		7		6		
	6				5		3	
1				6	7			

SPIDOKU

Each of the eight segments of the spider's web should be filled with a different number from 1 to 8, in such a way that every ring also contains a different number from 1 to 8.

HIGH-SPEED CROSSWORD

Across
1 "___, humbug!"
4 Narc's org.
7 "Mogambo" actress Gardner
8 Bobby of hockey fame
9 "Exodus" character
12 Singer Valens
14 Gen-___
15 "Goldberg Variations" composer
16 Nikon or Konica
18 Old anesthetic
20 Share a border with
21 Sandra ___ of "Gidget"
22 Every last thing: 2 wds.
25 Kind of newspaper
27 Halftime encouragement from the coach: 2 wds.
29 Football measurements: abbr.
32 Double-___ (kind of tournament, for short)
33 1950's Ford flop
35 Binds: 2 wds.
38 Grand Ole ___
39 "Yada, yada, yada"
40 Diet number
42 "Understand?"
43 Deception
44 Infomercials, e.g.
45 "Go on ..."
46 "Are we there ___?"

Down
1 ___ wire (stuff on a fence)
2 Fly a plane
3 Unfair article by a journalist: 2 wds.
4 "Stupid me!"
5 Clapton who sang "Layla"
6 Section
9 Product with sexy TV ads: 3 wds.
10 Show shown again on TV
11 Really mad
13 "Evita" role
17 When repeated, a fish
19 Country great McEntire
23 Every bit
24 Pepsi rival
26 24-hr. conveniences
27 "For ___ sake!"
28 A-list
30 Talk bad about
31 Most sneaky
34 Scooby-___ (cartoon dog)
36 The Bruins' sch.
37 Hurt
41 Was winning

WORDSEARCH WORKOUT

COUNTRIES OF THE WORLD

ANGOLA
CANADA
DENMARK
DJIBOUTI
GABON
IRELAND
ITALY
KIRIBATI
LATVIA
LITHUANIA
MACEDONIA
MONACO
NEPAL
NETHERLANDS
QATAR
SLOVAKIA
SYRIA
TUNISIA
VENEZUELA
WALES

DOUBLE FUN SUDOKU

TASTY TEASER

			5	6	9			
	5				1		3	
4	8		3		6	2	5	
8		3			9	1	2	
	5	6		2	3			
7	3	2		8	5		4	
	4	6	8			5	9	
1	3				8			
		2	7	6				

BRAIN BUSTER

	8	6		1	3			
1							6	
9		7		4		2		4
		2		4				
6							9	
	3		9					
5		9		3		1		4
2							5	
	4	9		5	8			

MATCHSTICK MAGIC

Move two matchsticks to make two squares.

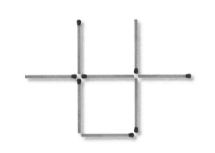

BRAIN TEASER

How many minutes before 12 noon is it if 72 minutes ago it was twice as many minutes past 9.00am?

? _____ ?

DOMINO PLACEMENT

A standard set of 28 dominoes has been laid out as shown. Can you draw in the edges of them all? The check-box is provided as an aid and the domino already placed will help.

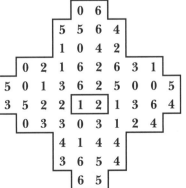

Did You Know?:

In a standard pack of playing cards, the king of diamonds, the king of clubs and the king of spades all have moustaches: the king of hearts has no moustache.

0-0	0-1	0-2	0-3	0-4	0-5	0-6

1-1	1-2	1-3	1-4	1-5	1-6	2-2
	✓					

2-3	2-4	2-5	2-6	3-3	3-4	3-5

3-6	4-4	4-5	4-6	5-5	5-6	6-6

CODEWORD CONUNDRUM

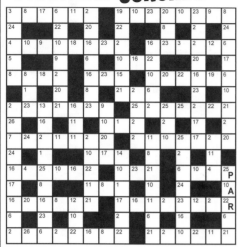

3	8	17	6		11	2		19	10	23	20	10	23	9	8
24			22			20		22				8		2	24
4	10	9	10	18	16	23	2		16	23	3	2	12	6	
5		9		6			10	16	22			20			17
8	18	2		16	23	15		10	20	22	16	19	6		
	1		20		8		21	10	6		23		10		
2	23	13	21	16	23		25	2	25	25	2		22	21	
26		16		11		10	1	2		2		17		2	
7	24	2	11	11	2	20		21	11	10	25	17	2	20	
24		1		10	17	14		8		2		11			
16	4	25	10	16	22		10	23	21		6	10	4	25 P	
17		8		11	8		1		10	24			10 A		
16	20	16	8	12	21		17	16	11	2	23	12	2	22 R	
6		23		10		2		16		16			6		
2	26	6	2	22	16	8	22		2	10	22	11	21		

A B C D E F G H I J K L M
N O P Q R S T U V W X Y Z

Reference Box

1	2	3	4	5	6	7	8	9	10 A	11	12	13
14	15	16	17	18	19	20	21	22 R	23	24	25 P	26

DOUBLE FUN SUDOKU

TASTY TEASER

	9		3	4			1	6
	3	5		6		9	7	
2				8				
9	7	2			4	3		
		6				1		
		3	9			4	8	7
			6					4
	5	4		1		7	2	
3	8			7	2		5	

BRAIN BUSTER

	3		4		8		1	
5			2		9			7
		4				9		
	8	7	3		6	5	2	
	9	6	1		2	7	4	
		3				8		
1			9		3			2
	5		6		4		7	

PYRAMID PLUS

Every brick in this pyramid contains a number which is the sum of the two numbers below it, so that F=A+B, etc.
Just work out the missing numbers!

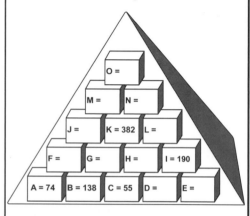

O =

M =   N =

J =   K = 382   L =

F =   G =   H =   I = 190

A = 74   B = 138   C = 55   D =   E =

HIGH-SPEED CROSSWORD

Across
1 Biblical shepherd
5 Ali and Frazier, e.g.
11 Brazilian soccer legend
12 Outfit for baby
13 "___ on Down the Road"
14 Malicious
15 "A Is for Alibi" author: 2 wds.
17 Actress Russo
18 Break down
21 Humpback, e.g.
26 "Pumping ___"
27 "Here comes trouble!"
28 Dancer's boss?
30 Big tests
31 What ice does if you leave it out
33 Largest city in South Dakota: 2 wds.
39 Fight back against
40 Extremely tired
41 "Catch-22" author Joseph
42 Peru's capital
43 Seaport of the Ukraine
44 "Baseball Tonight" channel

Down
1 "Planet of the ___"
2 Boyfriend
3 Different
4 Oscar winner for "Shampoo": 2 wds.
5 Martin's "Laugh-In" partner
6 Soon: 3 wds.
7 Blow off steam
8 About: 2 wds.
9 Animal with a mane
10 One of 100 in D.C.
16 King: Sp.
18 Criticize, slangily
19 Victorian, for one
20 Not a pro
22 Family last name on "The Cosby Show"
23 "Bingo!"
24 "Pink Panther" films actor
25 Hesitant syllables
29 Makes laugh
30 Will Ferrell comedy about Christmas
32 Additional
33 Future flower
34 Speck in the Pacific, e.g.
35 Peanut and vegetable
36 Hawaiian necklaces
37 Light
38 "South Park" boy
39 Greek letter

(Crossword grid with numbered cells 1–44)

1 MINUTE NUMBER CRUNCH

Beginner
124	− 16	÷ 9	x 7	+ 36	x 3	÷ 20	x 3	Answer

Intermediate
1973	− 982	+ 39	+ 148	÷ 19	x 7	− 48	÷ 2	Answer

Advanced
4	This to the power of 4	9/16 of this	11/12 of this	9/22 of this	x 18	− 677	+ 4/5 of this	Answer

Did You Know?:
The first car was designed in France in 1769 by Joseph Cugnot. You wouldn't recognise it as a car today, though, because it was steam-powered and ran on rails.

HIGH-SPEED CROSSWORD

Across
1 Where Adam and Eve were
5 Bobby Fischer's game
10 Block for kids
11 Part of a TV feed
12 Young wedding participant: 2 wds.
14 Plus
15 Speaks with the higher power
18 October birthstone
22 Chair part
23 Garden-variety
26 Mobile's state: abbr.
27 Sweet potato cousin
28 Novelist Levin
29 "Peace," in yoga class
31 Cabernet, for one
32 Board member, for short
33 Valentine's Day dozen
35 Difficult
38 Young wedding participant: 2 wds.
43 Love to pieces
44 Wander far and wide
45 Authority
46 Rival of NYSE

Down
1 One of Santa's little helpers
2 Md. neighbor
3 "I" problem?
4 "Forget it!": 2 wds.
5 Cadillacs and Chevrolets
6 Bigger than big
7 Newspaper worker
8 Respectful title
9 The sun
13 Some magazine pieces
15 Boeing 747, e.g.
16 "Calm down!"
17 "It's only ___!": 2 wds.
19 Couples
20 See eye to eye
21 Sporting advantages
24 Big wine holder
25 Arise
30 TV ad phrase: 2 wds.
34 "Gone With the Wind" last name
36 Shrek, e.g.
37 Coolest of the cool
38 Urban music style
39 Altar words: 2 wds.
40 CD-___
41 "The Three Faces of ___"
42 Man's name that means "king" in Latin

---

1 MINUTE NUMBER CRUNCH

Did You Know?:
The coconut crab lives on land and will drown if submerged in water. It lives on islands in the Indian Ocean and can grow to one metre across.

Beginner								Answer
9	x 8	Plus half of this	− 56	÷ 4	+ 94	− 11	÷ 6	

Intermediate								Answer
87	+ 56	x 3	Double it	− 669	4/9 of this	5/7 of this	220% of this	

Advanced								Answer
20	Cubed	99% of this	3/5 of this	+ 3/16 of this	− 3979	9/32 of this	x 7	

WORDSEARCH WORKOUT

```
W T U N I B B Y D A Z F E
Z E S U G E C C P B M N H
C V R O F O G I L I A N J
H C I U R G V O S C D N G
I H V S T I C T I G N E Y
L A T Y I A A R N E L A G
L Z C Y L B R F W E T C O
F Y R L P U I E E I T Y L
A D Y P H H Z L P E E R O
C C H A R T O G I M M E R
T W L D T A C O Z T E P O
O G I O H T C O N M Y T E
R A I N U D C J M L D H T
S S T D D D R Q W V O F E
R T Z K R P G B F T V H M
```

WEATHER

CHART
CHILL FACTOR
CLOUD
DRY
FAIR
FOG
GALE
HAZY
HOT
HURRICANE
ICY
LOCALLY
METEOROLOGY
MIST
RAIN
TEMPERATURE
TYPHOON
VISIBILITY
WET
WIND

DOUBLE FUN SUDOKU

TASTY TEASER

	1			8			7	
4			1		7			2
	7	2		5		8	9	
	4	5	3		8	7	6	
7			5		4			
	3	8	7		9	4	1	
	2	4		3		9	8	
9			8		1			6
	6			4			5	

BRAIN BUSTER

		3			2		9	7
	9			3				5
1		6				8		
			4			9	8	
	2	1			9			
		7			6		8	
5				4			1	
8	3		6			2		

WHATEVER NEXT?

In the diagram below, which letter should replace the question mark?

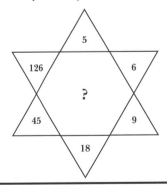

5
126   6
?
45   9
18

BRAIN TEASER

What number should replace the question mark?

? _____ ?

4	5	1
2	?	5
4	2	4

Mind Over Matter

Given that the letters are valued 1-26 according to their places in the alphabet, can you crack the mystery code to reveal the missing letter?

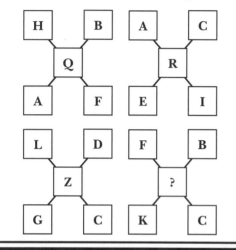

H		B		A		C
Q			R		
A		F		E		I
L		D		F		B
Z			?		
G		C		K		C

DOUBLE FUN SUDOKU

TASTY TEASER

5	8	4			1			9
				4				6
				5	9		7	
4		9	2		3	7		6
	2	8				3	5	
1		7	5		6	4		8
	7		9	3				
	1				2			
	4			6		9	8	2

BRAIN BUSTER

								8
			4	9				
	4	1	2	8		7	3	
5				3		6		
		7	5		8	3		
		6		4				7
	9	3		1	6	2	5	
			5	9				
6								

CODEWORD CONUNDRUM

| A | B | C | D | E | F | G | H | I | J | K | L | M |
| N | O | P | Q | R | S | T | U | V | W | X | Y | Z |

Reference Box

| 1 | 2 | 3 | 4 | 5 | 6 | 7 | 8 | 9 | 10 D | 11 | 12 | 13 |
| 14 | 15 | 16 | 17 | 18 | 19 | 20 L | 21 | 22 I | 23 | 24 | 25 | 26 |

HIGH-SPEED CROSSWORD

Across

1 Hack
5 Rushing sound
11 Italy's currency, before the euro
12 "There was no choice for me!": 3 wds.
13 Not many: 2 wds.
14 All-___ (late study sessions, casually)
15 Settler
17 Walters of TV news
22 Where two peas go: 3 wds.
26 Kitchen appliance
27 Jay Leno rival: 2 wds.
29 Winds up
30 Birthday cake item
31 Obliterate
33 Not questions
38 Edge
42 "___ to the Chief"
43 Be that as it may: 2 wds.
44 Capital of Norway
45 Quickness to anger
46 Mishmash

Down

1 Applaud
2 LP player
3 Cookie with florets on it
4 Weakest piece, in chess
5 "Nothing Compares 2 U" singer: 2 wds.
6 Machine's sound
7 Horse's morsel
8 "___ to Billie Joe"
9 Narrow waterway: abbr.
10 Christmas sounds
16 Black, in poetry
18 Delivered, as a baby
19 Enthusiastic
20 Movie holder
21 "___ of Green Gables"
22 Decorated, as a cake
23 ___ of the above
24 "No ifs, ___ ..."
25 History
28 Hudson and Chesapeake
32 Bring up
34 "___ next?"
35 "___ of Eden"
36 Anger, with "up"
37 At a snail's pace
38 Came into contact with
39 Monopoly property, often: abbr.
40 Band from Athens, Ga.
41 Economics stat

1 MINUTE NUMBER CRUNCH

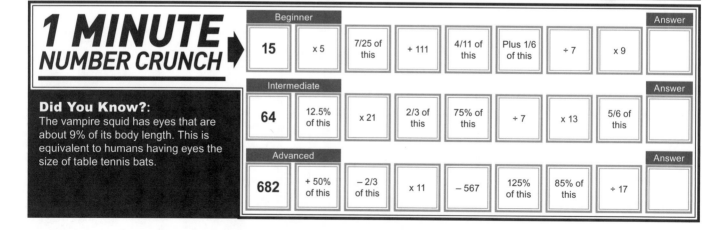

Beginner								Answer
15	x 5	7/25 of this	+ 111	4/11 of this	Plus 1/6 of this	÷ 7	x 9	

Intermediate								Answer
64	12.5% of this	x 21	2/3 of this	75% of this	÷ 7	x 13	5/6 of this	

Advanced								Answer
682	+ 50% of this	− 2/3 of this	x 11	− 567	125% of this	85% of this	÷ 17	

Did You Know?:
The vampire squid has eyes that are about 9% of its body length. This is equivalent to humans having eyes the size of table tennis bats.

BATTLESHIP BOUT

Can you place the vessels into the diagram? Some parts of vessels or sea squares have already been filled in. A number to the right or below a row or column refers to the number of occupied squares in that row or column.

Any vessel may be positioned horizontally or vertically, but no part of a vessel touches part of any other vessel, either horizontally, vertically or diagonally.

Did You Know?:
The planet Mars has two moons, Phobos and Deimos (Fear and Terror). Unlike Earth's moon, Luna, they are not spherical, and have the appearance of giant potatoes.

Empty Area of Sea:
Aircraft Carrier:
Battleships:
Cruisers:
Submarines:

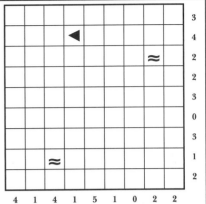

HIGH-SPEED CROSSWORD

Across
1 Breakfast food
4 Small amount
7 Neither fish ___ fowl
8 Singer Grant or novelist Tan
9 Grocery store holder
12 Make neat: 2 wds.
14 Ending for Japan or Surinam
15 Way, way off
16 U-Haul rival
18 Allots, with "out"
20 Soul great Redding
21 Not post-
22 Baseball announcer's phrase when a home run is hit: 2 wds.
25 Hole in your car
27 Fun on a lake: 2 wds.
29 Santa ___, Calif.
32 Advil target
33 More competent
35 Arsenic, e.g.
38 Border
39 Little pest
40 Nature's "opponent"
42 Discouraging words
43 Hawaiian instrument, for short
44 Ruin
45 Prepared
46 Untrustworthy

Down
1 Set up tents, e.g.
2 Jack Nicklaus or Tiger Woods
3 Top tunes for a band: 2 wds.
4 Blackout
5 "It's my turn!": 2 wds.
6 Sort
9 Where 3-down often appear: 3 wds.
10 Invite to the house: 2 wds.
11 "Silly" birds
13 "___ we having fun yet?"
17 Canceled: 2 wds.
19 Make, as a putt
23 The first "T" of TNT
24 Sammy of baseball fame
26 Functions
27 Tokyo's country
28 ___ Lodge (motel chain)
30 Nerve-related
31 Blood route
34 Baseball equipment
36 Burden
37 Put in the microwave
41 Not working any longer: abbr.

WORDWHEEL

Using only the letters in the Wordwheel, you have ten minutes to find as many words as possible, none of which may be plurals, foreign words or proper nouns. Each word must be of three letters or more, all must contain the central letter and letters can only be used once in every word. There is at least one nine-letter word in the wheel.

Nine-letter word(s):

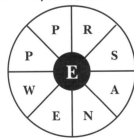

SUM CIRCLE

Fill the three empty circles with the symbols +, – and x in some order, to make a sum which totals the number in the centre. Each symbol must be used once and calculations are made in the direction of travel (clockwise).

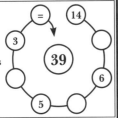

WORDSEARCH WORKOUT

```
S Y T T L R G F T V D L B
C Y F S O E N K R E X A A
A O I B S T I C T O T I A
L D O X S R L A R X B R G
E R D T Y A L J S K V E F
P W E H C U O H B I Z A K
V R V G C Q R G O T L O Z
N E N I U O A B C C O L E
O J T A P D M Z A H V G I
F R L R M N Q P J E Q N U
A O M T I K A O A N E I R
Q Z O S V E A F M N L D Y
O B T R X K R O P E I L V
R E W E R B N A T H T O U
P L Z Y Z E R I H Y S F N
```

LADDERS

AERIAL
ARTICULATED
COMPANION
ETRIER
FOLDING
HOOK
JACK
JACOB'S
KITCHEN
LOFT
QUARTER
ROLLING
ROOF
ROPE
SCALE
SIDE
STEP
STERN
STILE
STRAIGHT

DOUBLE FUN SUDOKU

TASTY TEASER

	8		9		5		7	
6		2		3		9		8
		7		6		4		
9		3	1		8	5		6
	1		4		6		9	
4		6	3		9	7		1
		5		9		1		
2		1		4		8		9
	6		5		1		2	

BRAIN BUSTER

			8					1
				9	2			5
5	8	4		3				9
		2					5	
6		7				1		8
	3					2		
9			1			4	6	2
2			5	7				
3				6				

1 MINUTE NUMBER CRUNCH

Beginner							Answer
34	Half of this	x 7	+ 49	÷ 8	300% of this	x 2	÷ 9

Intermediate							Answer
72	7/8 of this	x 4	1/3 of this	1/4 of this	Squared	x 3	÷ 9

Advanced							Answer
675	x 8/5	5/18 of this	+ 4/5 of this	7/9 of this	+ 3/10 of this	x 9	7/27 of this

Did You Know?:
Although the tin can was invented in 1810, and tinned food started to become popular around 1845, the tin-opener wasn't invented until 1858.

HIGH-SPEED CROSSWORD

Across

1 Actor O'Shea
5 Late singer Michael's nickname
10 Hardly any: 2 wds.
11 Additional
12 Pleasant, imaginary route: 2 wds.
14 The States
15 Wedding figure: 2 wds.
20 Cup
24 Motif
25 R-rated, maybe
26 Give off, as light
27 Words of agreement in church
29 Garden hassles
30 Eyelash stuff
32 Arnold Schwarzenegger lifts them
37 Pleasant, imaginary route: 2 wds.
40 Not sour
41 Two-color cookie
42 Jury members
43 Stinging insect

Down

1 Papa's mate
2 Thing
3 Flimsy, as an excuse
4 Aroma
5 "Ulysses" novelist James ___
6 "Finally!": 2 wds.
7 When doubled, a dance
8 Barbie's guy
9 Iron ___
13 Barbecue entree
16 Quaker's "you"
17 Enthusiastic volunteer's shout: 2 wds.
18 During
19 Brings home
20 Less than an ounce
21 Dalai ___
22 Air force heroes
23 Harmony
28 Mark Twain's Tom
29 "Hold it!"
31 Breaks
33 Cultivate
34 Greek goddess
35 Pegs carried by caddies
36 "Cut it out!"
37 Clairvoyance, e.g.
38 Leave in wonder
39 "Get it?"

CODEWORD CONUNDRUM

A B C D E F G H I J K L M
N O P Q R S T U V W X Y Z

Reference Box

1 A	2	3	4	5	6	7	8	9	10	11	12 M	13
14	15	16	17	18	19	20	21	22	23 R	24	25	26

DOUBLE FUN SUDOKU

TASTY TEASER

BRAIN BUSTER

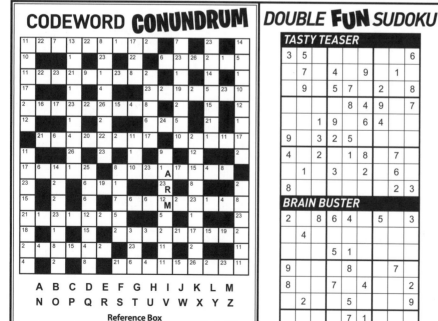

SPIDOKU

Each of the eight segments of the spider's web should be filled with a different number from 1 to 8, in such a way that every ring also contains a different number from 1 to 8.

HIGH-SPEED CROSSWORD

Across
1 Took care of: 2 wds.
6 "___ la vista!"
11 Get ready for a marathon
12 Part of "the works"
13 Where you'll see seven dwarfs running around
15 Vietnam's capital
16 Sneaky
17 "May ___ excused?": 2 wds.
19 Biblical paradise
21 She turned people to stone
23 Kind of gemstone
27 Grads
28 Funeral song
29 "Li'l Abner" cartoonist
30 Kitchen gadgets
31 C-___ (political channel)
33 Took a chair
34 A pint, maybe
37 Antipasto piece
39 Where you'll see lots of elves running around: 2 wds.
43 Inbox contents
44 Largest organ in the body
45 John, Jane and Judy
46 Coasters

Down
1 Normal: abbr.
2 "Exodus" character
3 No longer in fine form: 2 wds.
4 Louise of "Gilligan's Island"
5 Harmony
6 Mandel of "Deal or No Deal"
7 "I'll take that as ___": 2 wds.
8 Respected gentlemen
9 Cost to drive on a road
10 Rooney or Roddick
14 Little green man in film
17 Apple product
18 Actor Lugosi
20 Pinot ___ (kind of wine)
22 Baseball referees, for short
24 Keep for the future
25 The Taj Mahal's city
26 "___ we forget"
28 Boone and Day-Lewis
30 Ashy
32 Surveys
34 "Absolutely!"
35 ___ beans
36 Dutch cheese
38 Colorado resort
40 Conk out
41 Kennedy or Williams
42 "48 ___"

WORDSEARCH WORKOUT

```
E M P Y U G Y W F S R W B
N Y A W D E M J R I E L T
Y D X O Y N Q E B L A O N
T B I T O T Z B L C C S D
P D I V E B L A K P E N K
S E A I W E N W A M K P M
G L F R P D A R A I O X D
R I E Z T T R H S X R O Q
E V Q N E E T N P K V E Q
A U W R T T E R E E T V R
T M E T R N J H Y N C E E
O J N Y E T Y Y F N I Y B
U I S W A Y A V G E D L M
S P U V T R Z E L T A E U
E M M J Q H E C C C H E H
```

RIVERS OF BRITAIN

AIRE
AVON
BLACKWATER
DART
DOVEY
GREAT OUSE
HUMBER
KENNET
MEDWAY
NENE
PARRETT
RIBBLE
SPEY
TEIFI
THAMES
TOWY
TYNE
WELLAND
WENSUM
YARE

DOUBLE FUN SUDOKU

TASTY TEASER

	9	7		6		3	4	
4			5		3			1
		3		9		5		
	3	8	2		9	1	6	
9			6		1			3
	1	5	3		7	2	9	
		6		1		8		
8			9		5			7
	7	9		2		4	1	

BRAIN BUSTER

		1	8			5		
9	3			1				
8	7							
				6	2	7		
1			7			4		
2	8	5						
						3	8	
			4			1	7	
	6			9	4			

MATCHSTICK MAGIC

Remove three matchsticks to leave three squares.

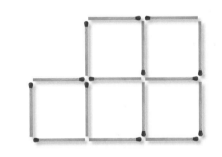

BRAIN TEASER

Frank has half as many again as Sally who has half as many again as Mary. Altogether they have 209.

How many has each?

?___?

1 MINUTE NUMBER CRUNCH

Beginner								Answer
99	Plus the sum of its two digits	÷ 3	+ 1/3 of this	Half of this	+ 58	÷ 12	x 5	

Intermediate								Answer
829	− 555	1/2 of this	+ 85	÷ 37	This cubed	3/9 of this	3/8 of this	

Advanced								Answer
94	x 11	÷ 0.5	+ 3/4 of this	− 2917	+ 8/9 of this	Plus half of this	14/9 of this	

Did You Know?:
The horn of a rhinoceros, though as solid as bone, is actually made of keratin – the same substance that forms the hair and nails of humans.

CODEWORD CONUNDRUM

| A | B | C | D | E | F | G | H | I | J | K | L | M |
| N | O | P | Q | R | S | T | U | V | W | X | Y | Z |

Reference Box

| 1 | 2 | 3 | 4 | 5 | 6 | 7 | 8 | 9 | 10 | 11 | 12 H | 13 E |
| 14 | 15 | 16 | 17 | 18 | 19 | 20 | 21 | 22 | 23 | 24 | 25 T | 26 |

DOUBLE FUN SUDOKU

TASTY TEASER

5	3	8				6	4	9
	6		8				5	
7			9	5				2
	4		7					8
		3	6		2	4		
1				5		9		
8				1	3			4
	7			9		2		
4	2	6			9	1	3	

BRAIN BUSTER

	7		2	9			8	
	1						9	
				8	6			
			1			7	3	
1	5		9		3		6	4
4	2			6				
		2	1					
	4				3			
	9		8	2		5		

PYRAMID PLUS

Every brick in this pyramid contains a number which is the sum of the two numbers below it, so that F=A+B, etc. Just work out the missing numbers!

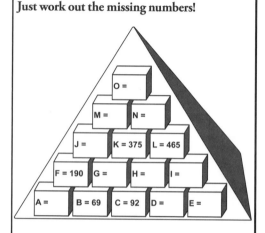

O =
M =   N =
J =   K = 375   L = 465
F = 190   G =   H =   I =
A =   B = 69   C = 92   D =   E =

HIGH-SPEED CROSSWORD

Across

1 Cry like a baby
5 "Two Women" Oscar-winner Sophia
10 Ashtabula's lake
11 "Hearts ___"
12 President after Richard Nixon: 2 wds.
14 "___ moment, please"
15 Affirmative vote
16 Electric shooter
18 Challenger
23 Lunch holder, maybe
25 Dash
26 What both 12-across and 41-across have brands of in their names
30 Body covering
31 AMA members
32 Nairobi's country
34 Scarlett of "Gone With the Wind"
38 Animal house
40 Herbert of the "Pink Panther" movies
41 Comic actor known for portraying 12-across: 2 wds.
45 Certain bellybutton
46 Black cat, maybe
47 Bargains
48 Chuck

Down

1 Brought forth
2 "Gladiator" setting
3 Sends money, perhaps
4 Actress Salonga or Thompson
5 Gentleman's counterpart
6 Bid
7 2016 Olympics city
8 Make a mistake
9 Actor Beatty
13 Former NFL player in Calif.
17 Black
19 Like someone from Dublin
20 Kilmer of "The Doors"
21 Part of a royal flush
22 Guitar great ___ Paul
24 George Burns role
26 "Don't ___!"
27 Don Ho instrument
28 Metallic element
29 Untamed horse
33 Tylenol alternative
35 "Remember the ___!"
36 "The Subject Was ___"
37 Church words
39 Peepers
41 Atlantic fish
42 Color
43 In-flight info
44 Burning

1 MINUTE NUMBER CRUNCH

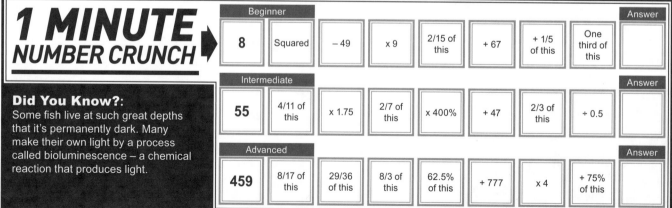

Beginner								Answer
8	Squared	− 49	x 9	2/15 of this	+ 67	+ 1/5 of this	One third of this	

Intermediate								Answer
55	4/11 of this	x 1.75	2/7 of this	x 400%	+ 47	2/3 of this	÷ 0.5	

Advanced								Answer
459	8/17 of this	29/36 of this	8/3 of this	62.5% of this	+ 777	x 4	+ 75% of this	

Did You Know?:

Some fish live at such great depths that it's permanently dark. Many make their own light by a process called bioluminescence – a chemical reaction that produces light.

HIGH-SPEED CROSSWORD

Across
1 Dust remover
4 Bill
7 Automobile
10 Singer Yoko ___
11 Peyton's brother
12 "I ___ you one"
13 Cats and dogs
15 Club ___
16 Big house
17 Prefix meaning "three"
19 African antelope
20 Sought help from: 2 wds.
23 Jazz genre
25 Weary cry: 2 wds.
26 Juan Peron's wife
27 Gave chow to
28 Fiesta food
31 Go to the other side of the street
33 Bracelet site, sometimes
34 Balloon filler
35 Marry
36 "Forget it!": 2 wds.
39 Health resort
41 Make all riled up
43 Not just him
44 Brown shade
45 Howard of "Happy Days"
46 Finale
47 Keep watch on
48 Two-out plays, in baseball stats

Down
1 Be itinerant
2 Palindromic woman's name
3 Regressing: 2 wds.
4 Get weepy: 2 wds.
5 100%
6 Casual eatery
7 Volunteering: 2 wds.
8 Leave in wonder
9 Traffic light color
14 Uni-
18 "Go team!"
21 Little piggies, so to speak
22 Chances
23 ___ carotene
24 Twitter co-founder Williams
29 "Bravo!"
30 Calm
31 Dog
32 Brawl
37 Above
38 Cravings
39 That lady
40 Be the author
42 Happy

DOMINO PLACEMENT

Did You Know?:
Neptune can't be seen with the unaided eye. It was the first planet to have been located by mathematical observation as opposed to being actually seen.

A standard set of 28 dominoes has been laid out as shown. Can you draw in the edges of them all? The check-box is provided as an aid and the domino already placed will help.

```
          3 4
        2 5 0 6
        1 3 0 6
    2 4 0 3 3 2 2 6
  4 5 6 1 5 2 0 1 0 3
  0 2 3 5 6 0 2 5 6 1
    1 1 4 2 1 4 4 4
        1 6 6 5
        0 5 4 5
          3 3
```

0-0	0-1	0-2	0-3	0-4	0-5	0-6
		✓				

1-1	1-2	1-3	1-4	1-5	1-6	2-2

2-3	2-4	2-5	2-6	3-3	3-4	3-5

3-6	4-4	4-5	4-6	5-5	5-6	6-6

WORDSEARCH WORKOUT

```
E C N A D S S Y E L L U P
Q S P E T S P I N N I N G
F E J R O T C U R T S N I
S H N O U L Q E S I G N G
L R O I G U L P J S G C Y
L E S R L G L L P G E G E
E W W R S O I L E Z D R T
B O I S S E P N E B M K P
B H M X T X R M G Y R P Z
M S M W H E E G A S S A M
U I I C G R B T K R A N B
D Y N T I C S S E N T I F
X E G M E I G G U A G O Y
B M O R W S Q A N T F O T
O C I F O E S U B V G I U
```

GYM WORK OUT

BAR-BELL
BENCH
DANCE
DUMBBELLS
EXERCISE
FITNESS
HORSE
INSTRUCTOR
JOGGING
MASSAGE
PRESS-UPS
PULLEYS
SAUNA
SHOWER
SPINNING
STEPS
SWIMMING
TRAMPOLINE
WEIGHTS
YOGA

DOUBLE FUN SUDOKU

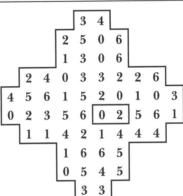

TASTY TEASER

7			9		6			1
	8			1			2	
1		5	8		4	9		7
	4		1	6	7		9	
3		6				1		5
	1		3	5	9		4	
2		8	6		3	4		9
	7			9			6	
6			5		1			2

BRAIN BUSTER

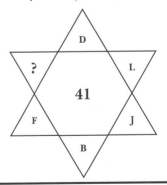

	3	1			2		8	
				6	1	7		
	8	7					6	
			2			8		
8		3				5		6
		9			6			
	6					2	1	
		4	7	1				
	9		6			3	5	

WHATEVER NEXT?

In the diagram below, which letter should replace the question mark?

D

? L

41

F J

B

BRAIN TEASER

How many circles appear here?

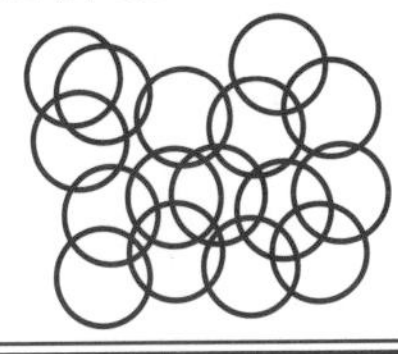

? ___ ?

Mind Over Matter

Given that the letters are valued 1-26 according to their places in the alphabet, can you crack the mystery code to reveal the missing letter?

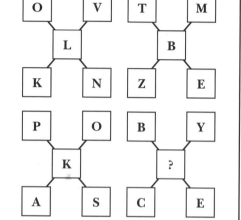

O	V	T	M
L			B
K	N	Z	E
P	O	B	Y
K		?	
A	S	C	E

DOUBLE **FUN** SUDOKU

TASTY TEASER

4		9			2			
		3		1	8		5	9
	8				5	4	2	
7		4			6		9	
2			5		4			3
	1		3			6		7
	6	5	8			7		
8	7		2	9		5		
			6			3	1	

BRAIN BUSTER

4			3		9	6	8	
5		9						
1			6	4				
	9					3		
6		2			8		7	
	5				4			
		4	2				1	
				7			3	
8	7	4		5				9

CODEWORD **CONUNDRUM**

| A | B | C | D | E | F | G | H | I | J | K | L | M |
| N | O | P | Q | R | S | T | U | V | W | X | Y | Z |

Reference Box

1	2	3	4 T	5	6	7	8	9	10	11	12	13
14 B	15	16	17	18	19	20 A	21	22	23	24	25	26

HIGH-SPEED CROSSWORD

Across

1 "Star ___"
5 Hairdos
10 Help, as a criminal
11 "L.A. Law" lawyer
12 City south of Hilton Head, SC: 2 wds.
14 Ziti, e.g.
15 Shampoo target
18 ___ oil
22 "Who ___?"
23 Kidney-related
24 Fix, in a way
25 Aged
26 Bouquet
29 Willing to believe anything
31 "Haystacks" painter
32 Less inept
33 Late hotelier Helmsley
35 Caribbean city: 2 wds.
40 Come to mind
41 ___-friendly
42 Goes for the gold?
43 Not crazy

Down

1 Functioned as
2 Lawyer's org.
3 Gun, as the engine
4 Piece of metal shot into paper
5 Fires
6 Henry Clay, for one
7 Breathe
8 Fruit often dried
9 Caribbean, e.g.
13 Drops off
15 "Beat it!"
16 Egypt's capital
17 Gas in air
19 One way to saute: 2 wds.
20 Opening part
21 Village leader
27 Lawyer ___ Belli
28 "Relax, and that's an order!": 2 wds.
29 "Peter Pan" dog
30 Old calculator
34 Some rolls of the dice
35 "Green Eggs and ___"
36 "Exodus" role
37 America
38 Big ___ (London attraction)
39 "We ___ the World"

1 MINUTE NUMBER CRUNCH

Beginner								Answer
22	x 7	Half of this	4/11 of this	+ 50% of this	− 9	x 4	7/11 of this	

Intermediate								Answer
27	x 3	− 56	80% of this	850% of this	7/10 of this	Double it	+ 823	

Advanced								Answer
96	x 14	+ 3/4 of this	5/6 of this	35% of this	+ 155	Square root of this	x 13	

Did You Know?:

Villagers in Romania re-elected Neculai Ivescu as their mayor even though he died shortly before the election.

1 MINUTE NUMBER CRUNCH

Beginner								Answer
1234	x 2	− 999	+ 31	90% of this	÷ 5	1/5 of this	x 3	

Intermediate								Answer
99	5/9 of this	5/11 of this	Square root of this	+ 20%	+ 5	Squared	x 3	

Advanced								Answer
96	x 4	+ 3/16 of this	5/6 of this	− 90% of this	+ 795	x 7	− 2978	

Did You Know?:
It's against the law to sail over Niagara Falls. Nevertheless, over the years several people have drowned trying to do so.

HIGH-SPEED CROSSWORD

Across
1 Aria, e.g.
5 Was just kidding around
11 "___ Brockovich"
12 Strike caller
13 Fishing equipment
14 Put in order
15 "The lady ___ protest too much"
16 Finale
17 Kinks hit
19 Site for bidders
23 Look through a peephole: 2 wds.
26 Beer variety
27 Fencing swords
28 Fit for a queen
30 Second-century date
31 Make a misstep
33 Old Chrysler
35 "Can ___ serious for a moment?": 2 wds.
36 "It's no ___!"
38 Song and dance, e.g.
41 "Goodness!": 2 wds.
44 Increase, with "up"
45 Two dots over a vowel, in German
46 Former NYC stadium
47 Courtroom plea
48 Thanksgiving dish

Down
1 E-mail, e.g.
2 Cookie often twisted
3 "The Loco-Motion" singer: 2 wds.
4 Off the cruise ship for a while: 2 wds.
5 Alaska's capital
6 Sign of the future
7 Not a heart, club or diamond
8 Bestseller
9 Before
10 Room where work gets done
18 Red ink amount
20 Nickname for a WWI weapon: 2 wds.
21 "Come on, be ___!": 2 wds.
22 Ivy League school
23 Eat like a bird
24 Long saga
25 Not false
29 Government outpost
32 Cartoon bird
34 Of the country
37 Blue books?
39 Abound
40 Fitness centers
41 Used a shovel
42 Australian runner
43 Role for Will Smith

WORDWHEEL

Using only the letters in the Wordwheel, you have ten minutes to find as many words as possible, none of which may be plurals, foreign words or proper nouns. Each word must be of three letters or more, all must contain the central letter and letters can only be used once in every word. There is at least one nine-letter word in the wheel.

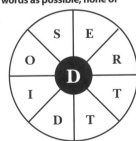

Nine-letter word(s):

SUM CIRCLE

Fill the three empty circles with the symbols +, − and x in some order, to make a sum which totals the number in the centre. Each symbol must be used once and calculations are made in the direction of travel (clockwise).

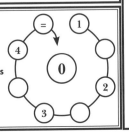

WORDSEARCH WORKOUT

```
T E S P S E R U T A E F A
O O L G X S L P H C S D L
G S L S D C L Q D E T L D
P P R S R M H L Y N I E O
P A A M P E S E E I U C R
B I Y N D W P T R B R N A
K X N O O N Q E I R F A N
C U N D U P U A A D I C G
B R N P E T P D R T E E E
L I S T A R T L G C S R S
W I N N I N G E U E A J C
J X O F F H P V D M I D E
G P M C O L L E C T S L E
Y X E Q N S F R B P E C U
A V L Y I O I M O I B A Y
```

FRUIT MACHINE

ARCADE
BARS
BELLS
CANCEL
CHERRIES
COLLECT
CREDITS
FEATURES
FRUITS
LEMONS

LEVER
NUDGE
ORANGE
PAYOUT
PLUMS
REPEAT
SLOT
START
WINDOW
WINNING

DOUBLE FUN SUDOKU

TASTY TEASER

1	6				3	8		
8			4	9			7	3
		7			8			
5	1				7		8	2
		3		5		9		
2	9		6				4	5
			2			6		
6	7			8	5			9
		4	1				2	7

BRAIN BUSTER

	6		3		2		1	
7			4		9			6
		1		7		2		
2		4				5		3
	8						2	
1		6				8		4
		2		4		7		
3			5		7			1
	5		1		8		9	

1 MINUTE NUMBER CRUNCH ▶

Beginner								Answer
14	x 6	Half of this	÷ 7	x 2.5	500% of this	x 3	÷ 15	

Intermediate								Answer
424	− 128	1/2 of this	÷ 4	x 7	+ 955	x 2	− 1957	

Advanced								Answer
558	+ 2/3 of this	7/10 of this	+ 5/7 of this	− 2/9 of this	− 277	8/3 of this	+ 3/8 of this	

Did You Know?:
New York City had a bedbug epidemic in 2007. Nearly seven thousand calls were made to pest control companies when the parasites infested hotels, hospitals, schools and homes.

HIGH-SPEED CROSSWORD

Across
1 Sticker on a windshield
6 Clearly surprised
11 Clear, as a disk
12 Far from fresh
13 Be off-target: 3 wds.
15 Chemical suffix
16 Long-term spy
17 Valuable stone
18 Couch
22 Groups of words
26 Brooks of "The Producers"
27 TV doctor
28 "Don't get any funny ___!"
30 "___ say!"
31 Corrode: 2 wds.
33 Onion's cousin
35 Carpet
36 Swedish retailer
38 Dove's sound
41 Country singer from Canada: 2 wds.
45 Groups of cattle
46 Symbol of the US
47 Live
48 Prom wear

Down
1 Moore of "G.I. Jane"
2 Andrews or Brockovich
3 Beer amount
4 Fool
5 "Hmmmm...": 3 wds.
6 Cain's brother
7 Chess and checkers
8 Santa ___ Winds
9 Golf score
10 Animal found in Finland
14 "Where the heart is"
17 Neon or argon
19 Sign of the future
20 Accomplishment
21 "Not to mention ..."
22 TV's Dr. ___
23 One of 18 on a golf course
24 Be a monarch
25 Placed
29 Archaeological site
32 Part of town
34 Varieties
37 Star___ (tuna brand)
38 Hamster's home
39 Sesame and olive
40 Mind ___ manners
41 That woman
42 Put a spell on
43 "Entourage" role
44 Armed conflict

CODEWORD CONUNDRUM

| A | B | C | D | E | F | G | H | I | J | K | L | M |
| N | O | P | Q | R | S | T | U | V | W | X | Y | Z |

Reference Box

DOUBLE FUN SUDOKU

TASTY TEASER

8	7		5					4
				8			3	2
4		5	9	1			7	
3			2			4	8	
		9	7		6	2		
	6	4			8			1
	2			3	5	1		7
	1	6			9			
5					7		6	9

BRAIN BUSTER

2		8	1		4	5		9
5								4
			5	2	9			
7		9	2		5	3		6
		3				2		
6		2	7		8	9		5
			3	8	6			
8								1
3		5	4		2	6		8

SPIDOKU

Each of the eight segments of the spider's web should be filled with a different number from 1 to 8, in such a way that every ring also contains a different number from 1 to 8.

HIGH-SPEED CROSSWORD

Across
1 Monies owed
6 Reid and Lipinski
11 Nebraska city
12 Scent
13 Acknowledged
14 Shish ___
15 "A Nightmare on ___ Street"
16 Leave amazed
18 Ending for rational or lion
19 Vardalos of "My Big Fat Greek Wedding"
20 "___ bad!"
21 Neither here ___ there
22 Plenty
24 Agreed-upon facts
26 Off in the distance
28 "___ Stone"
29 April rain
32 Other
35 One of two on the head
36 Soaking
38 Soap brand
39 The E in NYE
40 "Much ___ About Nothing"
41 Mischievous type
42 Word after time or money
44 San Antonio building
46 Put ___ to (stop): 2 wds.
47 18-wheelers
48 Goods
49 Sip

Down
1 Museum guide
2 Estevez of "The Breakfast Club"
3 1995 Val Kilmer movie: 2 wds.
4 Definite article
5 1978 Peace Nobelist Anwar ___
6 Sign on a tray of samples: 2 wds.
7 "Who ___ you?"
8 "Mrs. Doubtfire" actor: 2 wds.
9 Online bookstore
10 Scary swords
17 Pan used in Beijing
23 Tool with teeth
25 "Bravo!"
27 Money for finding lost pets
29 Go up and down
30 Cuba's capital
31 Wine color
33 Peak
34 Smoke out
37 Breakfast bread that may get burnt
43 Compass dir.
45 Grassland

WORDSEARCH WORKOUT

```
K R E W S N G L B V U K X
O T R A V A A H Q R D V P
N M D E S T G G D X A K C
E V B Y T A R A O Z M I Z
R O N O H S C I I R M M T
V L Z V F H E L C A P B E
E L L E N A D H N I N E U
Y N J S I M T K W M A R S
G T I D V N A O A X Z L B
C H I E I F M D D T W E R
N S T C L P A M O L L Y N
T P A M I E U Y L N I I O
Z Y T F A L D R F F N J H
H K K U B L E A H A O A C
E F I Y H W J F M Y T U Z
```

GIRLS' NAMES
DAWN
ELLEN
FELICITY
GAIL
HESTER
HONOR
HYACINTH
JOY
KIMBERLEY
LEAH
LIZA
MADELEINE
MADONNA
MAUD
MOLLY
MYRA
NATASHA
NINA
TRICIA
ZOE

DOUBLE FUN SUDOKU

TASTY TEASER

	6		9	1		4	2	
4					6			
	5	3			2			6
	8	1	3			9	7	
2				7				1
	7	5			4	6	8	
9			5			8	4	
			8					3
	3	4		6	7		1	

BRAIN BUSTER

				4				
5			1		8			6
	1	6			2	9		
1		9	2			3	5		8
	4			7			6	
8		5	9		4	3		2
		8	3		7	2		
7			4		1			3
				2				

MATCHSTICK MAGIC
Remove eight matchsticks to leave two squares.

BRAIN TEASER
The pictures below represent one face of each of five standard gaming dice. What is the total of the numbers on the reverse side of these dice?

SIMPLE AS A, B, C ?

Did You Know?:
The star-nosed mole has six times as many nerves running from its nose to its brain than a human has going from each hand to the brain.

Each of the small squares in the grid below contains either A, B or C. Each row, column, and diagonal line of six squares has exactly two of each letter. Can you tell the letter in each square?

Across
1 No two letters the same are directly next to each other
2 The Cs are further right than the Bs
3 The Bs are next to each other
4 The Bs are next to each other
5 The Bs are further right than the Cs
6 No two letters the same are directly next to each other

Down
1 Each C is directly next to and below an A
2 No two letters the same are directly next to each other
3 No two letters the same are directly next to each other
4 No two letters the same are directly next to each other
5 The As are next to each other
6 Each C is directly next to and below a B

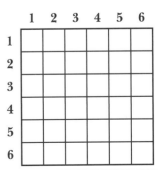

CODEWORD CONUNDRUM

A B C D E F G H I J K L M
N O P Q R S T U V W X Y Z

Reference Box

1	2	3	4	5	6	7	8	9	10	11	12	13
14	15 Y	16	17	18 D	19	20	21	22 R	23	24	25	26

DOUBLE FUN SUDOKU

TASTY TEASER

2				4		3		
9	7				5	4		
4		5	1	2		6		
	1	4		7				9
	8		3		9		7	
6			8		3	5		
	9		1	3	8			5
	6	9				2	3	
	5		7					1

BRAIN BUSTER

5	8					9	3	
	1				4			
9		7		3			6	
	6	5	1	7	3			
		1	2	8	4	9		
2		9		6				8
	6					3		
3	5					2	4	

PYRAMID PLUS

Every brick in this pyramid contains a number which is the sum of the two numbers below it, so that F=A+B, etc.
Just work out the missing numbers!

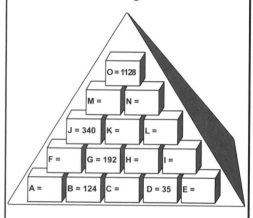

O = 1128

M =   N =

J = 340   K =   L =

F =   G = 192   H =   I =

A =   B = 124   C =   D = 35   E =

HIGH-SPEED CROSSWORD

Across
1 "Seinfeld" uncle
4 Marvelous, like the Beatles
7 Tombstone letters
10 Christmas creature
11 Anger
12 "First..."
13 ___ sprouts
15 Attorney's field
16 Last name that sounds hurtful
17 Vulcan mind tricks
19 Mel who hit 511 home runs
20 "... happily ___ after"
21 "Hop on Pop" author
23 Had the nerve
25 Score for Tiger Woods
26 Rolls-Royce or Maserati
27 Cupid's projectile
30 Spacious
32 John Paul II, e.g.
33 Historical time
34 Jasmine and basmati
35 Fancy pool shot
38 "A rat!"
39 Overly formal
41 Highest heart
42 Control
43 ___ foo yung
44 The P in MPG
45 "Yes" indication
46 Funny Romano

Down
1 Ballet move
2 "___ Enchanted"
3 Nuts: 3 wds.
4 Choice cuts
5 Kennel sound
6 Broadcast
7 Amusement park fun: 2 wds.
8 Imagined: 3 wds.
9 Seats with kneelers
14 Aardvark food
18 Actress ___ Marie Saint
21 Health resort
22 Secret Service agent's wear
24 Arid
28 "Well done!"
29 Vegetable oil brand
30 Tell again
31 Face-to-face exam
34 Do farm work
36 Big name in computer games
37 Hip
40 One roll of the dice

1 MINUTE NUMBER CRUNCH

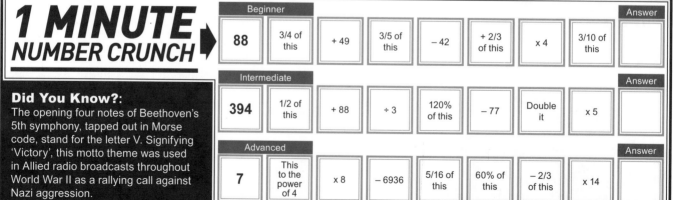

Beginner								Answer
88	3/4 of this	+ 49	3/5 of this	− 42	+ 2/3 of this	x 4	3/10 of this	

Intermediate							Answer
394	1/2 of this	+ 88	÷ 3	120% of this	− 77	Double it	x 5	

Advanced							Answer
7	This to the power of 4	x 8	− 6936	5/16 of this	60% of this	− 2/3 of this	x 14	

Did You Know?:
The opening four notes of Beethoven's 5th symphony, tapped out in Morse code, stand for the letter V. Signifying 'Victory', this motto theme was used in Allied radio broadcasts throughout World War II as a rallying call against Nazi aggression.

HIGH-SPEED CROSSWORD

Across
1 Beeped
6 Close, as a race
11 Amtrak service
12 Baseball blunder
13 Orson Welles classic: 2 wds.
15 Masthead names, briefly
16 Buddhist discipline
17 Born, in wedding announcements
18 Working together
20 Bicker
23 Full of lip
26 Amount of work
27 Drag
28 Danger
30 Red Square man
31 "Please enter!": 3 wds.
33 Chinese dictator
35 Bunk
36 Nile snake
39 Words before "Get your elbows off the table": 3 wds.
42 Blabs
43 Automaton
44 Send out a short message, maybe
45 Online call site

Down
1 Clip
2 Battery contents
3 Understands
4 QB Manning
5 Really wow
6 Court sport
7 Bother
8 Person with a III after their name
9 Sharpen
10 Elm or oak
14 Moray, e.g.
18 Video's counterpart
19 Consumed
20 Matterhorn or Mont Blanc
21 Fish eggs
22 Scary statue on top of a building
24 Go down a mountain
25 Japanese currency
29 Reappearing insect
30 Beverage bottle amounts
32 Neither's partner
33 Mr. Romney
34 Not many: 2 wds.
36 "Dear" lady with advice
37 Pig's food
38 Baseball great Rose
40 "Wonderful job!"
41 Just fine

1 MINUTE NUMBER CRUNCH

Beginner								Answer
78	+ 15	1/3 of this	x 4	+ 20	1/12 of this	x 8	1/2 of this	

Intermediate								Answer
291	+ 49	20% of this	1/4 of this	x 7	Double it	− 190	+ 32	

Advanced								Answer
342	5/19 of this	170% of this	+ 7/9 of this	x 0.625	5/34 of this	Cubed	4/5 of this	

Did You Know?:
British author Barbara Cartland wrote 723 novels. More than a billion copies of her books, in 36 languages, have been sold worldwide.

WORDSEARCH WORKOUT

```
K C L A R E N U F A W F M
C O M M I T T A L E B S F
P N C V O J C L D P I R H
N F R M D H Q D R T E A A
I I G U Z O I U P C P I W
P R N N I N S A Q P Y N Y
T M I V G R B E U N D I J
E A N E E Z U H H I N T N
R T E I G S C S G G U I U
R I P L U A T Y T N A A P
A O O I R T I I U A M T T
M N C N D L H R T T M I I
R Q V G R W T S R U N O A
I U Y O N A H C R A R N L
T Y N O M I R T A M M E S
```

CEREMONIES

AMRIT
BAPTISM
CHANOYU
CHUPPAH
COMMITTAL
CONFIRMATION
DOSEH
FUNERAL
INITIATION
INVESTITURE
MARRIAGE
MATRIMONY
MATSURI
MAUNDY
NIPTER
NUPTIALS
OPENING
TANGI
UNVEILING
WEDDING

DOUBLE FUN SUDOKU

TASTY TEASER

	7		6		1			
	2			8		1	6	9
	6		3	2	9			
3			4		5	8		
7	1					5	4	
		6	8		7			3
		9	4	6		3		
9	3	5		7			2	
		5		2		8		

BRAIN BUSTER

				7				
	5		4		3		6	
9			1		5			3
2	1		7		9		4	6
		5		8		7		
6	4		2		1		3	9
1			8		2			4
	2		3		7		8	
				1				

WHATEVER NEXT?

In the diagram below, which whole number should replace the question mark?

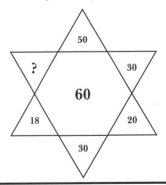

BRAIN TEASER

You have a range of weights available from 1-10 units. They are all single weights. Which one should you use to balance the scale and where should you place it?

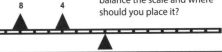

Mind Over Matter

Given that the letters are valued 1-26 according to their places in the alphabet, can you crack the mystery code to reveal the missing letter?

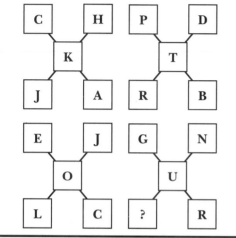

DOUBLE **FUN** SUDOKU

TASTY TEASER

8			9		7			
	5		1		2		6	4
	7		3		4			5
4		1	5				8	
	6			2			3	
	2			7	6			9
1		8		6		7		
7	3		2		1		9	
	5		3					6

BRAIN BUSTER

	6			8	4	5		
	5				2			1
3	9				8			
			1			2		
7								5
	4		7					
		9				6	3	
8			9				1	
	2	4	1		9			

CODEWORD **CONUNDRUM**

A	B	C	D	E	F	G	H	I	J	K	L	M
N	O	P	Q	R	S	T	U	V	W	X	Y	Z

Reference Box

1	2	3	4	5	6	7	8	9	10	11	12	13
								L				
14	15	16	17	18	19	20	21	22	23	24	25	26
				A						E		

HIGH-SPEED CROSSWORD

Across
1 Fearless
5 Cash or gold coins, e.g.
10 "I had no ___!"
11 Food in a "cook-off"
12 "Some Like It Hot" actor: 2 wds.
14 Operation with a pencil
15 Clint Eastwood TV show
20 Search for water
24 Satan
25 Opera tune
26 General or corporal
27 "___ in the Night" (Fleetwood Mac album)
29 Numbers
30 One way to cook pasta: 2 wds.
32 Puget Sound city
37 Hot dog brand: 2 wds.
40 Camelot, to Arthur
41 Go a few rounds
42 Hotel posting
43 Some male dolls

Down
1 Quick meal
2 Aroma
3 Olin of "Chocolat"
4 Quite a while
5 Integra automaker
6 Sharp, as a businessman
7 Be in session
8 Inventor ___ Whitney
9 "___ the season ..."
13 Fix
16 "My ___!"
17 "Terrible" czar
18 Little dent
19 Fraternal organization
20 Pieces of info
21 Spoken
22 Leaf-scattering force
23 Popular herb
28 Discounted: 2 wds.
29 Baseball feature
31 "___ of Endearment"
33 Job at hand
34 Sort
35 Slender
36 Blows it
37 Bobby of Boston Bruins fame
38 Baltic or Black
39 Pet with whiskers

1 MINUTE NUMBER CRUNCH

Beginner								Answer
232	− 34	1/2 of this	5/9 of this	4/11 of this	+ 19	2/3 of this	+ 42	

Intermediate								Answer
29	x 3	+ 78	÷ 11	+ 25	3/10 of this	x 7	÷ 3	

Advanced								Answer
702	7/39 of this	+ 224	7/10 of this	3/5 of this	2/3 of this	x 7	x 2.5	

Did You Know?:
Flying squirrels don't actually fly. The web of skin between their four limbs and body allows them to glide between trees. They can travel a distance of about 1,300 feet in this way.

DOMINO PLACEMENT

Did You Know?:
The first vending machine is thought to have been invented by Hero of Alexandria in 15 BC. Inserted in a slot, a coin could be used to release a drink of water to the customer.

A standard set of 28 dominoes has been laid out as shown. Can you draw in the edges of them all? The check-box is provided as an aid and the domino already placed will help.

```
          0  1
       5  5  2  6
       0  4  1  6
 4  1  5  1  6  1  1  6
 2  3  3  3  1  4  6  2  5  3
 2  5  2  6  2  4  3  0  5  0
 0  3  5  0  6  1  3  2
       4  5  0  3
       4  6  0  2
          4  4
```

0-0	0-1	0-2	0-3	0-4	0-5	0-6

1-1	1-2	1-3	1-4	1-5	1-6	2-2
			✓			

2-3	2-4	2-5	2-6	3-3	3-4	3-5

3-6	4-4	4-5	4-6	5-5	5-6	6-6

HIGH-SPEED CROSSWORD

Across
1 Stylish
5 Capital of France
10 Zeus's wife
11 ___ in (overflowing with)
12 1992 Edward James Olmos movie: 2 wds.
14 Completed
15 One way to fall in love
18 Legislate
23 Individual
24 "Hey there!"
25 What parents may "put up" with their kids: 2 wds.
28 Detroit baseball team
29 "Do the Right Thing" director
30 Therefore
31 Salad green
33 Train's sound
35 Mississippi music: 2 wds.
41 Wedding
42 Biblical birthright seller
43 Brewskis
44 Belgrade native

Down
1 When doubled, a dance
2 ___ and haw (stall)
3 Anger
4 Christmas ___
5 Rate
6 Not in the dark about: 2 wds.
7 Took off quickly
8 School of thought
9 "___-Devil" (Meryl Streep movie)
13 Climbing plant
15 Tooth's home
16 "Tomorrow" musical
17 Condescend
19 Swed. neighbor
20 "Fixing ___" (Beatles song): 2 wds.
21 Ice cream holders
22 Carries
24 Running backs gain them: abbr.
26 P.I., in old slang
27 ___ Set (kid's toy)
31 Corn holder
32 Cameos, e.g.
34 ___ Christian Andersen
35 Do a voice-over
36 One way to go: abbr.
37 Deception
38 "It's no ___!"
39 Swimmer's ___
40 Big sandwich

WORDWHEEL

Using only the letters in the Wordwheel, you have ten minutes to find as many words as possible, none of which may be plurals, foreign words or proper nouns. Each word must be of three letters or more, all must contain the central letter and letters can only be used once in every word. There is at least one nine-letter word in the wheel.

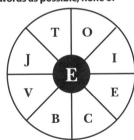

Nine-letter word(s):
_____

SUM CIRCLE

Fill the three empty circles with the symbols +, – and x in some order, to make a sum which totals the number in the centre. Each symbol must be used once and calculations are made in the direction of travel (clockwise).

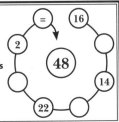

WORDSEARCH WORKOUT

```
T N L U Y O S L S T O O B
I O C A C F C T N O W O X
U G V G V O K O O B O E V
R P W E T I A Z O O L V S
F N K Y H P T T Q L K C O
S V C T P F Q S P S I R C
P T S L T L Z Q E C Y F T
O L E V I O Q I W F O E O
R S L A V W R B A S U T B
C M H A O E B E H D S W E
H E I H F R H M V O H B R
R N Z S O S K C S P B M Y
E N J C T Z X B F O Y N E
A I R S S E N T E W G N C
P D D A M P W H A T W W C
```

AUTUMN

APPLES
BOOTS
COAT
COOL
CRISP
CROPS
DAMP
FALL
FESTIVAL
FLOWERS
FRUIT
HAT
MIST
OCTOBER
PODS
REAP
SHEAF
STEW
STOOK
WETNESS

DOUBLE FUN SUDOKU

TASTY TEASER

6	1	7	8					
5		9		3	7			2
	3			5		1		4
			5	9			6	
	2	3				9	4	
	6			4	3			
2		8		1			5	
4			6	7		3		8
					2	7	9	1

BRAIN BUSTER

			6		9	3	5	
				7				8
		4		3	2	7		
	8		2		1	5	6	
6								2
	1	5	9		7		8	
	3	6	7		5			
7				3				
	4	1	8		6			

1 MINUTE NUMBER CRUNCH

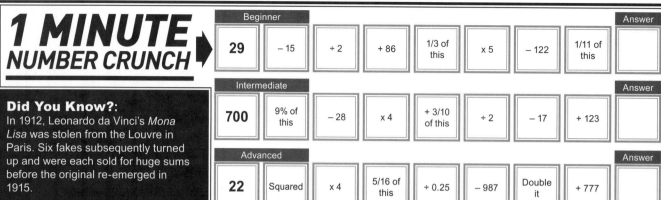

Beginner								Answer
29	− 15	÷ 2	+ 86	1/3 of this	x 5	− 122	1/11 of this	

Intermediate								Answer
700	9% of this	− 28	x 4	+ 3/10 of this	÷ 2	− 17	+ 123	

Advanced								Answer
22	Squared	x 4	5/16 of this	÷ 0.25	− 987	Double it	+ 777	

Did You Know?:
In 1912, Leonardo da Vinci's *Mona Lisa* was stolen from the Louvre in Paris. Six fakes subsequently turned up and were each sold for huge sums before the original re-emerged in 1915.

HIGH-SPEED CROSSWORD

Across
1 Country karaoke came from
6 Astound
11 Cognizant
12 Sprite flavor
13 Brawl
14 Lend ___ (assist): 2 wds.
15 Respected lady
17 Hi-___ graphics
18 "I ___ you one"
20 Baggy
22 Toy company
24 Tiny particle
27 Chips in
28 Foreword, for short
29 Advertising sign gas
30 Negates
31 Begin
33 "Help!"
34 Butter amount
36 Old Oldsmobile
38 Broadcasting: 2 wds.
40 Dutch cheese
43 Back in style
44 Bucolic
45 Sixth-grader, maybe
46 Sailing: 2 wds.

Down
1 Improvise musically
2 Leave astonished
3 South Carolina's nickname: 2 wds.
4 Length times width, for a square
5 Pokes fun at
6 San Antone landmark
7 Just OK
8 Bar drinks: 2 wds.
9 Area
10 Ultimate goals
16 "You've got mail" co.
18 Arab League member
19 Decline
21 Beach grains
23 Camping gear
25 Cookie often eaten with milk
26 What a rolling stone doesn't gather
28 Acura model
30 Website address, for short
32 Hank with 755 home runs
34 After-dinner drink
35 Again
37 Beat badly
39 Anger
41 Actor Daniel ___ Kim
42 Miss. neighbor

CODEWORD CONUNDRUM

A B C D E F G H I J K L M
N O P Q R S T U V W X Y Z

Reference Box

1	2 P	3	4	5	6	7	8	9 R	10	11	12	13
14	15	16	17	18	19 E	20	21	22	23	24	25	26

DOUBLE FUN SUDOKU

TASTY TEASER

			9	5	1			4
			3		6			7
4	3	9		2				6
		4	5		3		7	
8		2				5		3
	1		7		2	4		
6				7		9	8	1
2			1		8			
1			4	6	9			

BRAIN BUSTER

9			4		1			2
	1		7		6		4	
		6		8		3		
5		4				8		9
	9						7	
7		2				1		3
		1		4		5		
	4		3		8		9	
6			2		7			1

SPIDOKU

Each of the eight segments of the spider's web should be filled with a different number from 1 to 8, in such a way that every ring also contains a different number from 1 to 8.

HIGH-SPEED CROSSWORD

Across

1 ___ on the back
4 "Polythene ___" (Beatles song)
7 Stomach muscles
10 Paul Newman role
11 Vain person's issue
12 Montana or Biden
13 "The Little Drummer Boy" syllable
14 ATM code
15 Museum pieces
16 "Act your ___!"
17 Finds out new things
19 Deborah's "The King and I" co-star
20 Attention-getting shouts
21 Similar
23 "Kapow!"
25 Paquin or Chlumsky
26 Verve
28 Thin fish
29 Permitted
31 Coup d'___
33 "What ___ doing?": 2 wds.
34 Waves, perhaps: 2 wds.
37 Deeply philosophical
38 Fuss
39 Enjoy a Winter Olympics sport
41 "Lord, is ___?": 2 wds.
42 Word before gift or reflex
43 Chest muscle, for short
44 Photographer Goldin
45 Doc bloc
46 "Is it ___ wonder?"
47 Food from a hen

Down

1 Tropical fruit
2 Salad vegetable
3 Facebook format
4 Vigor
5 Catlike
6 Tourist's wear: 2 wds.
7 Almost closed, like a door
8 "___ in the USA" (Springsteen album)
9 Adjusts, as a clock
18 Make ___ (be a good vendor): 2 wds.
20 Place to get a massage: 2 wds.
22 Bending pair
24 What each of the three long entries in this puzzle begins with
27 Convention ID
30 Cloud with a silver ___
32 Clay of "American Idol" fame
34 Epic story
35 Sandler of "Big Daddy"
36 Exercise discipline with lots of stretching
40 Cold

(crossword grid)

WORDSEARCH WORKOUT

```
A R S N K R N A R A H A S
I S Z F U A R A H A N O F
R I C H I B R G I B S O N
O M F R O K I A U U O Z D
T P Y H E A H A K T N N E
C S D Q Y L M W N U U A A
I O A A R A B I A N M U T
V N S A C H I B O G W H H
T Y H A N A R O N O S A V
A T T L O R V E J Q Y U A
E A E I G I G R W P A H L
R K L B B E V A J O M I L
G U U Y V Y D P O U D H E
A C T A D U F A N N A C Y
W Q U N P E H Y H D R P U
```

DESERTS

AN NAFUD
ARABIAN
ATACAMA
CHIHUAHUAN
DASHT E LUT
DEATH VALLEY
GIBSON
GOBI
GREAT VICTORIA
KALAHARI
KARA KUM
LIBYAN
MOJAVE
NEGEV
NUBIAN
SAHARA
SIMPSON
SONORAN
SYRIAN
THAR

DOUBLE FUN SUDOKU

TASTY TEASER

6			5	8		1	2	
2	3		7					
		5	1			7		3
		8		6			9	4
	7		3		1		6	
3	9		4			2		
1		4			5	9		
					4		8	6
	5	9		2	7			1

BRAIN BUSTER

9			2		8			6
	5					1		
	6		4		3		5	
	3	4	7		2	6	9	
	9	7	1		6	4	2	
	1		9		7		8	
		8				7		
4			8		5			3

MATCHSTICK MAGIC

Here is an arrangement showing a diamond shape and a square shape. Move three matches to show a diamond, a square, and two equilateral triangles (an equilateral triangle has three angles of equal degrees and three sides of equal length).

BRAIN TEASER

What replaces the question mark?

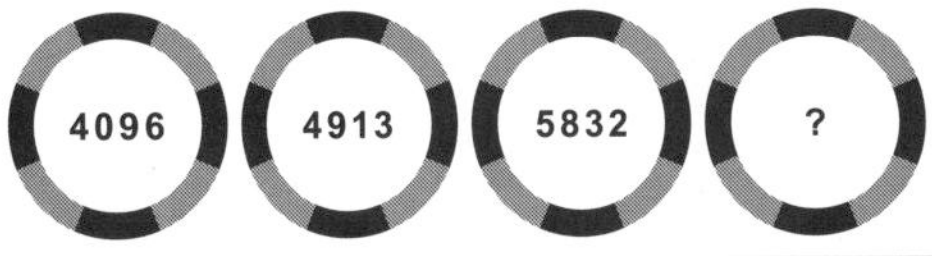

4096   4913   5832   ?

DOMINO PLACEMENT

Did You Know?:

Contrary to widespread belief, lemmings do not commit mass suicide. The myth was created by film-makers who mostly faked the 'evidence'.

A standard set of 28 dominoes has been laid out as shown. Can you draw in the edges of them all? The check-box is provided as an aid and the domino already placed will help.

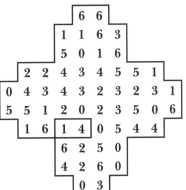

```
            6 6
          1 1 6 3
          5 0 1 6
      2 2 4 3 4 5 5 1
    0 4 3 4 3 2 3 2 3 1
    5 5 1 2 0 2 3 5 0 6
      1 6 1 4 0 5 4 4
          6 2 5 0
          4 2 6 0
            0 3
```

0-0	0-1	0-2	0-3	0-4	0-5	0-6

1-1	1-2	1-3	1-4	1-5	1-6	2-2
			✓			

2-3	2-4	2-5	2-6	3-3	3-4	3-5

3-6	4-4	4-5	4-6	5-5	5-6	6-6

CODEWORD CONUNDRUM

A B C D E F G H I J K L M
N O P Q R S T U V W X Y Z

Reference Box

1	2 C	3	4	5	6	7	8	9	10	11	12	13
14	15	16	17	18	19 E	20	21	22	23	24	25	26

DOUBLE FUN SUDOKU

TASTY TEASER

					4	5	7	2
	5		2	3		6		
9		8	5					1
	8	2		4				5
6		1		3				7
7			5		4	3		
2				8	9		4	
	3		1	7		2		
8	6	4	9					

BRAIN BUSTER

5		2		4				3
3		1		6		2		9
1	3					5	6	
	7	5				8	9	
6	8						4	2
7		6		1		4		5
2			5		9			8

PYRAMID PLUS

Every brick in this pyramid contains a number which is the sum of the two numbers below it, so that F=A+B, etc.
Just work out the missing numbers!

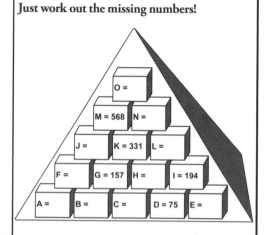

O =
M = 568   N =
J =   K = 331   L =
F =   G = 157   H =   I = 194
A =   B =   C =   D = 75   E =

HIGH-SPEED CROSSWORD

Across
1 Back of the neck
5 Insignia
11 Biblical twin
12 African nation whose capital is Lilongwe
13 Drink quickly
14 Flying high
15 MacLachlan of "Twin Peaks"
16 Backboard attachment
17 Not pro
19 Bidding site
23 "Forget about it": 2 wds.
25 Song for one
26 Iron ___
27 Sandwich order, for short
29 Awful
30 Functionalities
32 Saudi ___
34 Taboo act
35 Indiana city, or a man's name
36 Meadow
38 ___-Caribbean music
41 Grooms' mates
44 Hard punch
45 Has a good time
46 Weak, as an excuse
47 Disinclined
48 "For Your ___ Only"

Down
1 Adam's apple spot
2 Far from ruddy
3 TV celebrity chef from Savannah: 2 wds.
4 Oregon city
5 TV celebrity chef from Louisiana: 2 wds.
6 African nation
7 Charges
8 Back muscle, familiarly
9 She's a sheep
10 ___-Atlantic
18 Check
20 TV celebrity chef from New York City: 2 wds.
21 Jai ___
22 "Star Wars" role
23 It may be proper
24 About: 2 wds.
28 "La la" preceder
31 Fuse two pieces of metal
33 Fit for farming
37 Congers
39 City of the Coliseum
40 Has a mortgage
41 Undergarment
42 Holy title: abbr.
43 "___ got it!"

Crossword grid (numbered): 1 2 3 4 5 6 7 8 9 10 / 11 12 / 13 14 / 15 16 / 17 18 19 20 21 22 / 23 24 25 / 26 27 28 29 / 30 31 32 33 / 34 35 / 36 37 38 39 40 / 41 42 43 44 / 45 46 / 47 48

1 MINUTE NUMBER CRUNCH

Beginner								Answer
71	− 22	x 2	+ 26	50% of this	+ 19	1/3 of this	x 2	

Intermediate								Answer
59	x 3	− 114	+ 1/3 of this	5/12 of this	3/7 of this	x 13	+ 85	

Advanced								Answer
52	7/13 of this	x 9	1/6 of this	Squared	− 3/4 of this	5/9 of this	+ 60% of this	

Did You Know?:
Carnivorous animals won't eat an animal that has been killed by lightning because the victim has effectively been cooked, rendering it unpalatable to a wild animal.

HIGH-SPEED CROSSWORD

Across

1 Arms and legs
6 "Beat it!"
11 Honda brand
12 Texas food
13 Have a temper tantrum, maybe: 2 wds.
15 Holed up
16 Prior to
17 Go-___ (1980s band)
18 "___ you serious?"
19 Faint
20 Anger
21 "Beetle Bailey" creator Walker
23 Hit with a baseball
25 Waken from slumber
27 Hidden
30 Janitor's tools
34 Valuable mineral
35 "Dig in!"
37 By way of
38 High card
39 ___ Lanka
40 Christmas present wrapper, maybe
41 XXXIII
44 Kind of dye
45 Doozies
46 ___ Allan Poe
47 Pharaoh's land

Down

1 English poet John
2 Suzuki of baseball
3 "___ on the Orient Express"
4 "My man!"
5 Did a lumberjack's job
6 Plans
7 Greek letter
8 Try to answer on "Jeopardy!": 2 wds.
9 Former vice president: 2 wds.
10 Didn't hit
14 Small river, often
22 Three: It.
24 Store convenience, for short
26 Lousy, like a movie
27 Hate
28 Tried to appear larger, as a cat
29 ___ up (preparing to drive a golf ball)
31 Too
32 Get larger, as a workload: 2 wds.
33 Least risky
36 Deed
42 Biology abbr.
43 Embrace

1 MINUTE NUMBER CRUNCH

Did You Know?:
A once-common way to lose weight was to swallow live tapeworms. Once inside the stomach the worms would consume a proportion of the host's food.

Beginner								Answer
36	1/12 of this	x 20	+ 3	÷ 21	x 19	+ 18	1/3 of this	

Intermediate								Answer
13	x 9	+ 414	5/9 of this	÷ 5	+ 63	x 5	9/10 of this	

Advanced								Answer
26	Cubed	3/8 of this	+ 2/3 of this	60% of this	− 4607	5/16 of this	3/5 of this	

WORDSEARCH WORKOUT

```
V Y N P T U A S N I C X O
Z I Z W I B O A Y A O Q J
U O D Z U N K P R R R D E
Z N I A M C O E T U A G D
U I L O L A P T R I I H R
T R N X N B L M N N M V E
O A C F F A L V O O E A V
L B E P A R G A A Q I R R
R L B F H N I E N S O R S
E A L S I H D E T C I Y M
M A A J Z A N E S R L A P
T E M P R A N I L L O O B
H Z L S B E F O N Y I V E
E H R E N F E L S E R N P
Z T P I N O T B L A N C G
```

GRAPE VARIETIES

ALBARINO
BUAL
CINSAUT
EHRENFELSER
FIANO
KERNER
MALBEC
MALVASIA
MERLOT
OPTIMA
ORTEGA
PINOT BLANC
PINOT NOIR
RIESLING
SYRAH
TEMPRANILLO
VERDEJO
VIDAL BLANC
VIURA
ZINFANDEL

DOUBLE FUN SUDOKU

TASTY TEASER

	1					9	6
3		4		6		5	8
			1	8	2		
7	5	6			4		3
	1		8		5		6
4			6			9	2	5
			5	7	8		
	8	3		4		1		2
9	6				4		

BRAIN BUSTER

	2	3		4		9	1
	9		3		2		7
		6				3	
			9		6		
		8				2	
			2		4		
	1					8	
7		1		8		4	
5	2			9		7	6

WHATEVER NEXT?

In the diagram below, which letter should replace the question mark?

A B
F L   A E
E ?
B M   C F
E G

BRAIN TEASER

The average of two numbers is 41½; the average of three numbers is 72; what is the third number?

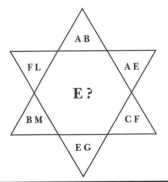

? ____ ?

Mind Over Matter

Given that the letters are valued 1-26 according to their places in the alphabet, can you crack the mystery code to reveal the missing letter?

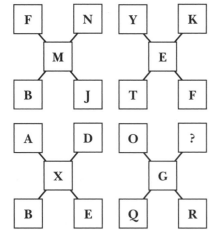

DOUBLE FUN SUDOKU

TASTY TEASER

				6	5	1	7	
	3		4		8	9		
	4	6			1		3	
6			1	7				5
7	1						4	8
2				5	4			7
	5		9			4	6	
	1	5		3		2		
	7	9	2	1				

BRAIN BUSTER

	8			9		1	4	5
	3		1					
	6			7	5			
5					9			
4	1						2	7
		3						8
			5	2			6	
					8		9	
8	4	2		3				5

CODEWORD CONUNDRUM

A B C D E F G H I J K L M
N O P Q R S T U V W X Y Z

Reference Box

1	2	3	4	5	6	7	8	9	10	11	12	13
	I		C									
14	15	16	17	18	19	20	21	22	23	24	25	26
										T		

HIGH-SPEED CROSSWORD

Across
1 To the ___ degree
4 To and ___
7 Karlsbad, for one
10 Nest egg money
11 Ending for velvet
12 ___ and cheese sandwich
13 "E.T." actor: 2 wds.
16 ___ oil
17 Ready for business
18 Make cleaner: 2 wds.
20 Big truck
23 Stands for painters
26 ___ Lodge
28 One of the Osmonds
29 Language
31 Emerald ___ (Ireland's nickname)
32 Became angry: 2 wds.
34 Since: 2 wds.
36 Mass holder
40 Longtime CNN newsman: 2 wds.
42 First name in the NFL
43 Aurora's counterpart
44 ___ Speedwagon
45 Caspian or North
46 Make a different color, like hair
47 Actress Poehler

Down
1 Small sips, as of booze
2 Oak or hickory
3 Head covers
4 Physics Nobelist Enrico ___
5 Ebb
6 Former partner of Lennon
7 Mall visitors
8 Cracker spread
9 "Absolutely!"
14 Using, as plates: 2 wds.
15 "Amen!": 3 wds.
19 Starchy food
20 TV ___
21 Green prefix
22 Country landlocked by China and Russia
24 "___ Abner"
25 "Understand?"
27 Away
30 Find work for
33 Come to mind
34 Amazes
35 Exclusive
37 Poet ___ Pound
38 Appear
39 QB Aikman
41 Four-poster, for example

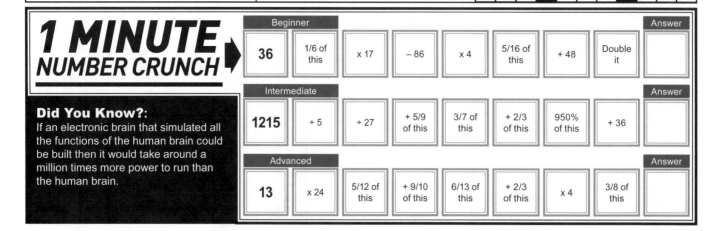

1 MINUTE NUMBER CRUNCH

Beginner								Answer
36	1/6 of this	x 17	− 86	x 4	5/16 of this	+ 48	Double it	

Intermediate								Answer
1215	÷ 5	÷ 27	+ 5/9 of this	3/7 of this	+ 2/3 of this	950% of this	+ 36	

Advanced								Answer
13	x 24	5/12 of this	+ 9/10 of this	6/13 of this	+ 2/3 of this	x 4	3/8 of this	

Did You Know?:
If an electronic brain that simulated all the functions of the human brain could be built then it would take around a million times more power to run than the human brain.

BATTLESHIP BOUT

Did You Know?:
The first quantity-produced car was made by the US company, Dureya. In 1896 Dureya produced a first run of 13 cars.

Can you place the vessels into the diagram? Some parts of vessels or sea squares have already been filled in. A number to the right or below a row or column refers to the number of occupied squares in that row or column.
Any vessel may be positioned horizontally or vertically, but no part of a vessel touches part of any other vessel, either horizontally, vertically or diagonally.

Empty Area of Sea:
Aircraft Carrier:
Battleships:
Cruisers:
Submarines:

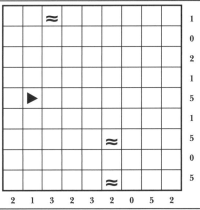

HIGH-SPEED CROSSWORD

Across
1 Wise bird
4 Absorbed, as a cost
7 Chair part
10 "___ won't be afraid" ("Stand by Me" line): 2 wds.
11 Toni Morrison novel "___ Baby"
12 "___ got it!"
13 "Seinfeld" role: 2 wds.
16 Another "Seinfeld" role
17 Dermatologist's hole
18 Helmsley of hotels
20 Away and in trouble
23 Everyday
27 Jeans name
29 Gawk
30 Old counter
32 Graze
33 "Come in!"
35 Play "Wheel of Fortune"
38 Hawaiian welcomes
42 Snide comment: 2 wds.
44 "Tarzan" extra
45 And so on
46 Confederate general
47 Battering device
48 "C'___ la vie!"
49 "___ & Order"

Down
1 "___ bitten, twice shy"
2 Cashmere, e.g.
3 Mona ___ (famous painting)
4 Make up (for)
5 Assume, as a role: 2 wds.
6 Go astray
7 Fancy wheels
8 For always
9 "Pretty Woman" star Richard
14 Old-fashioned woman's name
15 Besides: 2 wds.
19 Discouraging words
20 Pie ___ mode: 2 wds.
21 Spider's home
22 Eggs
24 Wild West?
25 "___ we alone?"
26 Was on the road to victory
28 Closest star to Earth, with "the"
31 Begins
34 Bumper sticker word
35 Wound reminder
36 ___ John's (pizza chain)
37 Thingy
39 Campus building
40 Part of town
41 Throw off, as poll results
43 "___-haw!"

WORDWHEEL

Using only the letters in the Wordwheel, you have ten minutes to find as many words as possible, none of which may be plurals, foreign words or proper nouns. Each word must be of three letters or more, all must contain the central letter and letters can only be used once in every word. There is at least one nine-letter word in the wheel.

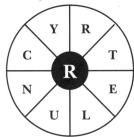

Nine-letter word(s):
_____

SUM CIRCLE

Fill the three empty circles with the symbols +, – and x in some order, to make a sum which totals the number in the centre. Each symbol must be used once and calculations are made in the direction of travel (clockwise).

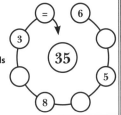

WORDSEARCH WORKOUT

COINS

ANGEL
BEZANT
COPPER
CROWN
DIME
DOUBLOON
DUCAT
FARTHING
GROAT
GUINEA
KRUGERRAND
NOBLE
OBOL
POUND
REAL
SIXPENCE
SOU
STATE
THALER
THREEPENNY BIT

DOUBLE **FUN** SUDOKU

TASTY TEASER

		2	3	1	8	7		
1		7	5			9		6
4			7				3	
	5			3				9
3		4				1		7
8			2				4	
	9			2				8
2		8			7	6		5
		6	8	4	9	3		

BRAIN BUSTER

7								8
5			6		7			3
	1	4		2		9	6	
		9		1		8		
			2		5			
		8		7		3		
	4	3		5		6	7	
9			1		4			2
8								1

1 MINUTE NUMBER CRUNCH

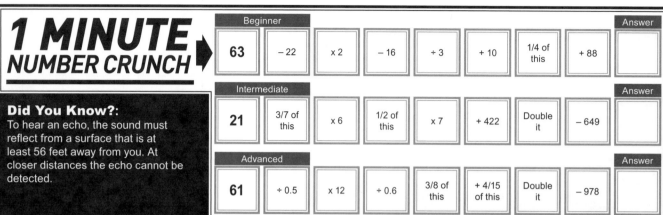

Beginner							Answer
63	− 22	x 2	− 16	÷ 3	+ 10	1/4 of this	+ 88

Intermediate							Answer
21	3/7 of this	x 6	1/2 of this	x 7	+ 422	Double it	− 649

Advanced							Answer
61	÷ 0.5	x 12	÷ 0.6	3/8 of this	+ 4/15 of this	Double it	− 978

Did You Know?:
To hear an echo, the sound must reflect from a surface that is at least 56 feet away from you. At closer distances the echo cannot be detected.

HIGH-SPEED CROSSWORD

Across

1 Publicity, casually
4 "Raiders of the Lost ___"
7 Six-pack muscles
10 Got outta Dodge
11 ___ and Jerry's (ice cream brand)
12 ___ Tuesday (Mardi Gras)
13 Neighbor of Canada
15 Time of the past
16 "Dig in!"
17 Authority
19 Cheat, in a way
21 "Don't ___!"
22 Palindromic woman's name
23 Hershey's candy bar
27 Spearheaded
28 "ER" network
29 Scottish "no"
30 Saw wrongly
32 Believer's suffix
33 DVD player's predecessor
34 Frosts, as a cake
35 Secret booze container
38 Strong tree
39 Calif. airport
40 Breakfast food
44 Good club?
45 Prefix with lateral
46 Baseball card stat
47 Take down the aisle
48 Athletes Cobb and Warner
49 Gelled

Down

1 Lyricist Gershwin
2 "China Beach" setting
3 Volleyball player's equipment
4 Not much: 2 wds.
5 ___ center
6 Backpack
7 Not many: 2 wds.
8 Empty, like a cupboard
9 Part of a constellation
14 Sunbeam
18 Plains city, for short
19 Placid
20 "The ___ Love": 2 wds.
21 Ann ___, Mich.
23 Flatten: 2 wds.
24 Fancy pants
25 Lessen
26 "___ go!"
31 Flat-screens, e.g.
34 "How Dry ___": 2 wds.
35 Blemish
36 Shoestring
37 Fired
38 Elevator name
41 "___ Which Way But Loose"
42 Honest prez
43 Ignited

CODEWORD CONUNDRUM

A B C D E F G H I J K L M
N O P Q R S T U V W X Y Z

Reference Box

1	2	3	4	5	6	7	8	9	10	11	12	13
L	O		I									

14	15	16	17	18	19	20	21	22	23	24	25	26

DOUBLE FUN SUDOKU

TASTY TEASER

4			1					6
		2	8	5		3		
5	1	8				2	9	4
1			7			5		
	2		4		9		8	
		3		6				2
2	9	1				7	3	8
		4		7	1	6		
7				3				9

BRAIN BUSTER

7	1			6				
	2		1					
		2		9	4			
	3	9			4			
	6		2				5	
		8			3	2		
	8	7		2				
					8		1	
			5			6	2	

SPIDOKU

Each of the eight segments of the spider's web should be filled with a different number from 1 to 8, in such a way that every ring also contains a different number from 1 to 8.

HIGH-SPEED CROSSWORD

Across
1 Catholic service
5 Common exercise
11 Soon, to a poet
12 Heir's concern
13 Data
14 President, say
15 After expenses
16 Lion's share
17 Movie actors with no lines
19 ___ butter
23 Sit in on, as a class
25 Actress Gardner
26 Aspect
28 TV host with a role in "The Color Purple"
30 Narcissist's problem
31 Took part in a democracy
33 ___ Virginia
35 Writing utensil
38 "Beware the ___ of March"
40 Man's name that reverses to another man's name
41 Swindler: 2 wds.
44 Promising words
45 Gentle wind
46 Department store section
47 Grow irate: 2 wds.
48 Approximately: 2 wds.

Down
1 Acadia National Park's state
2 Take by force, as a territory
3 Mexican entree: 2 wds.
4 ___-Caps
5 First female House Speaker
6 Functions
7 Sports figures
8 Owned
9 Western tribe for whom a U.S. state is named
10 Apiece
16 Fox comedy show
18 Wish you could take back
20 Alcoholic beverage: 2 wds.
21 ___ Marie Saint
22 "I see!"
24 Carries
26 Not many
27 Number of years
29 Fountain or ink
32 Began
34 It rings in the kitchen
36 "Reversal of Fortune" star Jeremy
37 Catch with a rope
39 Leave stunned
41 ABC rival
42 Miner's find
43 French word in wedding announcements
44 "What I think," when texting

Filled-in letters visible: 1 Across: LUIS / SN; 13 Across: INFO; 26 Down: Fe; 30: We; 33: W T; 38 Across: TIDES; MA; 45 Across: BREEZE; Re

WORDSEARCH WORKOUT

```
S Z S E K I S L L I B Y S
M H D C E P S F N X A K L
I D H L I V T R B G I S R
K F R P U P O Y R M C E B
E A H F R G O E P R V U F
M S F B E Q T I O Y L M X
H I T R N L N O R L X A E
N H C I A I G T S F H G D
T L T W M E S E H G P W T
Y T Z O B I Y I J B S I R
V E O X U E T K D K Y T E
F Y D P M Y M Y S C K C N
T V U A B Q R H N V A H T
L C O D L I N A N I G A F
M A R L E Y N H Y A T I C
```

DICKENS CHARACTERS

BILL SIKES
BULLS EYE
BUMBLE
CODLIN
FAGIN
FRED TRENT
MAGWITCH
MARLEY
NANCY
PIP
POTT
ROGER CLY
SCROOGE
SKIMPIN
SMIKE
STRYVER
TINY TIM
TOOTS
VUFFIN
WALTER GAY

DOUBLE FUN SUDOKU

TASTY TEASER

	6	3				2		
	8		6	5		7		9
	5		4		8		1	
				7	4	5		8
1			8		2			4
3		8	9	6				
	1		3		9		2	
9		4		1	7		5	
		7				3	9	

BRAIN BUSTER

2		1		6		7		8
	3						2	
9			2		8			1
	2			3		4		
		7		5				
	6		4		2			
7		4		2				9
	5					7		
6		3		9		8		4

MATCHSTICK MAGIC

Move four matchsticks to make three squares.

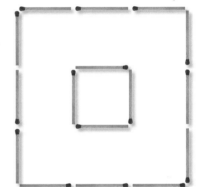

BRAIN TEASER

The price of one pair of socks is €3.50; the price of a pack of six pairs is €19.50. To the nearest whole number, by what percentage are the socks cheaper when you buy a pack of six?

? ___ ?

1 MINUTE NUMBER CRUNCH

Beginner								Answer
104	+ 17	2/11 of this	x 4	− 16	5/6 of this	+ 90	÷ 3	

Intermediate								Answer
390	7/10 of this	2/3 of this	Double it	75% of this	− 87	÷ 6	x 12	

Advanced								Answer
293	+ 739	− 5/8 of this	2/9 of this	x 7	5/14 of this	+ 3/5 of this	275% of this	

Did You Know?:
As well as being the largest animal on Earth, the blue whale is also the loudest. It can emit sounds at up to levels of 188 decibels.

CODEWORD CONUNDRUM

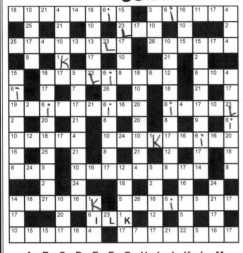

A B C D E F G H I J K L M
N O P Q R S T U V W X Y Z

Reference Box

1 K	2	3	4	5	6	7	8	9	10	11	12	13
14	15	16	17	18	19	20	21	22	23	24	25	26

DOUBLE FUN SUDOKU

TASTY TEASER

9			1		6			2
	1			7			6	
	6	2		5		7	3	
	9	5	4		7	6	8	
6			5		9			7
	4	7	6		3	9	1	
	2	9		4		3	7	
	8			9			5	
3			7		1			8

BRAIN BUSTER

	5	9		3		8	7	
		6	8		4	2		
2		5				6		7
9	8						2	4
1		3				5		8
		8	6		7	1		
	3	1		5		4	6	

PYRAMID PLUS

Every brick in this pyramid contains a number which is the sum of the two numbers below it, so that F=A+B, etc.
Just work out the missing numbers!

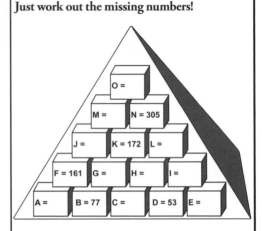

O =
M =   N = 305
J =   K = 172   L =
F = 161   G =   H =   I =
A =   B = 77   C =   D = 53   E =

HIGH-SPEED CROSSWORD

Across
1 Pub orders
6 Weapons
10 Fit for a king
11 Unlike the kiddie pool
12 Baby's garment
14 Roy's wife
15 Finishes up
16 Without walls
17 Send a message to
19 Dusk
21 One of Frank's exes
22 Hail Mary, e.g.
23 Nice stone
24 Affirmative vote
25 Church bench
28 Snack for an aardvark
29 Mining metal
30 Respectful greeting
33 Didn't dillydally
34 Coagulate
35 Former center O'Neal, casually
37 "Portnoy's Complaint" author Philip
38 Professor's guarantee
41 "Do ___ others as..."
42 Noun-forming suffix
43 Grizzly, e.g.
44 Naps

Down
1 Sib for sis
2 Director ___ Howard
3 An optometrist administers it: 2 wds.
4 Failed to be
5 Went down in a hurry
6 Extras
7 Brings in
8 Brouhaha
9 Exhausted
13 A teacher administers it: 2 wds.
17 Make "it," on the playground
18 Night before
20 Finds a niche for
22 Breathe hard
25 A teacher administers it: 2 wds.
26 Prior to
27 Join in holy matrimony
28 Name on a book's spine
30 Wash thoroughly
31 "Home ___"
32 "Whole ___ Shakin' Goin' On"
33 ___ Domingo (capital of the Dominican Republic)
36 Principal
39 Salmon ___ (sushi bar stuff)
40 Navy rank: abbr.

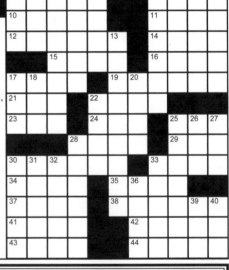

1 MINUTE NUMBER CRUNCH

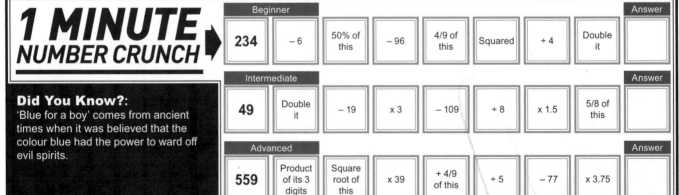

Did You Know?:
'Blue for a boy' comes from ancient times when it was believed that the colour blue had the power to ward off evil spirits.

Beginner								Answer
234	− 6	50% of this	− 96	4/9 of this	Squared	÷ 4	Double it	

Intermediate								Answer
49	Double it	− 19	x 3	− 109	÷ 8	x 1.5	5/8 of this	

Advanced								Answer
559	Product of its 3 digits	Square root of this	x 39	+ 4/9 of this	÷ 5	− 77	x 3.75	

HIGH-SPEED CROSSWORD

Across
1 Zines
5 Burning
10 Biol. subject
11 Travel book
12 "Young Frankenstein" woman
13 Not pen
14 Scary knives
16 Finale
17 ___ Mujeres, Mexico
18 Amiss
20 Motel
22 President before LBJ
25 Soaked
26 Go downhill
27 Portland's st.
28 Norton and Wood
29 "The Name of the Rose" author Umberto ___
30 Relatives
31 ___-bodied
33 Play on words
36 Run-down hotel
39 Sloth or panda
41 Forbidden act
42 Egyptian peninsula
43 Inflict upon: 2 wds.
44 Ringo of the Beatles
45 By the ___ of one's teeth

Down
1 Domestic
2 Late model ___ Nicole Smith
3 Funny presents: 2 wds.
4 Bucks
5 Long, long time
6 Pistol, e.g.
7 Hair critters
8 Norse god
9 Fuse
13 Bart Simpson specialty: 2 wds.
15 "Fur ___" (Beethoven work)
18 Have debts to
19 Gave grub to
21 Mythical weeper
22 It's full of funny things: 2 wds.
23 Thu. follower
24 Barbie's guy
32 Comes down to Earth
33 Quarterback's throw
34 Apartment
35 One of Columbus's ships
36 Just OK
37 Not pro-
38 Continue: 2 wds.
40 Ruin

(Crossword grid with filled answers: ANNA, GUIDE, PENCIL, E, STARR)

DOMINO PLACEMENT

Did You Know?:
The pufferfish is something of a delicacy, but parts of it contain a poison so deadly that a fatal dose weighs just four thousandths of an ounce.

A standard set of 28 dominoes has been laid out as shown. Can you draw in the edges of them all? The check-box is provided as an aid and the domino already placed will help.

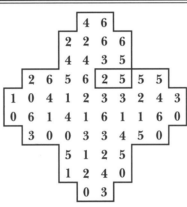

```
          4 6
        2 2 6 6
        4 4 3 5
    2 6 5 6 2 5 5 5
  1 0 4 1 2 3 3 2 4 3
  0 6 1 4 1 6 1 1 6 0
    3 0 0 3 3 4 5 0
        5 1 2 5
        1 2 4 0
          0 3
```

0-0	0-1	0-2	0-3	0-4	0-5	0-6

1-1	1-2	1-3	1-4	1-5	1-6	2-2

2-3	2-4	2-5	2-6	3-3	3-4	3-5
	✓					

3-6	4-4	4-5	4-6	5-5	5-6	6-6

WORDSEARCH WORKOUT

```
Q J M A R I E C U R I E B
N O S T R A D A M U S L L
N B A R D O T T B A E E Y
Z A K I C B I E R R F O C
D U M A S C R T I F M X A
B D A L T L R O I I Y Y R
E E A E I E T E T M S H E
L L E O C L N T N R M D G
P A Z S P R E O O H E C R
A I F T S R A L M G H I E
S R J R A I E M A I O R B
T E S N A D T U R N Y Y E
E A D Q T N L A E V P G D
U X H R K L C R M G C I X
R F R O E H S K K B K J I
```

FAMOUS FRENCH PEOPLE

BARDOT
BAUDELAIRE
BERLIOZ
BLERIOT
CHIRAC
DE BERGERAC
DE GAULLE
DELORS
DUMAS
EIFFEL
FRANCK
MARCEAU
MARIE CURIE
MATISSE
MITTERAND
MONET
NOSTRADAMUS
PASTEUR
RENOIR
SARTRE

DOUBLE FUN SUDOKU

TASTY TEASER

	4		1	6	3			
7				9		2		
8	2	3				6	1	9
	3		7			4		
6			8		2			3
		1			5		9	
4	6	5				9	3	8
	8		4				5	
		7	9	5		2		

BRAIN BUSTER

	6	7		5		8	9	
		2	1		8	3		
4		5				6		8
7	8						3	1
3		6				2		9
	8	9		2	4			
	5	4		6		1	2	

WHATEVER NEXT?

In the diagram below, which letter should replace the question mark?

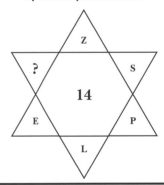

(Star diagram with letters Z, S, P, L, E, ? and center 14)

BRAIN TEASER

What day immediately follows the day three days before the day immediately before the day two days after the day immediately before Thursday?

? _____ ?

Mind Over Matter

Given that the letters are valued 1-26 according to their places in the alphabet, can you crack the mystery code to reveal the missing letter?

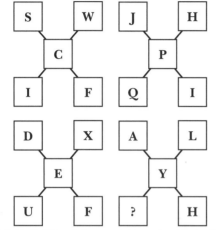

S	W	J	H
C		P	
I	F	Q	I
D	X	A	L
E		Y	
U	F	?	H

DOUBLE FUN SUDOKU

TASTY TEASER

	6	8		2		7	9	
5			1					
		9		3	8	4		2
	8				9	1	3	7
	2					4		
9	5	7	3				8	
8		1	5	7		6		
				2				3
	3	6		4		5	7	

BRAIN BUSTER

8			4			9	1	
	3			5		6		
4		9						7
2	9		5					
						2		8	3
9						3		4
		6		1			2	
	2	7			8			1

CODEWORD CONUNDRUM

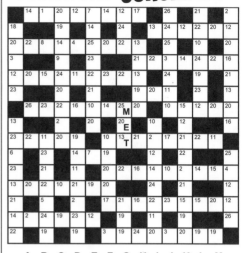

```
A B C D E F G H I J K L M
N O P Q R S T U V W X Y Z
```

Reference Box

1	2	3	4	5	6	7	8	9	10	11	12	13 T
14	15	16	17	18	19	20 E	21	22	23	24	25 M	26

HIGH-SPEED CROSSWORD

Across
1 "___ Rich Pageant" (R.E.M. album)
6 About: 2 wds.
10 James Bond, for one
11 Practice boxing
12 "Golden Girls" actress: 2 wds.
14 Celebrity
15 Female lobster
16 "This ___ travesty!": 2 wds.
18 Epic tale
22 Takes willingly
26 Common container
27 Not better
28 Sharp, as a pain
30 Time of the past
31 The ___ (upper Great Plains region)
33 Audition tape
35 Each
36 Chop (off)
38 Cookie since 1912
42 Country music great: 2 wds.
45 Be the owner of
46 First Greek letter
47 Bad day for Caesar
48 Dapper

Down
1 Friendly dogs, for short
2 "___ it now!": 2 wds.
3 Greek cheese
4 Contest submissions
5 Pig's home
6 Arthur of tennis fame
7 Whirls
8 Piece of body art
9 Taconite, e.g.
13 "Come again?"
17 Went fast
19 Be next to
20 "I've ___ Secret": 2 wds.
21 Cancels
22 Blown away
23 Apple center
24 Shove (in)
25 Benefit
29 Popular Toyota
32 Datebook abbr.
34 Mediterranean food
37 Small bills
39 Totally engrossed (by)
40 Real: Ger.
41 Just fine
42 Greek letter
43 Young fella
44 Forbid

1 MINUTE NUMBER CRUNCH

Beginner							Answer
38	+ 212	÷ 10	x 7	1/5 of this	Double it	− 7	2/9 of this	

Intermediate							Answer
424	− 148	2/3 of this	x 3	3/4 of this	8/9 of this	1/2 of this	+ 129	

Advanced							Answer
29	Cubed	− 15497	3/4 of this	5/9 of this	7/15 of this	Double it	− 2569	

Did You Know?:
Babies are born with more than 300 bones in their bodies. However, as some of the bones fuse together over time, the number reduces to just 206 by the time children have stopped growing.

1 MINUTE NUMBER CRUNCH

Beginner							Answer
104	25% of this	Double it	+ 53	÷ 5	+ 19	1/4 of this	x 39

Intermediate							Answer
127	+ 43	+ 20% of this	÷ 4	÷ 3	+ 283	31% of this	− 67

Advanced							Answer
43	x 7	+ 199	69% of this	9/15 of this	17/23 of this	4/9 of this	x 7

Did You Know?:
In 1977, a strong radio signal with an intensity much higher than the usual background noise was received from the direction of the constellation of Sagittarius. It lasted 72 seconds and may be the first evidence of intelligent life in outer space.

HIGH-SPEED CROSSWORD

Across
1 ___ talk (encouraging words)
4 The Colonel's restaurant
7 Software program, briefly
10 Mine stuff
11 Rounded shape
13 She won the U.S. Open in 1979 and 1981: 2 wds.
15 Common flower
16 Possesses, in the Bible
19 Quickly
23 Role for Paul
24 Try it out: 3 wds.
27 "Bloom County" character: 2 wds.
29 Metal named for an animal: 2 wds.
30 Compete
31 Gets a look at
32 Cravings
33 "Who's there?" reply: 2 wds.
37 1980s show about a detective from Texas: 2 wds.
43 Pencil parts
44 Amaze
45 Fly catcher
46 Came into contact with
47 Drops in the morning meadow

Down
1 Daisy holder
2 Go wrong
3 Little green vegetable
4 Lock openers
5 Apartment
6 Game with Colonel Mustard
7 Appropriate
8 Greek consonant
9 Writing instrument
12 Tel Aviv's nation
14 Meowing pet
16 Lock parts
17 Bandleader Shaw
18 Military tactic
20 Medical application
21 "Encore!"
22 Mugs for the camera
24 Not his
25 "Without further ___..."
26 Delivery vehicle
28 Drops in on
32 "Absolutely!"
34 Not us
35 Achy
36 Has to
37 Kitty's sound
38 "You ___ so right!"
39 Bill at a bar
40 Tiny amount
41 Have to repay
42 "What's ___?"

WORDWHEEL

Using only the letters in the Wordwheel, you have ten minutes to find as many words as possible, none of which may be plurals, foreign words or proper nouns. Each word must be of three letters or more, all must contain the central letter and letters can only be used once in every word. There is at least one nine-letter word in the wheel.

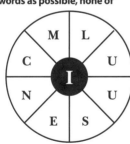

Wheel letters: M, L, U, U, S, E, N, C (centre: I)

Nine-letter word(s):

SUM CIRCLE

Fill the three empty circles with the symbols +, – and x in some order, to make a sum which totals the number in the centre. Each symbol must be used once and calculations are made in the direction of travel (clockwise).

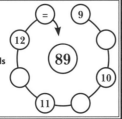

Circle: = , 9, 10, 11, 12, centre 89

WORDSEARCH WORKOUT

```
E Z J G N I M M I W S S M
I F Y L M V S O X Q T D B
E I O L T R J S O N T S Z
C O L A D E P L E R I I A
P H H D U D Y T U N V L C
O F A M V C E L N O D T L
S B L L N O B E K G I E U
T Q D O E A T U K N V U B
C E U M G T V W Q I I Q H
A H W A P Y C A Z B N I O
R M V E S P Z R R S G T U
D S W R C H L A E A I U S
C A B A R E T M R C C O E
I C E C R E A M L C H B H
X V S N Z G F I M R A E I
```

HOLIDAY CAMP

BINGO
BOUTIQUE
CABARET
CARAVAN
CHALET
CLUBHOUSE
CRAZY GOLF
CRECHE
DIVING
GAMES
ICE CREAM
PEDALO
POOL
POSTCARD
REDCOAT
SQUASH
SWIMMING
TENNIS
TENTS
TV ROOM

DOUBLE FUN SUDOKU

TASTY TEASER

		3		6	7	9	4	
4			2				6	
		1	3				7	8
6		5		2			3	
9			7		3			2
	1			9		7		4
2	3				4	5		
	8				5			7
	5	4	6	8		1		

BRAIN BUSTER

		7	3			9		
1	6				7			
3	5							
	2	3	9					
	7			5			4	
					8	2	5	
							6	3
			4				7	5
	8			1	4			

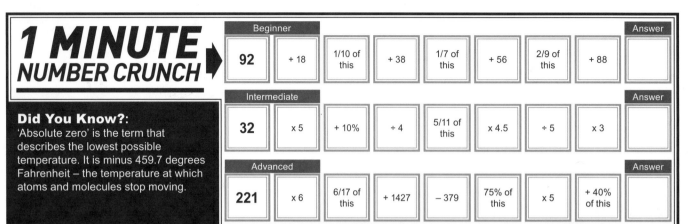

1 MINUTE NUMBER CRUNCH

Beginner								Answer
92	+ 18	1/10 of this	+ 38	1/7 of this	+ 56	2/9 of this	+ 88	

Intermediate								Answer
32	x 5	+ 10%	÷ 4	5/11 of this	x 4.5	÷ 5	x 3	

Advanced								Answer
221	x 6	6/17 of this	+ 1427	− 379	75% of this	x 5	+ 40% of this	

Did You Know?:
'Absolute zero' is the term that describes the lowest possible temperature. It is minus 459.7 degrees Fahrenheit – the temperature at which atoms and molecules stop moving.

HIGH-SPEED CROSSWORD

Across
1 Chichen Itza builders
6 Long, long time
10 Mexican brick
11 ___ Plus (shampoo brand)
12 Baseball feat: 2 wds.
14 Otherwise
15 Art class material
18 Store with a bull's-eye logo
23 Backstabber
24 Dentist's direction
25 "I had no ___!"
27 Forest growth
28 Gross dinner sound
30 Shook hands with
31 ___ tank
33 Alluring
34 Lady ___ (pop star)
36 Track and field sport: 2 wds.
42 "Take this!"
43 Newswoman Shriver
44 All tied up
45 Expertise

Down
1 "Spy vs. Spy" magazine
2 Fuss
3 "What did ___ say?"
4 "___ Road" (Beatles album)
5 Unload, as stock
6 Enter the picture
7 Come together
8 Historian's period
9 Oinker's place
13 Guess: abbr.
15 Magician ___ Angel
16 Soup server
17 Consumed quickly: 2 wds.
19 Hoop
20 Garden statue, sometime
21 County of England
22 Cantankerous
26 Paintings, photography, etc.
29 See 9-down
32 "Silent" prez
33 Pat of "Wheel of Fortune"
35 Nice rocks
36 Word in many movie titles
37 Show off, on a Harley
38 Wrath
39 Spoon-bender Geller
40 Dot follower, in some e-mail addresses
41 Amigo

CODEWORD CONUNDRUM

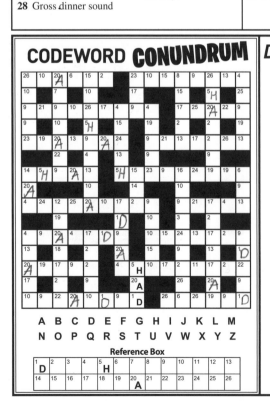

A B C D E F G H I J K L M
N O P Q R S T U V W X Y Z

Reference Box

1 D	2	3	4	5 H	6	7	8	9	10	11	12	13
14	15	16	17	18	19	20 A	21	22	23	24	25	26

DOUBLE FUN SUDOKU

TASTY TEASER

		5	2		8	1		
6	4			9			8	5
	1			6		7		
7	6		8		9		1	3
		3	6		7	8		
8	9		5		3		2	6
	2			8			3	
4	3			7			5	8
		6	3		2	4		

BRAIN BUSTER

2	5			9			8	7
		1				2		
3			7		2			5
	9			4			2	
		6		8				
	2			1			4	
8			2		4			3
		6				8		
9	1			3			7	4

SPIDOKU

Each of the eight segments of the spider's web should be filled with a different number from 1 to 8, in such a way that every ring also contains a different number from 1 to 8.

HIGH-SPEED CROSSWORD

Across
1 Submachine gun
4 Cartoon "devil"
7 Golf course score
8 ___ code (5- or 9-digit number)
11 Bird: prefix
12 One of four in a deck
13 ___ Lanka
14 Before ninth
16 Camp water
17 Get older
18 From ___ (completely): 3 wds.
20 Charon's river
21 Stirred up
24 Little dog, for short
25 "Ciao!"

26 "___ Maria"
27 Mt. ___ (where Noah landed)
29 Worker's weekend shout
30 "Lovely" Beatles girl
31 "2001" computer
32 Canine cry
34 "Absolutely!": 2 wds.
37 "___ you there?"
38 100 percent
39 Olive ___ (Popeye's love)
40 Lock opener
41 Ground cover
42 ___ center
43 Apr. addressee

Down
1 ___ the crack of dawn: 2 wds.
2 12th president: 2 wds.
3 Anger
4 ___ Bo (exercise system)
5 Flying ace
6 Son of reggae star Bob, who sang "Tomorrow People": 2 wds.
8 Hungarian who slapped a cop in L.A.: 3 wds.
9 Aggravate
10 Apple or cherry
15 Bewitch

16 Singer Rawls
19 One of five on a foot
20 Day ___ (place for a pedicure)
22 Curse: 2 wds.
23 Dict. entry
25 Louisville Slugger, e.g.
28 Tear
29 Thanksgiving, e.g.: abbr.
32 Talk and talk
33 Before
35 Former GM car
36 Special attention, for short
38 "___ Lay Me Down": 2 wds.

WORDSEARCH WORKOUT

```
L E I Y B Y R R S W V S W
E A N I G E R A U B A N X
E D Y I H M S U K C N H M
Q Y M R G K O X B U C O J
Z U Q O A N O N N D O J A
Z B E T N G Y T T S U T S
B G O B D T L M N R V S P
W O E V E E O A E O E M E
N C L P R C F N C S R A R
W I W Z I N U V I K Q O L
M Q T H U N D E R B A Y T
B L O N D O N U H W P U A
V C F A X A F I L A H F L
V I C T O R I A W A T T O
I C R G C H U R C H I L L
```

CANADIAN TOWNS AND CITIES

CALGARY	QUEBEC
CHURCHILL	REGINA
EDMONTON	SASKATOON
GANDER	ST JOHNS
HALIFAX	SUDBURY
INUVIK	THUNDER BAY
JASPER	TORONTO
LONDON	VANCOUVER
MONTREAL	VICTORIA
OTTAWA	WINNIPEG

DOUBLE FUN SUDOKU

TASTY TEASER

3				5	6			
4		9		5			8	7
			3	8	2			
	4	5			7	2	6	
	3		8		7		5	
5	7	1			4	9		
		7	1	8				
9	8		4		2			3
	5	6						4

BRAIN BUSTER

		6		5	3			
5	8			9				
	2				3			
				1	4	7		
	9			5			8	
	5	7	3					
	2					5		
		8				2	6	
	1	5		4				

MATCHSTICK MAGIC

Move four matchsticks to make three squares.

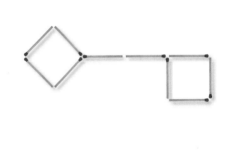

BRAIN TEASER

What number should go under the letter E?

F E H

30	?	36

SIMPLE AS A, B, C?

Did You Know?:
The bar-tailed godwit flies over 7,000 miles non-stop on its migration between Alaska and New Zealand, losing more than half its body weight in the process.

Each of the small squares in the grid below contains either A, B or C. Each row, column, and diagonal line of six squares has exactly two of each letter. Can you tell the letter in each square?

Across
1 No two letters the same are directly next to each other
2 The As are next to each other
3 The Bs are further right than the As
4 The Bs are further right than the As
5 The Cs are further right than the As
6 The Cs are between the As

Down
1 The As are next to each other
2 No two letters the same are directly next to each other
3 The Cs are lower than the As
4 No two letters the same are directly next to each other
5 The Cs are next to each other
6 The Bs are between the Cs

	1	2	3	4	5	6
1						
2						
3						
4						
5						
6						

CODEWORD CONUNDRUM

```
A B C D E F G H I J K L M
N O P Q R S T U V W X Y Z
```

Reference Box

| V | 2 | 3 | 4 | L | 6 | 7 | 8 | 9 | 10 | 11 | 12 | 13 R |
| 14 | 15 | 16 | 17 | 18 | 19 | 20 | 21 | 22 | 23 | 24 | 25 | 26 |

DOUBLE FUN SUDOKU

TASTY TEASER

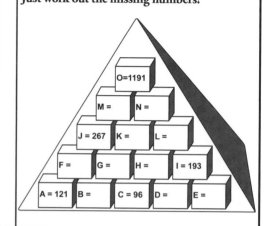

BRAIN BUSTER

PYRAMID PLUS

Every brick in this pyramid contains a number which is the sum of the two numbers below it, so that F=A+B, etc.
Just work out the missing numbers!

O=1191

M =   N =

J = 267   K =   L =

F =   G =   H =   I = 193

A = 121   B =   C = 96   D =   E =

HIGH-SPEED CROSSWORD

Across
1 Do the laundry
5 Golfer's bag carrier
11 Money before a poker hand
12 Get there
13 Celebrity
14 Person who loves books
15 Brad of "Thelma & Louise"
16 Apple computer
17 Poet ___ Pound
19 Doing: 2 wds.
23 One of Santa's Little Helpers
25 Clarify in detail
27 Soccer scores
29 More than on time
30 Pilot
32 ___-Mex cuisine
33 Actress Laura of "Rambling Rose"
34 "___ Tuesday" (Rolling Stones hit)
36 Cow's food
38 In the distance
41 Money for putting a song on the radio
44 ___ Parks of the civil rights movement
45 Graduates from a school
46 Witty words
47 Put down
48 Board in a bed

Down
1 Stinging insect
2 Against: pref.
3 Fun place to go on rides and eat food: 2 wds.
4 Rival of Avis, Enterprise and Budget
5 Company that sells used autos
6 Section
7 Famous vampire
8 Performed
9 "___ been thinking about you!"
10 Suffix with mountain or musket
18 Relax
20 Spilling a beer, for example: 2 wds.
21 Scrabble piece
22 Dark mineral
23 "My goodness!"
24 Valentine's Day celebrates it
26 South American country whose capital is Lima
28 Cosmetics brand
31 Certify, as a priest
35 Root beer brand
37 Arm bone
39 Largest of the continents
40 At full attention
41 Tablet
42 Samuel Adams Summer ___
43 "That tastes good!"

1 MINUTE NUMBER CRUNCH

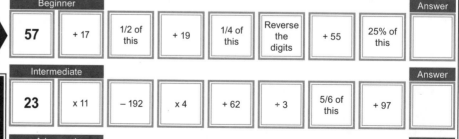

Did You Know?:
Near the end of World War II, 1,000 Japanese soldiers went into a mangrove swamp to evade capture by the British. Only 120 returned – the rest had been devoured by crocodiles.

Beginner								Answer
57	+ 17	1/2 of this	+ 19	1/4 of this	Reverse the digits	+ 55	25% of this	

Intermediate								Answer
23	x 11	− 192	x 4	+ 62	÷ 3	5/6 of this	+ 97	

Advanced								Answer
19	x 15	x 3	5/19 of this	x 14	70% of this	3/5 of this	7/9 of this	

HIGH-SPEED CROSSWORD

Across
1 Power
7 Ruin
10 Popeye the Sailor has a tattoo of one
11 ___ and aft
12 Mother ___ (noted humanitarian)
13 Onassis and Emanuel
14 Tennis star Tommy
15 Leave the union
17 Web connecting businesses, for short
18 Sailing the waves
19 Prophet
20 Chaperone
21 Your planet
23 Prophet
26 Work units
30 Prejudiced person
31 Fix, as a medical condition
32 Extreme fear
34 Half-hitch or granny
35 Not new, like a car
36 Didn't dine at home
38 Palindromic candy company
39 Read through casually
40 Finale
41 Person who judges food

Down
1 Singer Johnny
2 Nervous feeling
3 Minor tiff
4 1950s-70s label known for blues, jazz and rock
5 ___ Angeles Lakers
6 Historical times
7 To a greater degree
8 More dry and hot
9 Find a new chair for
11 They spot false claims
16 "___ of Eden"
20 Previously
22 Choir voice
23 More than 90 degrees, as an angle
24 Candy company
25 "Amen!"
27 Leave in a hurry
28 Complain
29 Irish ___ (big dog)
33 At full attention
37 Chai or chamomile

BATTLESHIP BOUT

Did You Know?:
In the 18th century, the passenger pigeon was the world's commonest bird. By 1914 the bird was recorded extinct.

Can you place the vessels into the diagram? Some parts of vessels or sea squares have already been filled in. A number to the right or below a row or column refers to the number of occupied squares in that row or column.
Any vessel may be positioned horizontally or vertically, but no part of a vessel touches part of any other vessel, either horizontally, vertically or diagonally.

Empty Area of Sea:
Aircraft Carrier:
Battleships:
Cruisers:
Submarines:

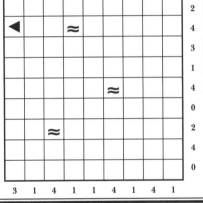

WORDSEARCH WORKOUT

```
U R V Z C I F P T P R L Q
H T E R A S E C I E V L X
A C W L A C H D N I B I H
Q Q S N I A Y N U T G R E
O I D A R O A V I Q T D T
E E O G T C B S F C W K U
R R E N S W G U I T A R M
D R I H I G Q S H J A O B
F T D F E S H J D Z W L L
R P M A L A E W O E A T E
E V Q D V G T R R N O M D
E O F E B N B E K I H U R
Z A R W Z P U E R R D U Y
E F Z S R E T S A O T O E
R M N T L Q B R L N J S R
```

ELECTRICAL APPLIANCES

BLANKET
BOILER
CHARGER
DRILL
FIRE
FREEZER
GUITAR
HEATER
HI-FI UNIT
IONISER
IRON
LAMP
MOWER
RADIO
RAZOR
SANDER
SCANNER
SHAVER
TOASTER
TUMBLE-DRYER

DOUBLE FUN SUDOKU

TASTY TEASER

6		4		2			3	
	2	5		8	1			
7		1				8	9	
4					2	8		
2	7		6		9		5	4
		3	7					1
8	9				5		3	
		1	9		6	7		
	5			6		4		2

BRAIN BUSTER

8	5				9	2		
		3			7			
7			3		2			8
	8			4			3	
1			2		6			9
	3			7			2	
5			1		3			6
	6				4			
3	9					7	1	

WHATEVER NEXT?

In the diagram below, which number should replace the question mark?

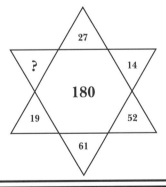

27
?
14
180
19
52
61

BRAIN TEASER

What number should replace the question mark?

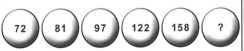

72 81 97 122 158 ?

Mind Over Matter

Given that the letters are valued 1-26 according to their places in the alphabet, can you crack the mystery code to reveal the missing letter?

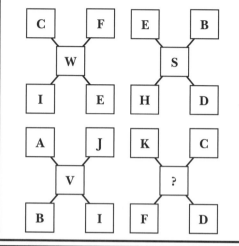

DOUBLE FUN SUDOKU

TASTY TEASER

	6		9				5	
3	2	9				1	6	4
4			3	2				7
7				5		4		
		4	6		1	3		
	9		8					2
6				8	9			5
9	4	1				7	3	8
	8				7		1	

BRAIN BUSTER

7		2		3		4		5
		5	9		8	6		
9								8
		3		4				
8								7
			7		6			
4								1
		3	1		7	5		
1		7		6		9		3

CODEWORD CONUNDRUM

A B C D E F G H I J K L M
N O P Q R S T U V W X Y Z

Reference Box

1	2	3	4	5 O	6	7	8	9	10	11	12	13
14	15	16	17	18 T	19	20	21	22	23	24	25 L	26

HIGH-SPEED CROSSWORD

Across
1 "Dancing Queen" band from Sweden
5 Spa treatment
11 Easy victory
12 Makes into law
13 Addition, subtraction and such
14 "I see it the same way!"
15 Guinea pig
17 Say it never happened
18 Some turns on the road
22 Showed over again
23 Set aside (for)
24 Not working today
25 Put ___ fight: 2 wds.
26 Songs for one person
29 Tennessee football player
31 The Sphinx's country
32 1998 movie with Jennifer Lopez and Woody Allen's voices
33 Get there
35 One of a kind
38 "Alice's Restaurant" singer Guthrie
41 Argues against
42 "Yeah, sure!": 2 wds.
43 Least convincing, like an excuse
44 No, to Russians

Down
1 What a shoulder holds
2 Constricting snake
3 Caterpillar of the future
4 Goddess for whom Greece's capital is named
5 Accomplishment
6 Actress Bassett
7 Library desk
8 Cold cubes
9 Devoured
10 Drug also called "acid"
16 Dictionary entry: abbr.
17 Clear up, as a cold windshield
19 What a 3-down may do: 2 wds.
20 November birthstone
21 Laurel or Mikita
22 Valentine's Day flower
27 Not translucent
28 Walks sassily
29 ___ chi (Chinese exercise)
30 Fruitlessly: 2 wds.
34 Relax
35 Web address, for short
36 Teacher's union
37 Computer company
39 "I Hope You Dance" singer ___ Ann Womack
40 Mel of baseball fame

1 MINUTE NUMBER CRUNCH →

Beginner								Answer
131	– 28	x 2	+ 39	÷ 5	2/7 of this	x 6	50% of this	

Intermediate								Answer
1947	Double it	– 1821	÷ 3	+ 104	÷ 15	x 4	– 79	

Advanced								Answer
330	4/15 of this	10/11 of this	5/8 of this	x 5.5	7/25 of this	+ 33	– 7/10 of this	

Did You Know?:
Flatfish, when they are young, look like ordinary fish, with an eye on each side. However, as they mature and gradually become flatter, one eye moves around to lie adjacent to the other. Both eyes are on the top of a flatfish at full maturity.

weigt
weight

DOMINO PLACEMENT

Did You Know?:
On the International Space Station, all toilet waste is stored in a craft which, when full, is released towards Earth where it burns up on entering the atmosphere.

A standard set of 28 dominoes has been laid out as shown. Can you draw in the edges of them all? The check-box is provided as an aid and the domino already placed will help.

```
            3 5
        4 5 4 6
        3 6 0 6
    2 3 3 4 0 0 3 3
    5 0 6 2 6 1 5 5 3 1
    2 2 2 5 6 3 4 0 2 4
      1 1 1 2 0 1 1 6
        4 4 0 2
        0 1 5 5
          4 6
```

0-0	0-1	0-2	0-3	0-4	0-5	0-6
✓						

1-1	1-2	1-3	1-4	1-5	1-6	2-2

2-3	2-4	2-5	2-6	3-3	3-4	3-5

3-6	4-4	4-5	4-6	5-5	5-6	6-6

HIGH-SPEED CROSSWORD

Across
1 Talk about
8 ___ Aviv (city in Israel)
11 Toronto's province
12 Pie ___ mode
13 Dish with parmesan cheese and croutons
15 Prepares to pray
16 Nevada senator Harry
17 Skinny fish
18 Tube-shaped pasta
19 Alcoholic's affliction, for short
20 Computer accessory
22 Finnish steam room
23 Handsome
26 ___ Perignon champagne
29 Amusing water creature
30 He lost to Bush in 2000
31 Geek
32 Beautiful ladies
34 Sandwich bread choices
36 Never-proven mental ability
37 Place for F-16 fighter jets
38 "What can I do for you?"
39 Color that's also a Stephen King movie

Down
1 Decreased for a penalty, as pay
2 Caught, like fish
3 Strengthens (oneself), as for a shock
4 Situations
5 Risk territory named for a Eurasian mountain range
6 Respectable gentlemen
7 "Mayday!"
8 Natural skill
9 "Seinfeld" woman
10 Way up a wall
14 Scene of conflict
18 ___-pong
20 Sock grouping
21 Point, in baseball
22 Gets rid of, like extra pounds
23 Kind of animal Eddie Murphy voices in "Shrek"
24 In a relaxed state
25 Pieces of bacon
26 Rival of Hertz and Enterprise
27 "You won't like the alternative"
28 ___ up (botched the job)
30 Boston newspaper
32 Verve
33 Goes wrong
35 Lobe's home

(Crossword grid with handwritten answers: DISCUSS, CEASER SALAD, PENNE, PING, DONKEY, NERD, ESP)

WORDWHEEL

Using only the letters in the Wordwheel, you have ten minutes to find as many words as possible, none of which may be plurals, foreign words or proper nouns. Each word must be of three letters or more, all must contain the central letter and letters can only be used once in every word. There is at least one nine-letter word in the wheel.

M B E R R A T U O

Nine-letter word(s):
_____

SUM CIRCLE

Fill the three empty circles with the symbols +, – and x in some order, to make a sum which totals the number in the centre. Each symbol must be used once and calculations are made in the direction of travel (clockwise).

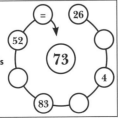

= 26
52
(73)
4
83

WORDSEARCH WORKOUT

```
B E B H A V A N A O Z U T
V Z L O Q K W A E O A D M
S A C O G J C D M T I B Z
A P A T T O I W A I A U S
N A Y S R V T U S U L E A
T L E E H G A K Q A N N
O S N T S A N J O S E O S
D R N A N T M B U A T S A
O O E A I N R N W N C A L
M T M A H A C A V J A I V
I L G H S I T X M U R R A
N O Y I O T O L H A A E D
G E L N O C J P D N C S O
O I Y T I C A M A N A P R
A C D N O T G N I H S A W
```

AMERICAN COUNTRIES CAPITALS

ASUNCION
BOGOTA
BRASILIA
BUENOS AIRES
CARACAS
CAYENNE
HAVANA
LA PAZ
LIMA
MANAGUA
MONTEVIDEO
OTTAWA
PANAMA CITY
QUITO
SAN JOSE
SAN JUAN
SAN SALVADOR
SANTIAGO
SANTO DOMINGO
WASHINGTON DC

DOUBLE FUN SUDOKU

TASTY TEASER

	6			1	2		8	
		7			9	3		
5	8	3				1	2	9
	1				4	9		
2			5		3			8
		8	7			6		
6	4	2				8	9	5
		5	6			4		
	7		9	4		3		

BRAIN BUSTER

			4					
7	8		4	1			6	5
				7	5			
		5		8			4	
	2		9		5		8	
	4			3		2		
						7	3	
3	1			9	6		2	8
					9			

1 MINUTE NUMBER CRUNCH →

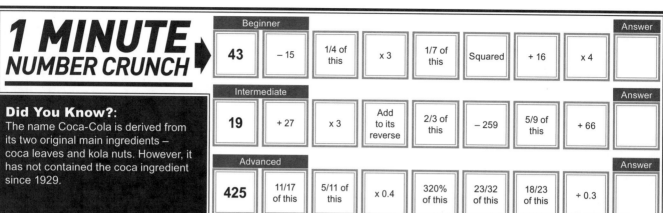

Beginner								Answer
43	– 15	1/4 of this	x 3	1/7 of this	Squared	+ 16	x 4	

Intermediate								Answer
19	+ 27	x 3	Add to its reverse	2/3 of this	– 259	5/9 of this	+ 66	

Advanced								Answer
425	11/17 of this	5/11 of this	x 0.4	320% of this	23/32 of this	18/23 of this	÷ 0.3	

Did You Know?:
The name Coca-Cola is derived from its two original main ingredients – coca leaves and kola nuts. However, it has not contained the coca ingredient since 1929.

HIGH-SPEED CROSSWORD

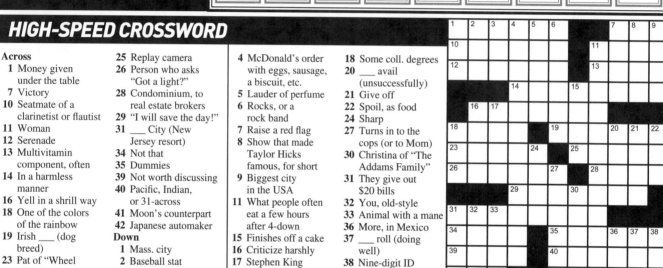

Across
1 Money given under the table
7 Victory
10 Seatmate of a clarinetist or flautist
11 Woman
12 Serenade
13 Multivitamin component, often
14 In a harmless manner
16 Yell in a shrill way
18 One of the colors of the rainbow
19 Irish ___ (dog breed)
23 Pat of "Wheel of Fortune"
25 Replay camera
26 Person who asks "Got a light?"
28 Condominium, to real estate brokers
29 "I will save the day!"
31 ___ City (New Jersey resort)
34 Not that
35 Dummies
39 Not worth discussing
40 Pacific, Indian, or 31-across
41 Moon's counterpart
42 Japanese automaker

Down
1 Mass. city
2 Baseball stat
3 Charged particle
4 McDonald's order with eggs, sausage, a biscuit, etc.
5 Lauder of perfume
6 Rocks, or a rock band
7 Raise a red flag
8 Show that made Taylor Hicks famous, for short
9 Biggest city in the USA
11 What people often eat a few hours after 4-down
15 Finishes off a cake
16 Criticize harshly
17 Stephen King title dog
18 Some coll. degrees
20 ___ avail (unsuccessfully)
21 Give off
22 Spoil, as food
24 Sharp
27 Turns in to the cops (or to Mom)
30 Christina of "The Addams Family"
31 They give out $20 bills
32 You, old-style
33 Animal with a mane
36 More, in Mexico
37 ___ roll (doing well)
38 Nine-digit ID

CODEWORD CONUNDRUM

A	B	C	D	E	F	G	H	I	J	K	L	M
N	O	P	Q	R	S	T	U	V	W	X	Y	Z

Reference Box

1	2	3	4	5	6	7	8	9	10 M	11 A	12	13
14	15	16	17	18	19	20	21	22	23 N	24	25	26

DOUBLE FUN SUDOKU

TASTY TEASER

		3	5	9			7	
1	8	2			6			
7			1			6		2
5				4		2	3	
8			3		9			5
	1	7		2				4
6		1			4			9
		2				4	5	7
	4			3	7	8		

BRAIN BUSTER

	9		4		6		7	
				1				
6			2		7			3
4	8		1		9		3	2
		6		5		1		
2	3		8		4		9	7
8			7		1			5
				4				
	4		5		8		2	

SPIDOKU

Each of the eight segments of the spider's web should be filled with a different number from 1 to 8, in such a way that every ring also contains a different number from 1 to 8.

HIGH-SPEED CROSSWORD

Across

1 Simple earrings
6 Feeling of unease
11 Baseball great Banks
12 Specialty
13 Leona Helmsley's nickname, with "the"
15 1996 Olympics host nation
16 Geneticist's letters
17 Inflated sense of self-worth
18 Extreme ending
19 Mean person, in kid-speak
21 Vegetable used in soups
23 Mineral deposit
24 Quick scissors cut
26 Cotton ___ (Q-tip)
29 2,000 pounds
31 Dishonest way to make money
33 Tony Soprano, for example
37 Ginger ___ (soft drink)
38 Copy
39 Radio host ___ Glass
40 Prius, e.g.
41 Benny Goodman's nickname, with "the"
44 ___ a high note
45 Lack of fighting
46 Takes a breather
47 Acceptances

Down

1 Book after another book
2 Bridge features
3 Like leftovers
4 Six-sided roller
5 Puts in the mail
6 International ___ (diplomat's area)
7 ___ de plume (pen name)
8 Language Sophocles wrote in
9 Play place
10 Choir voice
14 "I'm ___ you!" ("You don't fool me!")
20 The latest
22 First aid ___
25 Elixirs
27 Small trees
28 You don't want to lose this during a bike race
30 Soft ball brand
32 Combines two corporations
33 Creator
34 Express a point of view
35 Is flexible
36 Like some singing voices
42 Obtained
43 Little, in Scotland

WORDSEARCH WORKOUT

```
X S E K S C T D L L V J I
S N L W A M I I U N I T S
Q O O A T R G E R D J V G
S B C I G H C H A S E U E
Z L K K T V S A N L L T U
G W E N E A E B B P X R V
N J Y E N T L G E L G D Z
I K C V V B I L W A E G D
T E R R N E U U A Y R S O
C U R R E N T L D T V T E
U U T R E W O P B N S S H
D L O H C T I W S P O N B
T U B I N G T X U R U C I
P M X N V F Z R I R V J L
T N N H G Q A Z Y I L B E
```

ELECTRICAL

BULB
CABLES
CHASE
CONDUIT
CURRENT
DUCTING
EARTH
GRID
INSTALLATION
LIGHT
LIVE
PLUG
POWER
ROSE
SLEEVE
SOCKET
SPUR
SWITCH
TUBING
UNITS

DOUBLE FUN SUDOKU

TASTY TEASER

3			6		8	4		1
		7		1			9	
4			2		7	8		
2			9			5	8	
1				6				7
	7	3			4			6
		9	1		5			4
	4			3		2		
7		5	8		6			9

BRAIN BUSTER

	8	2		7				
		3		2				5
	6				5			
4	2		5					
	7			2			8	
					1		4	9
		6					2	
1		2		9				
				8		3	6	

MATCHSTICK MAGIC

Remove nine matches so that no squares with lengths of equal sides will remain.

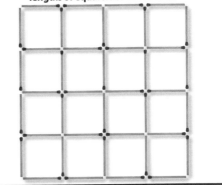

BRAIN TEASER

If the temperature rises 15% from x°C to 103.5°C, what was the previous temperature?

?____?

DOMINO PLACEMENT

Did You Know?:
A pinhead-sized piece of your brain contains sixty thousand nerve cells called neurons. Signals from your nerves take less than a hundredth of a second to get to your brain.

A standard set of 28 dominoes has been laid out as shown. Can you draw in the edges of them all? The check-box is provided as an aid and the domino already placed will help.

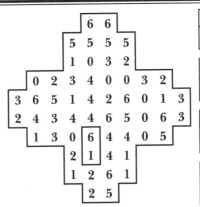

0-0	0-1	0-2	0-3	0-4	0-5	0-6
1-1	1-2	1-3	1-4	1-5	1-6 ✓	2-2
2-3	2-4	2-5	2-6	3-3	3-4	3-5
3-6	4-4	4-5	4-6	5-5	5-6	6-6

CODEWORD CONUNDRUM

A B C D E F G H I J K L M
N O P Q R S T U V W X Y Z

Reference Box

1	2	3	4	5	6	7 A	8	9	10	11	12	13
14 R	15	16	17	18	19	20	21 I	22	23	24	25	26

DOUBLE **FUN** SUDOKU

TASTY TEASER

BRAIN BUSTER

PYRAMID PLUS

Every brick in this pyramid contains a number which is the sum of the two numbers below it, so that F=A+B, etc.
Just work out the missing numbers!

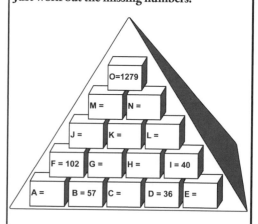

O = 1279
M =   N =
J =   K =   L =
F = 102   G =   H =   I = 40
A =   B = 57   C =   D = 36   E =

HIGH-SPEED CROSSWORD

Across
1 Phony
5 ___-toothed tiger
10 Got better, as cheddar
11 Make oneself look nice
12 Passes a law against
13 Rice dish made with saffron
14 Q followers
15 Mr. Onassis
16 Steve Jobs computer
17 Terre Haute sch.
18 100 yrs.
19 Mel of baseball fame
20 Insect with transparent wings
22 Take ___ time
23 Evict
25 Woody's last name, on "Cheers"
27 Hospital staff members
30 Last part
31 My, in Marseilles
32 Explosive letters in Angry Birds
33 Polished off
34 East: Ger.
35 In the past
36 Some summer births, astrologically
38 Vegetable fried in the South
39 Fire remnant
40 Defeated
41 Last name that means "kings" in Spanish
42 Schools of thought

Down
1 Silk or polyester
2 Sampras rival
3 First leg of the Triple Crown
4 Mag workers
5 County where 13-across originated
6 "___ you kidding me?"
7 Last leg of the Triple Crown
8 Tell, like a story
9 Makes law
13 Middle leg of the Triple Crown
15 Rock band named for an electrician's term
21 Assistance
22 Your and my
24 Send packing
25 Jerry Mathers TV role
26 Not late
28 How memory traces are stored (anagram of MANGER)
29 Worn furs
31 Othello and others
37 "That's cool!"
38 ___-Wan Kenobi ("Star Wars" role)

1 MINUTE NUMBER CRUNCH

Did You Know?:
When the inventor of the telephone, Alexander Graham Bell, asked Mark Twain to invest in his idea, Twain declined saying that he saw 'no future in it'.

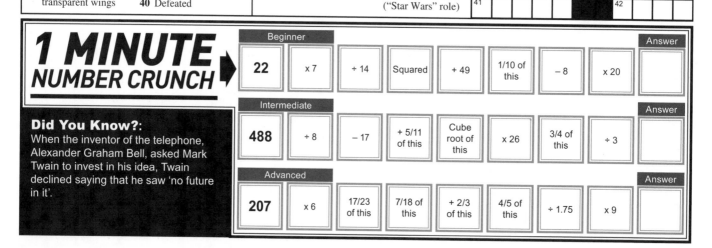

Beginner								Answer
22	x 7	÷ 14	Squared	+ 49	1/10 of this	− 8	x 20	

Intermediate								Answer
488	÷ 8	− 17	+ 5/11 of this	Cube root of this	x 26	3/4 of this	÷ 3	

Advanced								Answer
207	x 6	17/23 of this	7/18 of this	+ 2/3 of this	4/5 of this	÷ 1.75	x 9	

HIGH-SPEED CROSSWORD

Across

1 Nights before holidays
5 Does a housecleaning task
10 Half a quart
11 Repeated phrase
12 Thought
13 "I agree completely!"
14 Exact replica
16 ___-free diet
17 Vail visitor, usually
19 Evil spirit
23 Candy with its own dispenser
24 Yoko from Tokyo
25 Place for gladiators
28 People of Copenhagen
30 Defeating by a small margin
32 Overtime rule in soccer where the first team to score wins immediately
36 Deteriorate
37 Red Muppet
38 "Please play some more songs!"
39 Financial claim, as on a house
40 Side dish in a Mexican restaurant
41 Perfectly rational

Down

1 Of historic importance
2 "Livin' la ___ Loca"
3 Inspire
4 Home to horses
5 Boogied down
6 Negated, as work
7 Use your feet
8 3, in cards
9 Pathetic
11 Herb used in making tea
15 Not just my
17 Masseuse's employer, sometimes
18 "___-plunk"
20 Big country between China and Russia
21 "First..."
22 Words of rejection
26 ___ Rockefeller, vice president under Ford
27 Venomous snakes
28 Commotion
29 Heavenly harpists
31 Trait carrier
32 Vanished
33 Killer whale
34 Sunday shout
35 Solo
36 Spider's home

---

1 MINUTE NUMBER CRUNCH

Did You Know?:
Donated blood is separated into its constituent red and white cells and plasma. This means that each donation can potentially help three different people who each need only one component.

Beginner								Answer
73	+ 17	5/9 of this	+ 8	1/2 of this	Reverse the digits	50% of this	+ 16	

Intermediate								Answer
93	x 3	5/9 of this	− 47	7/12 of this	÷ 7	x 75	+ 97	

Advanced								Answer
104	8/13 of this	Square root of this	x 72	175% of this	5/12 of this	+ 9/10 of this	Add to its reverse	

WORDSEARCH WORKOUT

```
A V P Q G B E D T I A K Z
N X V U C H A N G C H U N
L H C A Y A N G Z H O U N
E O U N B K G U K D F X A
S P H Z Y Y O A A I O D N
H G C H L H Y T W H S Q J
A N N O Z U O K I A H I I
N A I U G N A H C N A N N
K I S S G O N O U G N G G
U J H D U F U O G Z Z O V
N U O E Q U H E S H J A C
M I N H S Z S G G O L O M
I J X L N H N U R U M Q I
N D C A N O A G Y L P Q Y
G V L B J U W N M O V Y X
```

CHINESE TOWNS AND CITIES

ANSHUN	KUNMING
CHANGCHUN	LANZHOU
DATONG	LESHAN
FOSHAN	NANCHANG
FUZHOU	NANJING
HAIKOU	QINGDAO
HANGZHOU	QUANZHOU
HESHAN	SUZHOU
HSINCHU	URUMQI
JIUJIANG	YANGZHOU

DOUBLE FUN SUDOKU

TASTY TEASER

	3		9		1		4	
6		8		2		3		1
4				8				5
8		5	1		2	7		4
	7		8		5		1	
2		1	3		7	8		9
9				1				7
7		6		5		1		3
	8		7		9		6	

BRAIN BUSTER

6	3						8	9
				9				
		5	3	8			1	7
			6			1	4	
		1				6		
	6	7			4			
4	8			2	9	7		
				6				
1	2					9	6	

WHATEVER NEXT?

In the diagram below, which letter should replace the question mark?

C N
F ?   E L
17
H I   A P
G J

BRAIN TEASER

What weight should be placed at the question mark in order to balance the scales?

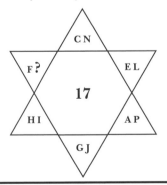

8   4   ? 6

Mind Over Matter

Given that the letters are valued 1-26 according to their places in the alphabet, can you crack the mystery code to reveal the missing letter?

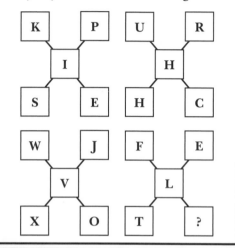

K	P		U	R	
	I			H	
S	E		H	C	
W	J		F	E	
	V			L	
X	O		T	?	

DOUBLE **FUN** SUDOKU

TASTY TEASER

3	2	9		7				6
			6	9				8
					2			5
	6	2	1		4	5	8	
4	3						1	9
	8	7	5		9	3	2	
7			4					
8				1	6			
2			5		4	6	3	

BRAIN BUSTER

9		7				6	8	
	5		4	1				
7						3	1	
	9				7			
	6	2				7	8	
		3				2		
2	4						7	
			7	1		4		
6	1			3			2	

CODEWORD **CONUNDRUM**

A B C D E F G H I J K L M
N O P Q R S T U V W X Y Z

Reference Box

1	2	3	4	5	6	7	8	9	10	11	12	13
									K N			
14	15	16	17	18	19	20	21	22	23	24	25	26
		I										

HIGH-SPEED CROSSWORD

Across
1 Nuts and ___
6 River-blocking structure
9 Neighbor of a Nevadan or a Coloradan
11 Seep
12 Township in South Africa
13 Former Russian ruler
14 Yo-yos, tops, kites, etc.
15 "Remington ___" (1980s show)
17 "___'s Gold" (1997 movie about a beekeeper)
18 Becomes smaller, as the moon
19 Sexual deviant, in slang
20 Emerges victorious in, as a game
21 Bob of sausage fame
23 Coleman of "Boardwalk Empire"
26 Historical periods
30 100% necessary
31 Zero, in tennis
32 Hardest to locate
34 Garden of ___
35 Poet Pound
36 People who don't throw their money away
38 Cow shouts
39 "Be that as it may..."
40 Letters after em
41 Computer key

Down
1 Destroy, as a crime ring
2 Peter of "Goodbye, Mr. Chips"
3 Attorney
4 Waters of the world, poetically
5 Took a chair
6 Baker's amounts
7 Common shrub
8 Tiniest
10 Rejections
11 2001 George Clooney movie
16 Bed size
20 Path
22 Doggie docs
23 1985 Pointer Sisters hit
24 Book buyer's favorite river
25 Beasts of burden
27 Rat or mouse
28 Hostile (to)
29 Motion detector
33 Mao ___-tung
37 Many a Monopoly property: abbr.

1	2	3	4	5			6	7	8
9				10		11			
12						13			
14			15	16					
17			18						
19			20						
		21	22						
23	24	25			26	27	28	29	
30			31						
32			33	34					
35		36	37						
38			39						
40			41						

1 MINUTE
NUMBER CRUNCH

Beginner								Answer
33	− 4	x 5	− 15	x 3	− 90	5/6 of this	+ 14	

Intermediate								Answer
89	+ 57	− 29	5/9 of this	4/5 of this	x 7	x 0.75	÷ 3	

Advanced								Answer
33	x 25	2/3 of this	9/11 of this	28% of this	5/14 of this	+ 89	÷ 0.25	

Did You Know?:
Norwegian soccer player Svein Grondalen once had to miss an international match because of an injury incurred when he crashed into a moose while jogging.

BATTLESHIP BOUT

Can you place the vessels into the diagram? Some parts of vessels or sea squares have already been filled in. A number to the right or below a row or column refers to the number of occupied squares in that row or column.

Any vessel may be positioned horizontally or vertically, but no part of a vessel touches part of any other vessel, either horizontally, vertically or diagonally.

Did You Know?:
There are more than a million species of animal on the planet, including over 70,000 kinds of spider but only about 4,600 kinds of mammal.

Empty Area of Sea: ≈
Aircraft Carrier:
Battleships:
Cruisers:
Submarines:

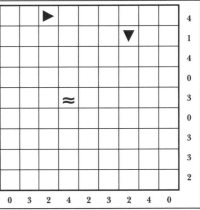

HIGH-SPEED CROSSWORD

Across
1 Cigarette remains
6 Condition of sale, sometimes
10 Old love
11 End of ___
12 1998 Robert De Niro movie
13 Element that's tested for in people's basements
14 Charged particle
15 Lake maker, sometimes
17 First off
18 Worker busy in Apr.
19 ___-cones
20 Rejections
21 Arthur who won the U.S. Open in 1968
23 Kid who's skipping school
25 Actress Gilbert or singer Manchester
27 Longtime colleague of Jennings and Rather
29 ___ and crafts
32 Actor Chaney
33 Sheep's greeting
35 Great anger
36 Toronto's province: abbr.
37 Heavenly sphere
38 Popular kind of Buddhism
39 Lighted sign at a radio station
41 Splotches, as of paint
43 Junior ___ (movie theater candy)
44 Zellweger of "Jerry Maguire"
45 Caspian and Caribbean
46 Makes very wet

Down
1 Cameroon's continent
2 Boats with one mast
3 TV character played by Miley Cyrus
4 Big record label
5 Mails
6 Palindromic woman's name
7 Resort city south of the Grand Canyon
8 Like some patches
9 Least crazy
11 Protective covers
16 Pacifist
22 "I just saw a mouse!"
24 Neighbor of Canada: abbr.
26 The 12 ___ of Hercules
27 Flowers
28 Reagan nickname
30 "Jeopardy!" host
31 Gets the feeling (that)
34 Short forms, for short
40 "___ no problem!"
42 Shortest sign of the zodiac

WORDWHEEL

Using only the letters in the Wordwheel, you have ten minutes to find as many words as possible, none of which may be plurals, foreign words or proper nouns. Each word must be of three letters or more, all must contain the central letter and letters can only be used once in every word. There is at least one nine-letter word in the wheel.

Nine-letter word(s):
_____

SUM CIRCLE

Fill the three empty circles with the symbols +, – and x in some order, to make a sum which totals the number in the centre. Each symbol must be used once and calculations are made in the direction of travel (clockwise).

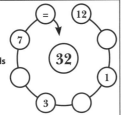

WORDSEARCH WORKOUT

```
S E J C N H J R I O W P Y
E S C A L E S X A P O U R
H U L P G F E O S P I E H
S O F P P N H E T O N L L
I H N H J O G W E S I L X
F M B R G I Y Z N I M L F
O O E G O T G O A T E I R
P O R E H C R A L I G B J
S N I W T N I E P O S R M
U U H R M U F R A N Z A I
C D A O L J W L P D R V K
R H R S T N H T R A I P E
C Z A X K O E Y B R C N Z
W C X H B C E D G T I J G
G Y W H Q X L O H C G O C
```

ASTROLOGY

ARCHER
CAPRICORN
CHART
CONJUNCTION
CUSP
FISHES
GEMINI
GOAT
HOUSE
LEO
LIBRA
MOON
OPPOSITION
PLANETS
RAM
READING
SCALES
TWINS
VIRGO
WHEEL

DOUBLE FUN SUDOKU

TASTY TEASER

5			6	9			7	4
		7			5			
1	8				4	5		
2	9		8				6	3
		4		3		9		
3	1			7			5	2
		6	1				2	7
			2		8			
8	7			5	3			9

BRAIN BUSTER

	5		7		4		6	
		2				8		
	4	6				3	1	
6			9	3	2			8
4			1	8	7			5
	2	9				1	4	
		4				5		
	3		6		5		9	

1 MINUTE NUMBER CRUNCH

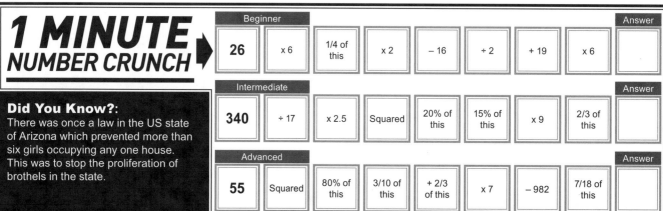

Beginner								Answer
26	x 6	1/4 of this	x 2	− 16	÷ 2	+ 19	x 6	

Intermediate								Answer
340	÷ 17	x 2.5	Squared	20% of this	15% of this	x 9	2/3 of this	

Advanced								Answer
55	Squared	80% of this	3/10 of this	+ 2/3 of this	x 7	− 982	7/18 of this	

Did You Know?:
There was once a law in the US state of Arizona which prevented more than six girls occupying any one house. This was to stop the proliferation of brothels in the state.

HIGH-SPEED CROSSWORD

Across
1 Where dandruff forms
6 Word in many Florida city names
11 FDR's affliction
12 Bird on the U.S. Great Seal
13 Fictional detective, or pseudonym of his creators
15 Playing hard to get
16 Greek letter after sigma
17 Palindromic woman's name
18 Singer Kristofferson
20 Of the coldest season
22 Period after Mardi Gras
23 Prefix with classical
24 Defeats by a small amount
26 Law school class
30 Total: abbr.
32 Boat's underside
33 Loud noisemaking
36 Indian woman's clothing
37 Put on TV
38 Drink made from leaves
40 Study
41 Creepy author from Maine
44 Bert's puppet buddy
45 Family tree female
46 Put off
47 Scary snake

Down
1 Dotted pattern
2 Used crayons
3 Teaming up (with)
4 It isn't true
5 Seattle or St. Louis
6 "Hush!"
7 ___ de toilette (perfume)
8 Real estate ___
9 Obvious
10 Old-school comedian Youngman
14 Show signs of being tired
19 Power for old trains
21 Breakfast corners
25 Put out a fire, one way
27 Prepared
28 Stamp or Trent D'Arby
29 Word after hash or gun
31 Elm or oak
33 Prepared to rob, as a house
34 Petrol amount
35 "___ we all?"
39 Another palindromic woman's name
42 Apple or cherry
43 Joke around with

CODEWORD CONUNDRUM

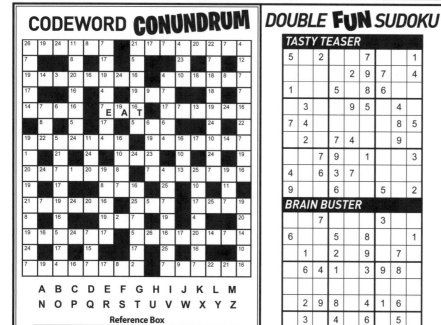

A	B	C	D	E	F	G	H	I	J	K	L	M
N	O	P	Q	R	S	T	U	V	W	X	Y	Z

Reference Box

1	2	3	4	5	6	7 E	8	9	10	11	12	13
14	15	16 T	17	18	19 A	20	21	22	23	24	25	26

DOUBLE FUN SUDOKU

TASTY TEASER

5		2			7			1
				2	9	7		4
1			5		8	6		
	3			9	5		4	
7	4						8	5
	2		7	4			9	
		7	9		1			3
4		6	3	7				
9			6			5	2	

BRAIN BUSTER

		7			3			
6			5		8			1
	1		2		9		7	
	6	4	1		3	9	8	
2	9	8		4	1	6		
	3		4		6		5	
9			7		5			2
		5			4			

SPIDOKU

Each of the eight segments of the spider's web should be filled with a different number from 1 to 8, in such a way that every ring also contains a different number from 1 to 8.

HIGH-SPEED CROSSWORD

Across
1 Medieval weapon, or modern spray weapon
5 Different
10 Milky gemstones
12 "Hand over the money!": 2 wds.
13 "Be quiet!": 2 wds.
14 Kick out
15 Concealed
16 Sought office
18 Period of time
19 "Nevertheless..."
21 Will Smith musical genre
22 Moan and groan
24 Pacino and Capone
25 ___ cards (spooky deck)
27 First five of 26
29 Chicken ___ king: 2 wds.
30 Walk proudly
32 Little doggy
33 Part of a baseball game
36 Mischief maker
37 Big primate
38 "C'est la ___!"
39 Shaquille or Tatum
41 Piece of pizza
43 Some teachers grade on one
44 Lugs (around)
45 Obnoxious people
46 Funeral fire

Down
1 Kind of coffee
2 Be ___ in the neck: 2 wds.
3 You see a lot of them on November 1st: 2 wds.
4 Quarterback Manning
5 Ready for business
6 Money for the government
7 Behavior some kids may exhibit on November 1st
8 The ___ City (capital of the Land of Oz)
9 Fall back, as into a bad pattern of behavior
11 Narrow waterways
17 "The Fountainhead" novelist Rand
20 "Which person?"
23 Honest and sincere
25 Kind of pudding
26 Male graduate
28 Part of a hamburger
31 Waiter's money
34 More pleasant
35 Silly birds
37 Ginger ___ (some soft drinks)
40 Wide road: abbr.
42 Cut (off)

(Completed grid, handwritten answers):
MACE, HER; OPAL, S, YMO; COGNIT, PEU; HID, R, ERT; ANYWAY, RAIN; WHINE, LN; TAROT, ABCDE; ALA, STRUT; PUP, INNING; IMP, APE, VIE; ONEIL, SLICE; CURVE, TOTES; ASS, TYRE

WORDSEARCH WORKOUT

```
H J L Y L A N M Y H K R A
P A V Q H J P H T P Q C P
H A Z I L Y D A T N I M H
H U G E L Y E N O H E I Z
C E I H L L C D P H N U Z
R E P M A H H Y P D A B X
R V V H H I L A R I O U S
E K V T A G N A H H C U J
T A K Q O R N E E D T V Y
N N Z R X C L R D R E L L
U J E O E L B E N D L O I
H I V M O S H H U I I F F
H O G Q J H X W H U I H F
C I T L S I Y M V H I R U
E V E T A I L I M U H N H
```

H WORDS

HAMPER
HANDY
HARLEQUIN
HAZEL
HAZILY
HELLO
HEMP
HERBS
HIDDEN
HIEROGLYPHIC

HI-FI
HILARIOUS
HILLY
HINDRANCE
HONEY
HUFFILY
HUGELY
HUMILIATE
HUNTER
HYMNAL

DOUBLE FUN SUDOKU

TASTY TEASER

1	5			8	3			2
4	3	9	7					
		8		1			9	6
			1	5		4		
	8	2				6	5	
		4		6	8			
2	7			9		1		
					2	5	3	9
6			4	3			8	7

BRAIN BUSTER

9				3				2
		2	8		1	4		
	8						1	
4	1		6		8		5	9
			4		3			
8	7		9		5		4	3
	3						7	
		7	1		9	6		
6				5				4

MATCHSTICK MAGIC

Divide this area into five pieces of equal size, using 11 matchsticks.

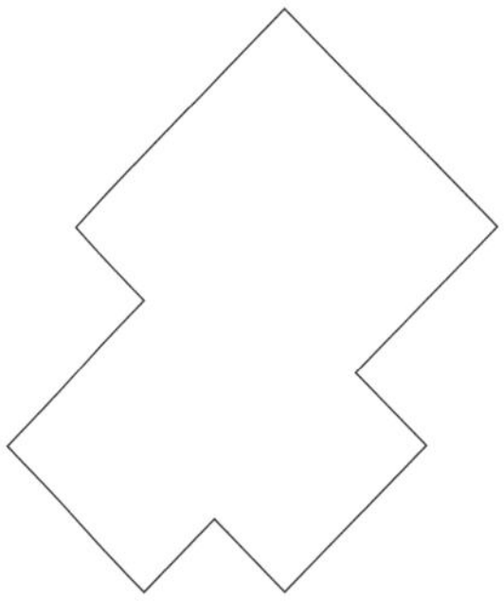

BRAIN TEASER

Divide 600 by one quarter and add 15. What is the answer?

? _____ ?

1 MINUTE NUMBER CRUNCH

Beginner							Answer
52	÷ 4	x 7	+ 17	1/9 of this	+ 142	50% of this	− 38

Intermediate							Answer
501	− 180	2/3 of this	Double it	+ 3/4 of this	− 627	+ 178	22% of this

Advanced							Answer
77	7/11 of this	− 4/7 of this	Cubed	1/9 of this	2/3 of this	Double it	x 7

Did You Know?:
French artist Henri de Toulouse-Lautrec owed his strange shape and gait to breaking his legs in his early teens. His legs subsequently stopped growing, so as an adult he had a fully grown torso but very short legs.

CODEWORD CONUNDRUM

Reference Box

DOUBLE FUN SUDOKU

TASTY TEASER

					8	1		
	6	2	9	5			4	
4	7			2			9	3
5	8	7	4					9
6								2
9				5	4	7	1	
7	1		6			3	5	
	3			7	1	9	8	
		5	2					

BRAIN BUSTER

	3	4				9	5	
		9		3				
1		5				3		8
8			5		6			3
			1		2			
9			4		7			6
4		3				7		9
			2		8			
	8	7				1	2	

PYRAMID PLUS

Every brick in this pyramid contains a number which is the sum of the two numbers below it, so that F=A+B, etc.
Just work out the missing numbers!

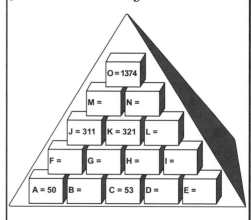

O = 1374

M =   N =

J = 311   K = 321   L =

F =   G =   H =   I =

A = 50   B =   C = 53   D =   E =

HIGH-SPEED CROSSWORD

Across
1 Big pieces, as of meat or marble
6 Celebrity
10 Slander's cousin
11 Not reacting
12 Walk casually
13 Session after a speaker's talk, for short
14 Frenchwoman who won two Nobel Prizes
16 Protestant work ___
17 Since
20 "Where are you?" response
24 Use needle and thread
25 Take to the stage
26 Like people who are "out"
27 Montana's capital
29 Not all
30 Uneasy feeling
32 New York's governor, 1983-94
37 Pasta with ridges
38 Goodbye, to the French
39 Carries (around)
40 Medium-distance runner
41 Blown away
42 Blog write-ups

Down
1 Poetry ___ (literary competition)
2 Peru's capital
3 Shortened form, for short
4 Faith
5 Dangerous winter weather
6 Collar stuff
7 "Beloved" author Morrison
8 Assistant
9 Letters on some TVs
11 Strain to view something
15 Largest city in the Midwest
17 Cigarette stuff
18 "What did I tell you?"
19 Bird in the Harry Potter books
21 Driving force
22 Aries is one
23 Palindromic body part
25 Oakley and Leibovitz
28 Made, as money
29 Place to record an album
31 Rascal
32 Cat's sound
33 Money before a poker hand
34 Some paints
35 Shake hands with
36 Yours and mine
37 School org.

1 MINUTE NUMBER CRUNCH

Beginner								Answer
74	+ 47	÷ 11	x 13	+ 9	50% of this	+ 38	50% of this	

Intermediate								Answer
39	x 5	2/3 of this	x 1.6	3/4 of this	+ 92	x 3	+ 146	

Advanced								Answer
23	Squared	+ 633	÷ 0.25	− 3/8 of this	x 3	4/15 of this	1/2 of this	

Did You Know?:
Waterspouts are literally tornadoes at sea, the funnel transferring water droplets from surface to cloud in much the same way that their land-based cousins pick up debris.

HIGH-SPEED CROSSWORD

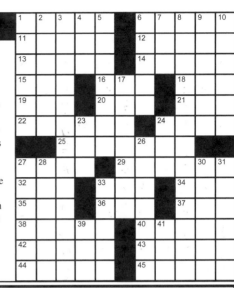

Across
1 Michelob and others
6 Like secret messages
11 Find a total
12 Up
13 Greek letter after rho
14 Lucky number
15 "Make ___ double!"
16 Number cruncher of April
18 Debt letters
19 Oslo's nat.
20 More number crunchers of April
21 Firecracker that doesn't go off
22 Mom's mom
24 Guarded entrance
25 Based on sound reasoning
27 Common seasoning
29 Earls and such
32 Fla. neighbor
33 "___ no problem!"
34 Letters in many black church names
35 Dull brown hue
36 ___-com (Internet startup)
37 "30 Rock" network
38 Force
40 Stomach issue
42 Sleep loudly
43 Demi or Dudley
44 Levels
45 Discharge

Down
1 Establishing
2 Magazine worker
3 "The Raven" author
4 Bacardi, e.g.
5 Document formatting concern
6 Houses, in Spain
7 Have to pay
8 Country singer who did "You Never Even Called Me by My Name"
9 Barely manage, as a living
10 Remove covering from
17 Ask too many questions about
23 Negating particle
24 Talk casually
26 Halloween getup
27 Person who loves inflicting pain
28 Graduates
30 Glowing campfire remnants
31 Juicy information
33 Keeps the engine in neutral
39 Go wrong
41 Lincoln ___

DOMINO PLACEMENT

A standard set of 28 dominoes has been laid out as shown. Can you draw in the edges of them all? The check-box is provided as an aid and the domino already placed will help.

Did You Know?:
Mosquitos are attracted to the smell of a person's feet, which is why people are bitten in this area more than other parts of the body. Mosquitos are also attracted to people who have eaten bananas.

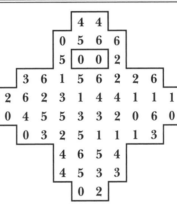

```
            4 4
        0 5 6 6
        5 0 0 2
    3 6 1 5 6 2 2 6
  2 6 2 3 1 4 4 1 1 1
  0 4 5 5 3 3 2 0 6 0
  0 3 2 5 1 1 1 3
        4 6 5 4
        4 5 3 3
          0 2
```

0-0	0-1	0-2	0-3	0-4	0-5	0-6
✓						

1-1	1-2	1-3	1-4	1-5	1-6	2-2

2-3	2-4	2-5	2-6	3-3	3-4	3-5

3-6	4-4	4-5	4-6	5-5	5-6	6-6

WORDSEARCH WORKOUT

```
I T B M F B C B S H Y P G
A L D A H R H V J U E E I
I Y W J T I A C P J L A L
P L P U I T L M O X L R L
A T A C K T E J E D A S I
D I R M J E L N I T R E E
L N K A D N Z M S W F U S
E S C H D I R I B S A R M
I L U P N A H T A N J K E
F E B U I B W W G C C D E
S Y W D O L E X N K L Z S
N R C W N O S D U H L Q Q
A A E Q S N O D R C L X Q
M N Y D D Z E X P Q I V J
H D L E I F H C R U B F R
```

FAMOUS NEW ZEALANDERS

ALDA
ALLEY
ATACK
BATTEN
BOWEN
BRITTEN
BUCK
BURCHFIELD
FRAME
GILLIES
HUDSON
MACDIARMID
MANSFIELD
MURDOCH
NATHAN
PARK
PEARSE
TINSLEY
UPHAM
WAKE

DOUBLE FUN SUDOKU

TASTY TEASER

	7			3		6		
8			9		5		1	3
1			4		7		5	
4			6			5	2	
3				9				7
	8	7			1			9
	6		3		2			1
7	2		5		9			6
	1		8			4		

BRAIN BUSTER

	2			5			8	
		8	7		4	6		
6								3
2	3		4		5		9	6
			2		3			
5	4		8		9		2	7
7								9
		2	9		7	1		
	1			3			4	

WHATEVER NEXT?

In the diagram below, which letter should replace the question mark?

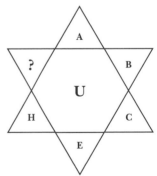

BRAIN TEASER

The cost of hiring a private rail carriage is shared equally by all the passengers who all paid an exact number of Euros which was less than €100. The carriage has seats for 50 passengers and the total bill amounts to €1887. How many seats were not occupied?

Mind Over Matter

Given that the letters are valued 1-26 according to their places in the alphabet, can you crack the mystery code to reveal the missing letter?

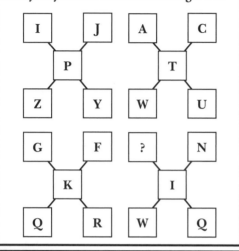

DOUBLE **FUN** SUDOKU

TASTY TEASER

4	5				3	2		
2			9	7			8	3
		8			2			
6	7		5				9	1
	3		1		7			
1	4			8			2	6
		6			5			
5	8			2	1			7
	9	4				6	8	

BRAIN BUSTER

8								9
9			2		6			1
	5	3				6	2	
	3			5			9	
4			8		3			5
	7			4			8	
	1	6				8	4	
2			6		1			7
7								3

CODEWORD CONUNDRUM

A	B	C	D	E	F	G	H	I	J	K	L	M
N	O	P	Q	R	S	T	U	V	W	X	Y	Z

Reference Box

1	2	3	4	5	6	7	8	9	10	11	12	13
								S				
14	15	16	17	18	19	20	21	22	23	24	25	26
						A						

HIGH-SPEED CROSSWORD

Across
1 Stole
7 Bacon source
10 Mother ___ (she helped the poor in Calcutta)
11 State that borders Minnesota and Illinois
12 Unpleasant smell
13 Plenty
14 Where to find valuable nuggets
16 "Peace ___ time"
19 And so forth
20 "Be quiet!"
21 Gets rid of, as extra weight
24 Garden of ___
25 Yellowish-brown shade
26 Swedish cars
28 "Tom Sawyer" author
29 Simple bed
30 Angel's instruments
31 Merry-go-round
34 Run ___ (go crazy)
35 Get there
39 Hit or ___ (unpredictable)
40 Fix, as a male cat
41 Bradley and McMahon
42 Informative pieces

Down
1 Roads: abbr.
2 Soaked
3 Extreme wrath
4 Publisher with a cute animal as its logo
5 Accompany
6 "Charlie and the Chocolate Factory" author
7 Black and white vehicle
8 Victorious shout
9 Way through a fence
11 Beatles hit with nonsense lyrics
15 ___ Moines, Ia.
16 Italian ___ (summertime desserts)
17 Nothing at all
18 It's SWIPED in this puzzle
22 Faucet problem
23 NBA team from Phoenix
27 Man's name formed from three consecutive letters of the alphabet
28 "Where ___ a will..."
31 Showed up
32 In the center of
33 Not nuts
36 Call ___ day
37 "Oy ___!"
38 Where some nurses work: abbr.

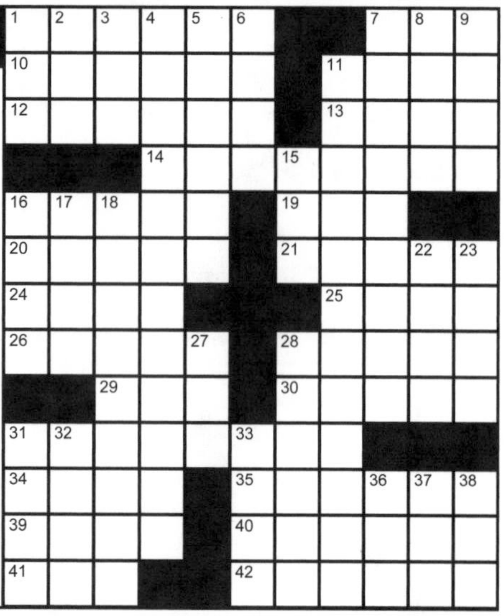

(Crossword grid numbered 1–42)

1 MINUTE NUMBER CRUNCH

Beginner							Answer
8	Squared	3/16 of this	+ 15	x 2	− 19	x 2	6/7 of this	

Intermediate							Answer
942	÷ 3	+ 6	3/8 of this	2/5 of this	÷ 6	x 1.75	Squared	

Advanced							Answer
195	7/13 of this	+ 4/5 of this	2/7 of this	− 1/6 of this	x 11	3/5 of this	Add to its reverse	

Did You Know?:
In 1976, children playing in a soccer match found their heads glowing bright blue. It was an appearance of St Elmo's fire – a discharge from an electrical field, caused by thundery weather.

1 MINUTE NUMBER CRUNCH

Beginner								Answer
58	+ 19	4/7 of this	÷ 4	+ 83	50% of this	− 15	1/2 of this	

Intermediate								Answer
18	x 3	1/2 of this	+ 2/9 of this	x 11	Double it	+ 1/3 of this	÷ 8	

Advanced								Answer
64	+ 72	5/8 of this	x 6	4/17 of this	÷ 0.75	9/32 of this	Squared	

Did You Know?:
The Belly Button Festival is held every year in the Japanese city of Shibukawa. It's traditional for revellers to paint faces around their navels and dance in the streets.

HIGH-SPEED CROSSWORD

Across
1 Tiger's ex
5 Libra's symbol
11 TV "Warrior Princess"
12 Dictatorial ruler
13 Muhammad Ali's old name
15 Newton of gravitational fame
16 Mia of soccer
17 When some local news starts
18 Starch often candied
21 Hawaiian necklace
22 Biblical garden site
24 Girl or woman
26 "White Album" ballad
28 Talk
31 Some fast-food places
35 Pie ___ mode
36 Mountain ___ (green soft drink)
38 Money for later years
39 Fictitious Cincinnati radio station
41 The ___ Brothers ("Shout" singers)
43 Traditional part of Lent
46 Juneau's state
47 Attractive
48 Flower that's dying
49 "Planet of the ___"

Down
1 Bring a thrill to
2 Didn't buy, as a car
3 Totally nuts
4 Letters on the space shuttles
5 Good name for a guy who makes gumbo?
6 Baseball great Young et al.
7 St. Louis landmark
8 Random chorus syllables
9 Tooth covering
10 One of the Little Rascals
14 More than cool
19 Blazing
20 Gibson or Blanc
23 ___-picking
25 January honoree, for short
27 Take down the aisle
28 Appalachian fruit
29 Base that dissolves in water
30 Of the ankle
32 Put gas in, as your tank
33 Make
34 Agree
37 Come out on top
40 "Hey, you!"
42 Pet-lover's org.
44 Pres. Eisenhower
45 Paddle's cousin

WORDWHEEL

Using only the letters in the Wordwheel, you have ten minutes to find as many words as possible, none of which may be plurals, foreign words or proper nouns. Each word must be of three letters or more, all must contain the central letter and letters can only be used once in every word. There is at least one nine-letter word in the wheel.

Wheel letters: H, M, L, S, E (centre), A, P, B, E

Nine-letter word(s):
_____

SUM CIRCLE

Fill the three empty circles with the symbols +, − and x in some order, to make a sum which totals the number in the centre. Each symbol must be used once and calculations are made in the direction of travel (clockwise).

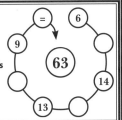

= 6
9   63   14
13

WORDSEARCH WORKOUT

```
Q F O H F O F T H Z V T K
A U C P L E W A Q E L M L
T I Q L G J E Z C L U B J
T K E G X P A A U S U E B
C A R I E C L K A T Z R R
R U S L Y G O N D E T I I
F H A M E J Q J R I A N K
O Y O D A U K H A N L G S
X X R N I N U H B M E D D
H E T N E M A P B Y T C A
M A T F B R X S U B S A L
V I L O V T P M H A C F L
N E L A I D W O Z Y H Q W
B D R F E Z R E T S A P V
T D F R A N Z J O S E F A
```

GLACIERS
ALETSCH
BERING
BRIKSDAL
FEE
FOX
FRANZ JOSEF
FURGG
HARVARD
HORN
HUBBARD
HUMBOLDT
JAMTAL
MER DE GLACE
PASTERZE
RHONE
SAN QUINTIN
STEIN
TASMAN
VATNAJOKULL
YALE

DOUBLE FUN SUDOKU

TASTY TEASER

2		5	1				3	
		4	8	5				6
	8				6		9	2
9	7	1	5	2				
6								4
			3	1	9	2	7	
8	1		4				7	
7				9	8	3		
	2				3	6		5

BRAIN BUSTER

		3	8		7	2		
4			6		1			9
	7					5		
8	6		3		2		9	1
5	9		7		6		4	2
	1						8	
7			1		5			3
		4	2		8	9		

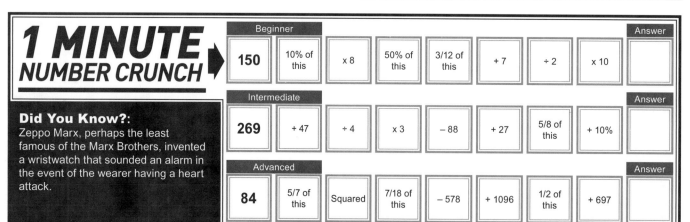

1 MINUTE NUMBER CRUNCH

Beginner								Answer
150	10% of this	x 8	50% of this	3/12 of this	+ 7	÷ 2	x 10	

Intermediate								Answer
269	+ 47	÷ 4	x 3	− 88	+ 27	5/8 of this	+ 10%	

Advanced								Answer
84	5/7 of this	Squared	7/18 of this	− 578	+ 1096	1/2 of this	+ 697	

Did You Know?:
Zeppo Marx, perhaps the least famous of the Marx Brothers, invented a wristwatch that sounded an alarm in the event of the wearer having a heart attack.

HIGH-SPEED CROSSWORD

Across
1 Circus performers
7 Once around the track
10 Lasso
11 Woman of the house
12 Marcos with a lot of shoes
13 Sign of the future
14 "The Da Vinci Code" author: 2 wds.
16 Gush (forth)
19 Actor Mineo of "Rebel Without a Cause"
20 Scientist Marie or Pierre
22 Badge with a photo on it, for short: 2 wds.
26 Walk ___ in someone else's shoes: 2 wds.
27 It's tougher than string
28 Time away from work, for short: 3 wds.
29 ___ & Garfunkel
30 Fake hair
32 Fender-bender result
33 One of five "Great" bodies of water: 2 wds.
37 Allies' foes, in WWII
38 "___ and upward!"
42 40-day period
43 Music system
44 Throw in at no extra cost
45 "Amen!": 3 wds.

Down
1 151, in Roman numerals
2 On the ___ (fleeing the police)
3 Valuable mineral deposit
4 1999 Will Smith/Kevin Kline movie: 3 wds.
5 Zippo
6 Musial and Laurel
7 Big car for a celeb
8 Several: 2 wds.
9 Sean of "Mystic River"
11 Internet: 3 wds.
15 Puts worms on a hook, e.g.
16 Damage permanently
17 Mountain lion
18 "___ Brockovich"
21 Creepy
23 Magazine that chooses a Person of the Year
24 With an unknown author: abbr.
25 Fellow
31 Disgusting
33 Random chorus syllables
34 Fired, in slang
35 Gentle
36 "___ the Groove" (Madonna hit)
39 "Where ___ we?"
40 Outdoor sports chain
41 Period

CODEWORD CONUNDRUM

A B C D E F G H I J K L M
N O P Q R S T U V W X Y Z

Reference Box

1	2	3	4	5	6	7	8	9	10	11	12	13
						P						

14	15	16	17	18	19	20	21	22	23	24	25	26
							A					L

DOUBLE FUN SUDOKU

TASTY TEASER

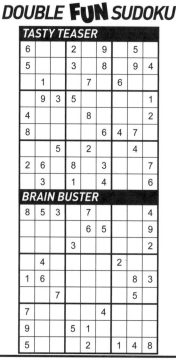

BRAIN BUSTER

SPIDOKU

Each of the eight segments of the spider's web should be filled with a different number from 1 to 8, in such a way that every ring also contains a different number from 1 to 8.

HIGH-SPEED CROSSWORD

Across
1 "Two ___ up!"
7 Papa
10 To be sure
11 Four times around the track, maybe
12 Motion detector
13 Since
14 Chemistry, biology and geology
16 Circle parts
19 Shakespeare title word
20 Nasty strain
22 Chews (on)
26 "It's impossible!"
27 One of the Barrymores
28 Heavy, like a muffin
29 Seaside
30 Owns
32 "Brown ___ Girl" (Van Morrison hit)
33 Looking on the bright side of life
37 Weakest chess piece
38 Starch in Chinese cooking
42 Cleveland's lake
43 President Cleveland
44 Barrier for Roger Federer
45 Elvis hit "Return to ___"

Down
1 Sets in the living room
2 "___ Haw"
3 Coffee holder
4 "Little" title role of 2006
5 Voting group
6 Nation that borders Turkey
7 The D of CD
8 Plant with fleshy leaves
9 Dict. entries
11 1999 Jim Carrey movie
15 Defeats by a little bit
16 Enthusiastic
17 Ingredient in paella
18 Prefix in many juice names
21 It comes off an ironing board
23 Hello, at sea
24 "Where ___ you?"
25 Kids take it down hills
31 Belts out a tune
33 Sign on a store
34 Slim (down)
35 Moron
36 Still hurting
39 Relative of the CD
40 Civil War general
41 Go wrong

WORDSEARCH WORKOUT

```
R V Y H I M B Y R R E H S
E S W W Y P P A H W X E T
P I N E M M A N U E L N E
A L W U L E T T C B O X E
P R E C E C S D H E L N W
G F U G J T I S L A D E S
N A G M N N G C I G J X P
I F R C P A O C I A T O I
P R B L N U Y H Q G H W R
P A O E A C N I U Z A Z I
A J T I K N W C C G R H T
R X W R M L D I H G F B J
W R F B K M O N C A R D S
H D S A Z L G G T Q Q G Z
Y T H G I N T N E L I S E
```

CHRISTMAS

ANGEL	NOEL
BAUBLE	OXEN
CARDS	PINE
EMMANUEL	RUM PUNCH
GABRIEL	SHERRY
GARLAND	SILENT NIGHT
HAPPY	SLADE
ICICLE	SPIRIT
ICING	SWEETS
MESSIAH	WRAPPING PAPER

DOUBLE FUN SUDOKU

TASTY TEASER

	7	4	2	5	1			
	8	9	6			7	2	
4			7				3	
	9			4				6
	7	2			3	4		
3			1			5		
	5			1				9
	6	8			7	5	1	
		4	5	3	9	8		

BRAIN BUSTER

		8			7			
								1
			6	5		9	4	
	8	9			3	7		
2				9				6
	1	8			9	4		
6	4		9	2				
9								
		5			3			

MATCHSTICK MAGIC

Here are two cocktail glasses. Move six matchsticks and change them into a house.

BRAIN TEASER

Which letter should replace the question mark?

(A) (H) (L) (T) (?)

SIMPLE AS A, B, C ?

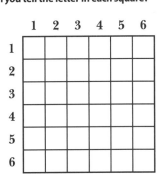

Did You Know?:
Brazilian priest Adelir de Carli took off in a chair attached to 1,000 helium-filled balloons in 2008. The charity stunt went tragically wrong, however, when he was blown out to sea. The lower half of his body was found in the sea 60 miles away, three months later.

Each of the small squares in the grid below contains either A, B or C. Each row, column, and diagonal line of six squares has exactly two of each letter. Can you tell the letter in each square?

Across
1 The Bs are next to each other
2 The Cs are next to each other
3 The As are further right than the Bs
4 Each A is directly next to and right of a C
5 The Bs are next to each other
6 The Bs are further right than the Cs

Down
1 No two letters the same are directly next to each other
2 The As are lower than the Bs
3 The Bs are next to each other and lower than the As
4 Each B is directly next to and below a C
5 The As are next to each other
6 Each B is directly next to and below a C

	1	2	3	4	5	6
1						
2						
3						
4						
5						
6						

CODEWORD CONUNDRUM

A B C D E F G H I J K L M
N O P Q R S T U V W X Y Z

Reference Box

1	2	3	4	5	6	7	8	9	10	11	12	13
I				S								
14	15	16	17	18	19	20	21	22	23	24	25	26
					E							T

DOUBLE FUN SUDOKU

TASTY TEASER

		5	1		7			9
	8		9				4	6
	2	1				3	8	
3			7				5	
	4	7	9		1	8	6	
	6			4				2
5	7				2	1		
6	9		4		3			
8		4		2	5			

BRAIN BUSTER

7		6				1		
	6	7			4		8	
2	3			6				
8			7					
9				5				
	5							4
	1			3	6			
9	4		1	2				
	7		8			9		

PYRAMID PLUS

Every brick in this pyramid contains a number which is the sum of the two numbers below it, so that F=A+B, etc.
Just work out the missing numbers!

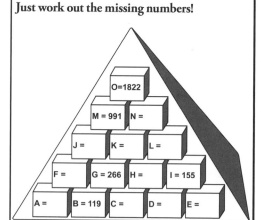

O=1822

M = 991 N =

J = K = L =

F = G = 266 H = I = 155

A = B = 119 C = D = E =

HIGH-SPEED CROSSWORD

Across
1 "Don't take that ___ with me!"
5 Succeed
11 Masterwork
12 Instantly
13 Non-permanent employee
14 Stuffed (oneself)
15 Before, in poems
16 Huge heap
17 Third of 12
19 Did up, as one's sneakers
23 Tic-tac-toe line
24 Untrustworthy person
25 Whine when you don't get your way
27 Small bird
28 Ladies of the family
30 Big roll of cash
31 Sing like Sinatra
32 Church instrument
35 Breakfast area
37 Baboon's cousin
38 Washington neighbor
41 Big speakers at a rock concert
42 English-speaking country of Central America
43 Animal fur
44 Backbones
45 Finds work for

Down
1 ___ pole
2 Mozart's "Don Giovanni," e.g.
3 The best of the best
4 Ability tested by Zener cards
5 "The Gift of the ___"
6 Coral islands
7 1950's conflict
8 Language you speak: abbr.
9 Freezer cubes
10 Turner who founded CNN
16 Vietnamese soup
18 Eli Whitney invented it
20 What this puzzle's three theme entries end in
21 Manage (a living)
22 Room in the Brady Bunch household
25 Ms. ___-Man (video game)
26 Your and my
29 Button many hit in the morning
30 Pan used in China
33 Steve Jobs' company
34 Bird houses
36 Small bills
38 No longer used, as a word: abbr.
39 Dem. rival in DC
40 ___ Lilly pharmaceuticals
41 "The Simpsons" small business owner

(crossword grid)

1 MINUTE NUMBER CRUNCH

Beginner								Answer
77	3/7 of this	x 4	3/12 of this	− 1	50% of this	x 9	5/12 of this	

Intermediate								Answer
456	2/3 of this	÷ 4	x 1.5	x 3	5/9 of this	Less 10%	2/19 of this	

Advanced								Answer
599	÷ 0.25	Double it	375% of this	3/10 of this	− 5/9 of this	x 0.75	− 878	

Did You Know?:
A Mexican man inserted hooks into his upper body and used them to suspend himself from a tree. He was protesting against the discrimination of people with tattoos and body piercings.

HIGH-SPEED CROSSWORD

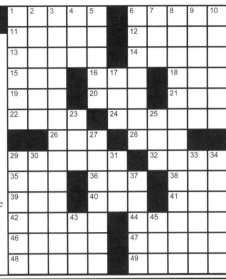

Across

1 Academy Award
6 Stopped, like a deer in the headlights
11 Polo designer Lauren
12 Corsage's place
13 "In a perfect world..."
14 Highfalutin' art form
15 Fuel
16 Dance style
18 Letters between M and Q
19 Extreme anger
20 Money for the server
21 "What can I do for you?"
22 No votes
24 Get rid of, as a dictator
26 Owned by you and me
28 Actress Joanne of "All the King's Men"
29 Drunken state
32 Approximately
35 Golf course score
36 Japanese electronics giant (hidden in PINE CONE)
38 Cool
39 Dry ___ (it makes "smoke" in theater productions)
40 Hassle
41 Big bird
42 ___ flush
44 Hits with an open hand
46 Make changes
47 Country great Haggard
48 Endures
49 Hall & ___ (1980s pop duo)

Down

1 Source
2 Big African desert
3 Surprise announcement?
4 iPhone program
5 Butler in "Gone With the Wind"
6 Didn't do well at all, as a movie
7 Talk casually
8 1987 #1 hit for Madonna
9 Terrible scores
10 Go by
17 Assist
23 Eat poshly
25 In favor of
27 McDonald and Reagan
29 Nice football pass
30 Washington state city
31 Communist
33 Easy as pie
34 Masterworks
37 Women's magazine noted for sex quizzes, for short
43 Small worker
45 Broadway actress Salonga

---

1 MINUTE NUMBER CRUNCH

Did You Know?:
When a German man, Udo Ried, cut off a toe when he dropped a kitchen knife on his foot, his cat ran off with the toe while Ried waited for an ambulance.

Beginner								Answer
56	+ 13	1/3 of this	Reverse the digits	− 4	x 2	+ 4	1/15 of this	

Intermediate								Answer
49	6/7 of this	÷ 3	x 5	÷ 0.2	4/5 of this	÷ 70	Cubed	

Advanced								Answer
578	÷ 2	Square root of this	+ 68	80% of this	x 1.75	Double it	− 109	

WORDSEARCH WORKOUT

```
A B A N A B U P A A W R V
A P X Q Z T I J I I P E B
N E R D A T H T J T K I D
V S T U C C A R E K A T M
A U N A E B O N C N Z U X
E A I P I M N B A N R L S
V R W R I A U L P U I B U
N A I T J R R V R P R T H
U K N J P E N O A J V U S
R Y N U I S A S A D F R N
J E O O A F I B O R N E O
G V T P P L M V A T H A H
S Y N S V R E A R O R K K
O H A W A I I V U A I L Q
N U C G C E J T U G J Z S
```

ISLANDS OF THE SOUTHERN SEAS

BANABA
BORNEO
CANTON
EASTER
FIJI
GUAM
HAWAII
HONSHU
JARVIS
KANDAVU
KIRIBATI
LANAI
MURUROA
NAURU
PITCAIRN
RAIATEA
SERAM
TIMOR
VANUA LEVU
VANUATU

DOUBLE FUN SUDOKU

TASTY TEASER

		9	1			6	8	
1	5		8			4		
	4		2		5			7
		1		6	8	9		
	8	6				2	5	
		3	5	9		6		
8			4		9		3	
	9				7		1	5
7	6			8	3			

BRAIN BUSTER

	9		4		8		2	
3	6					9	8	
		1			5			
2			3	1	4			8
1			7	6	5			9
	2				8			
8	3				7	5		
	7		9		2		6	

WHATEVER NEXT?

In the diagram below, which letter should replace the question mark?

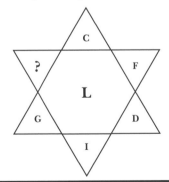

BRAIN TEASER

What number should replace the question mark?

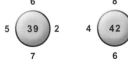

Mind Over Matter

Given that the letters are valued 1-26 according to their places in the alphabet, can you crack the mystery code to reveal the missing letter?

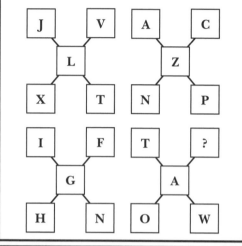

J V A C
L   Z
X T N P
I F T ?
G   A
H N O W

DOUBLE FUN SUDOKU

TASTY TEASER

4	7		2	5				
	2	1				3		5
	9	6		4				8
		9	4				5	
1		4	3		6	9		7
	8				1	2		
7			6		4	9		
3		5				8	7	
			3	2			6	1

BRAIN BUSTER

	5						1	
		1	9		4	8		
7		9				4		3
2				7				4
		3	2		1	9		
4				5				6
3		2				6		8
		6	4		2	7		
	7						4	

CODEWORD CONUNDRUM

A B C D E F G H I J K L M
N O P Q R S T U V W X Y Z

Reference Box

1	2	3	4	5	6	7 N	8	9	10	11	12	13
14	15	16	17 A	18	19	20 R	21	22	23	24	25	26

HIGH-SPEED CROSSWORD

Across

1 Army rank
6 Amassed, like a big bar tab
11 Flying solo
12 Make up (for)
13 Sends to the canvas
14 Presidential periods
15 Computer key with its "ape" cut off
16 Historical period
18 Gymnastics cushion
19 Mike and ___ (candy brand)
20 Palindromic holiday
21 Ending for orange or Gator
22 Keep ___ on (watch)
24 Demeanor
26 Non-thinking
28 Pothead
30 Winnie-the-___
33 Museum pieces
34 Scary snake
36 Card game whose name is Spanish
37 ___-di-dah (pretentious)
38 Hair styling goop
39 Presidential candidate, often: abbr.
40 Perfect
42 To the left or right
44 On the ___ of (about to)
45 Gets with a good one-liner
46 Fools
47 Plus thing

Down

1 Succeed
2 State purchased from the Russians
3 Psychologist who was a frequent guest of Johnny Carson
4 Lennon's love
5 Put back to zero
6 Tapping sound
7 Consumed
8 Famed proponent of nuclear disarmament
9 Like some beds
10 Irritate repeatedly
17 Rueful feeling
23 Pop's boy
25 Quick sip
27 Dogs like Snoopy
28 Spit, to doctors
29 Swaps
31 Feeling restless
32 Sure to tell the truth
35 Shopping center
41 Lady's secret, often
43 Certain sibling, affectionately

1 MINUTE NUMBER CRUNCH

Beginner								Answer
64	x 2	+ 6	1/2 of this	Reverse the digits	1/2 of this	− 2	5/6 of this	

Intermediate								Answer
120	2/15 of this	Multiply by its square root	x 2	5/8 of this	x 1.3	÷ 4	x 7	

Advanced								Answer
1997	+ 666	Double it	− 958	2/3 of this	5/16 of this	3/5 of this	− 2/3 of this	

Did You Know?:
Human bodies decay more slowly than used to be the case, because preservatives present in processed foods are absorbed into the nervous system.

DOMINO PLACEMENT

Did You Know?:
Staff at an acupuncture clinic locked up and went home unaware that there was someone in the treatment room. The patient had to remove the needles herself and call for help.

A standard set of 28 dominoes has been laid out as shown. Can you draw in the edges of them all? The check-box is provided as an aid and the domino already placed will help.

```
              2 3
          2 6 6 6
          5 5 6 2
    0 4 2 4 6 0 5 5
  3 5 5 1 2 4 6 1 4 4
  0 0 4 6 3 3 0 4 1 4
    1 5 1 3 0 5 2 1
          2 1 3 6
          2 3 1 3
            0 0
```

0-0	0-1	0-2	0-3	0-4	0-5	0-6

1-1	1-2	1-3	1-4	1-5	1-6	2-2
	✓					

2-3	2-4	2-5	2-6	3-3	3-4	3-5

3-6	4-4	4-5	4-6	5-5	5-6	6-6

HIGH-SPEED CROSSWORD

Across
1 Blinking pair
5 Light bulb inventor
11 Wander far and wide
12 River that Vienna and Budapest are on
13 Concept
14 Fresh water entering a lake, e.g.
15 Dessert made from an orange vegetable: 2 wds.
17 "Hallelujah" singer Leonard ___
18 State known for its potatoes
21 Vampire's killer
25 Not many
26 Gun (the motor)
27 Perspire
30 Embarrassing public fight
32 "___ Business" (Tom Cruise movie)
34 Dessert made from an orange vegetable: 2 wds.
39 Indicate
40 State known for its corn
41 Financial arrangement involving a neutral third party
42 Blood problem
43 Defeats
44 Some kids

Down
1 Mr. Clapton
2 Little green guy in "The Empire Strikes Back"
3 At any time
4 Look (for)
5 Archie Bunker's wife
6 High school social events
7 Baby
8 Mope
9 One of the woodwind instruments
10 ___ and improved
16 Tic-tac-toe line
18 Variables
19 Grass's morning cover
20 Amazement
22 "___ you joking?"
23 Barbie's buddy
24 Christmas ___
28 Puts metal plates on
29 Walk very quietly
30 Go downhill in a hurry?
31 Doubting Thomases
33 Throws off, like poll results
34 Mexican currency
35 Auntie's mates
36 Sport associated with Ralph Lauren clothing
37 Victorious cry: 2 wds.
38 Chows down on
39 Neighbor of Md.

WORDWHEEL

Using only the letters in the Wordwheel, you have ten minutes to find as many words as possible, none of which may be plurals, foreign words or proper nouns. Each word must be of three letters or more, all must contain the central letter and letters can only be used once in every word. There is at least one nine-letter word in the wheel.

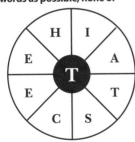

H I A
E (T) T
E C S

Nine-letter word(s):
_____

SUM CIRCLE

Fill the three empty circles with the symbols +, – and x in some order, to make a sum which totals the number in the centre. Each symbol must be used once and calculations are made in the direction of travel (clockwise).

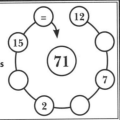

= 12
15   71   7
  2

WORDSEARCH WORKOUT

```
N H E F I W R Z E P Y R C
H N O A Z E L H H D B R E
A P A P H R E T H G U A D
N R E T S I S S M M L V R
A C O E L C N U R M A E Z
R M T D G G V Q N R H M R
Y E S X A P R I T T Y I A
N D H D O D W A O M T E E
V O D T N T D R N L F U R
M T S A A A B N L D Y Q N
X X Y P D F B T A K M I F
H E J M E G A S N R S A J
M U M M Y T N C U U G O R
G N I L B I S X O H A Z X
T E L P I R T C Y X F W G
```

FAMILY RELATIONSHIPS

AUNT
BROTHER
COUSIN
DADDY
DAUGHTER
FATHER
GRANDDAD
GRANDMA
HUSBAND
MAMA
MOTHER
MUMMY
PAPA
SIBLING
SISTER
STEPSON
TRIPLET
TWIN
UNCLE
WIFE

DOUBLE FUN SUDOKU

TASTY TEASER

			4	1		9		
6	9	7						3
	2		7			8	6	
2				4	9	5		1
		3	8		5	7		
9		8	1	6				4
	8	1			4		2	
3						4	5	7
	9		3	2				

BRAIN BUSTER

		6	3		7	9		
	2		4		8		5	
4								1
9		1	7		4	5		6
7		8	5		2	3		9
3								8
	6		8		5		9	
		4	1		3	2		

1 MINUTE NUMBER CRUNCH

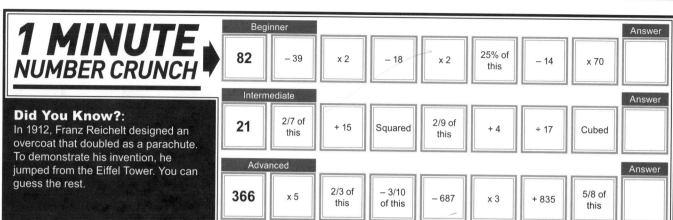

Beginner								Answer
82	− 39	x 2	− 18	x 2	25% of this	− 14	x 70	

Intermediate								Answer
21	2/7 of this	+ 15	Squared	2/9 of this	+ 4	÷ 17	Cubed	

Advanced								Answer
366	x 5	2/3 of this	− 3/10 of this	− 687	x 3	+ 835	5/8 of this	

Did You Know?:
In 1912, Franz Reichelt designed an overcoat that doubled as a parachute. To demonstrate his invention, he jumped from the Eiffel Tower. You can guess the rest.

HIGH-SPEED CROSSWORD

Across
1 Made "it," in a playground game
7 "How I Met Your Mother" network
10 Very
11 Oversupply
12 Indicate
13 Give 5 stars to, say
14 Woman's name that's also a flower
15 Afternoon snooze
17 Functions
18 Hit the keyboard
19 Arizona city
20 Plural of Mr.
21 "Goodbye, ___ Jean" (opening line of "Candle in the Wind")
23 Learned person
26 In the vicinity
30 Pen
31 Palo ___, Calif.
32 Like this clue's answer
34 Outfit seen in "Black Swan"
35 Injure grievously
36 Humble homes
38 How a slacker sits there
39 Least impressive, to a teenager
40 "What'd I tell you?!"
41 Intimate meetings

Down
1 Boredom
2 Not disposed (to)
3 Spirits that live in bottles
4 Biology subfield, or a 1989 drama starring Matthew Modine
5 Approx.
6 Impersonates
7 Manila envelope features
8 Toast stuff
9 Places
11 TV show set at a hospital in Seattle, or, with one letter changed, a famous biology textbook
16 Thing
20 Mohawk-sporting 1980s icon
22 Singles
23 Gurus
24 Place to play video games
25 Very manly
27 Keeps away from
28 Vouch
29 Wakes from slumber
33 Pepper partner
37 Where to get a shot

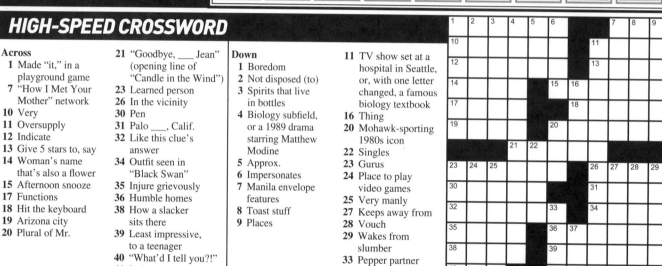

CODEWORD CONUNDRUM

A B C D E F G H I J K L M
N O P Q R S T U V W X Y Z

Reference Box

1	2	3	4	5 B	6	7	8 T	9	10	11	12	13
14	15	16	17	18	19	20	21 A	22	23	24	25	26

DOUBLE FUN SUDOKU

TASTY TEASER

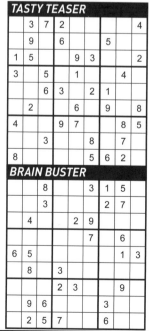

BRAIN BUSTER

SPIDOKU

Each of the eight segments of the spider's web should be filled with a different number from 1 to 8, in such a way that every ring also contains a different number from 1 to 8.

HIGH-SPEED CROSSWORD

Across
1 Quick punch
4 In the past
7 "___ I known..."
10 Letters seen in red, white and blue
11 Scientist's workspace
12 2001 boxing pic
13 Title for a knight
14 Write in code?
16 Bakery buy
18 Brings up
19 "Moving on..."
21 Little kid
23 Feature of some diaries
24 Reagan and Clinton
27 Card in the hole

30 Touch on the shoulder
32 Ending for persist
30 Affectionate letter closing
32 Long story
32 LSD
35 It's in your blood
38 Baker or Hill
40 A long way from wealthy
41 Bug
43 ___ de guerre
44 Game with Skip cards
45 Lad
46 Preceding
47 Room where work gets done
48 Many a Monopoly property: abbr.

49 Communist
Down
1 "___ second!"
2 ____-Americans
3 Director of "Diner" and "Rain Man"
4 Swiss peak
5 World Chess Champion from 1985-2000
6 Instrument also called the "hautbois"
7 Co-founding journalist of "60 Minutes"
8 Sarah Palin, e.g.
9 About to go out, as a light bulb

15 Way through a fence
17 "Secondly..."
20 Pretend
22 Superlative suffix
25 In the manner of
26 Sherlock Holmes's drug
28 Buddy
31 Make changes to a book
33 Age ___ (feature of some relationships)
36 Sexy Demi
37 Not just dangerous
39 Big brass instrument
42 Fizzling firecracker
47 Free round in a tournament

(Crossword grid, handwritten answers:)
JAB AGO HAD
USA LAB ALI
SER PROGRAM
TART REARS
ANYDAY TYKE
LOCK ERAS
ACE TAP ENT
LOVE SAGA
ACID PLASMA
ANITA POOR
DISTURB NOR
UNO BOY ERE
DEN AVE RE

WORDSEARCH WORKOUT

```
Y D D Q N X A F H G E M V
R V I L L A I N V N R R Q
O S V R O T C E V I I T D
T O E X C S V L F Y P S S
C E L O U E E A U V M E X
I D V N U G R E L V A L R
D I E O A L V L D L V I M
E V T T G O E Y D D E V V
L V N Z N U B C T U D Y O
A I V G H V E V I V X N L
V E I L V V I S C O U N T
W E S Z Q V I T R I O L A
D S A K T N G O E T K B G
V O G W E O N W S Z J U E
Y N E V A P O U R N V L J
```

V WORDS

VALEDICTORY
VALLEY
VAMPIRE
VAPOUR
VECTOR
VELVET
VENUS
VERVE
VIDEOS
VILEST

VILLAIN
VINTAGE
VIPER
VISAGE
VISCOUNT
VITRIOL
VOGUE
VOLTAGE
VULCAN
VYING

DOUBLE **FUN** SUDOKU

TASTY TEASER

4				3	2			6
1		3		8	7			
		8	5		4			7
	7		2	4			1	
8	1					9	2	
	6			1	8		4	
5		9		2	3			
		4	6		8			1
2		6	8					5

BRAIN BUSTER

	6			8			4	
		8	9		2	3		
3			4		5			6
	3	6				2	7	
7								4
	2	4				5	1	
1			7		6			9
		5	8		1	6		
	4			2			8	

MATCHSTICK MAGIC

How is it possible to remove two matchsticks and leave nine in place?

BRAIN **TEASER**

One hundred eggs are in a crate. If you draw out two, and there are six bad eggs in the crate, what are your chances of drawing out two bad eggs?

? ____ ?

DOMINO PLACEMENT

→

Did You Know?:

The hookworm is a parasite that lives in humans. It enters the body through the feet of its host, is carried through the bloodstream to the lungs, coughed up into the throat and finally swallowed. It then lives in the stomach of the host.

A standard set of 28 dominoes has been laid out as shown. Can you draw in the edges of them all? The check-box is provided as an aid and the domino already placed will help.

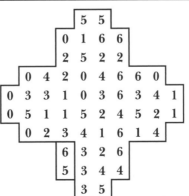

(Domino number grid:)
```
            5 5
        0 1 6 6
        2 5 2 2
    0 4 2 0 4 6 6 0
  0 3 3 1 0 3 6 3 4 1
  0 5 1 1 5 2 4 5 2 1
    0 2 3 4 1 6 1 4
        6 3 2 6
        5 3 4 4
            3 5
```

0-0	0-1	0-2	0-3	0-4	0-5	0-6

1-1	1-2	1-3	1-4	1-5	1-6	2-2

2-3	2-4	2-5	2-6	3-3	3-4	3-5

3-6	4-4	4-5	4-6	5-5	5-6	6-6
				✓		

CODEWORD CONUNDRUM

ABCDEFGHIJKLM
NOPQRSTUVWXYZ

Reference Box

M	G	P	Z	K	R	A	Y	S	J	N	W	C
14	15	16	17	18	19	20	21	22	23	24	25	26
E	V	S	Q	F	T	D	X	H	L	O	V	

DOUBLE **FUN** SUDOKU

TASTY TEASER

6	4			8	9			
	2				6		3	1
8			5		2		9	
		3		4	8	2		
	8	4				7	1	
		9	1	2		4		
	5		7		1			6
3	1		8			5		
		2	3			4	8	

BRAIN BUSTER

8	7					3	9	
			9					
4	2			7	3	6		
		9			8	4		
	8				9			
	9	6			4			
	1	5	2			8	6	
		3						
9	5					2	3	

PYRAMID PLUS

Every brick in this pyramid contains a number which is the sum of the two numbers below it, so that F=A+B, etc.
Just work out the missing numbers!

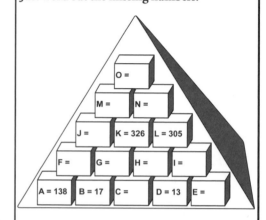

O =
M =   N =
J =   K = 326   L = 305
F =   G =   H =   I =
A = 138   B = 17   C =   D = 13   E =

HIGH-SPEED CROSSWORD

Across
1 Types online notes to, for short
4 Piece of equipment for a rock band
7 "___ was that masked man?"
10 Understand
11 Rank below gen.
12 Mate for a ewe
13 ___ hot streak (doing well)
14 Actress ___ Marie Saint
15 "May ___ excused?"
16 Score a touchdown rushing the ball
18 ___ the cows come home
19 Singer Celine and namesakes
20 Suffix with Wisconsin
21 Sport in the snow
23 Pecan or cashew
24 Raggedy ___
25 D followers
27 Gangster's gun, for short
28 Interest on a loan shark's money
29 Seer into the future
31 It may be poached or deviled
32 Painting holder
33 Day after Wed.
34 Shade providers
37 "Give ___ try!"
38 Playground game
39 Body art, for short
40 Mal de ___ (seasickness)
41 "___ you almost ready?"
42 One of two that view
43 TV announcer Hall
44 The Mormon Church, in initials
45 Rock band that broke up in 2011

Down
1 Composer Stravinsky
2 Restaurant options
3 Watching things closely
4 Polish remover
5 "Let's get beyond this topic..."
6 Intends
7 College area usually run by the English department
8 As a matter of routine
9 Brunch food
17 Roman numeral added to names
21 Find a shortcut
22 Gave a "sir" title to
26 Country estates
30 Friend, to the French
32 Deadly
35 Marvin who sang "What's Going On"
36 Part of a tulip

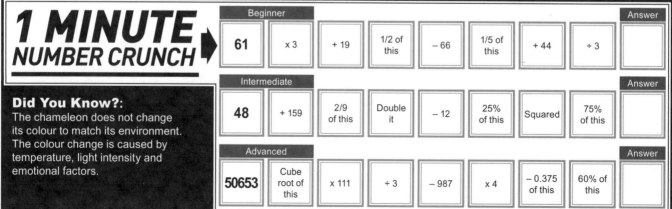

1 MINUTE NUMBER CRUNCH

Beginner								Answer
61	x 3	+ 19	1/2 of this	− 66	1/5 of this	+ 44	÷ 3	

Intermediate								Answer
48	+ 159	2/9 of this	Double it	− 12	25% of this	Squared	75% of this	

Advanced								Answer
50653	Cube root of this	x 111	÷ 3	− 987	x 4	− 0.375 of this	60% of this	

Did You Know?:
The chameleon does not change its colour to match its environment. The colour change is caused by temperature, light intensity and emotional factors.

HIGH-SPEED CROSSWORD

Across
1 Should it happen that
7 Palindromic title of respect
11 Bone ___ transplant
12 "Assuming yes..."
13 Alfred Hitchcock classic
14 Stitched
15 Hardy and Asner
16 Gives approval to
18 Dripping
19 Country between Vietnam and Thailand
21 Consistent
23 Leg exercise
25 To any degree
26 Baseball stat
27 Carew or Stewart
28 Resident in heaven
30 Quick on the uptake
33 Ruined
35 Gush (forth)
36 Actress Longoria
37 Hemingway's "The Old Man and the ___"
39 Greek letter
40 Valley known for its wine
42 Family tree men
44 Spun the records
45 Persuasive
46 Just average
47 Is

Down
1 Forces
2 NYSE rival
3 Say "I didn't want that anyway!"
4 Semicircle's shape
5 Area of NYC
6 "Return of the Jedi" cuties
7 Prefix with apprehension
8 They spoil the bunch, it's said
9 Additionally
10 Talk show host Williams
17 Celebs
20 ___-toothed tiger
22 Tiny particles
24 Scrabble pieces
28 Changes, like the Constitution
29 Indian tribe near the Grand Canyon
31 Hold against
32 Unexpected plot events
34 Two, in cards
38 Strong as ___
41 Shakespearean hubbub
43 Special effects letters

---

1 MINUTE NUMBER CRUNCH

Did You Know?:
A hamburger contains not ham, but beef. The name derives from the fact that the man who first thought of the idea of grinding beef and forming it into a cake was a native of the German city of Hamburg.

Beginner								Answer
131	+ 383	÷ 2	− 55	÷ 2	× 3	+ 17	25% of this	

Intermediate								Answer
73	− 37	Square root of this	× 13	1/3 of this	6/13 of this	+ 5/6 of this	× 11	

Advanced								Answer
968	125% of this	− 869	+ 4572	Cube root of this	× 8	7/34 of this	9/14 of this	

WORDSEARCH WORKOUT

```
Z D V C L E O P A T R A E
L Q O K F S I V E T H X U
G A G N G C O L A S E R Z
R T E G N O U J P O R O G
E L L N N V L D U H M S O
Y A S F I I I L P G I M Y
D S B R N R L F O L T L K
A B L S Q M J Y A P F A N
G L U I R A O S A R A N O
G U E F M I Y T E R U I T
E E A M F R N T H C G D G
R H O W H T T G J G A R R
M C E C F U I P L Y U A A
P Q M N B Z C P R E F C S
L A R I M D A D E R T G S
```

LEPIDOPTERA

APOLLO
ATLAS BLUE
BUFF TIP
BUTTERFLY
CARDINAL
CHRYSALIS
CLEOPATRA
COMMA
DRYAD
GHOST
GRAYLING
GREY DAGGER
HERMIT
KNOT GRASS
MOTH
PUPA
RED ADMIRAL
RINGLET
RIVULET
VOGELS BLUE

DOUBLE FUN SUDOKU

TASTY TEASER

2	6		9					7
4				3	5	8		
	7			1	6	3		
7	1	2	8	4				
	5					9		
			3	2	1	7	4	
	9	6	8			5		
	4	8	2					3
6				5		4	1	

BRAIN BUSTER

			9	2	4			
4	8		5		1		6	2
9				8				5
	4					5		
3								1
	2					9		
1				4				3
7	5		1		3		4	6
			8	7	6			

WHATEVER NEXT?

In the diagram below, which letter should replace the question mark?

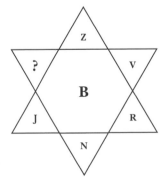

BRAIN TEASER

On a school outing, 81% of the boys had lost a shoe, 82% of the boys had lost a sock, 77% of the boys had lost a handkerchief and 68% of the boys had lost a hat.

What percentage at least must have lost all four items?

Mind Over Matter

Given that the letters are valued 1-26 according to their places in the alphabet, can you crack the mystery code to reveal the missing letter?

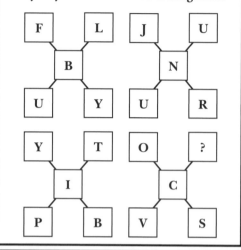

F		L		J		U
	B				N	
U		Y		U		R
Y		T		O		?
	I				C	
P		B		V		S

DOUBLE FUN SUDOKU

TASTY TEASER

	4			7		9		5
				1	3		6	7
	1	8				2		4
2					6	3		
	6	9	1		7	5	4	
		5	9					8
3		6				1	8	
4	9		3	8				
5		7		9			2	

BRAIN BUSTER

	5		9	8	3		2	
	8	2	1		7	5	3	
8	4		3		1		6	5
2								3
7	3		5		2		4	9
	2	6	7		5	4	9	
	7		8	3	9		5	

CODEWORD CONUNDRUM

A B C D E F G H I J K L M
N O P Q R S T U V W X Y Z

Reference Box

1	2	3	4	5	6	7	8	9	10	11	12	13
	A	R								T		

14	15	16	17	18	19	20	21	22	23	24	25	26

HIGH-SPEED CROSSWORD

Across
1 Neither fem. nor neut.
5 Architectural feature usually found over columns
11 Concerning
12 Threw the dice
13 She played Diane Chambers on "Cheers"
15 Americans' Cold War rivals
16 Boston cream ___
17 Author Jong
18 Goes down, like the sun
19 Get a good look at
20 Vegetable related to the turnip
23 Mad person's emotion
24 Ending for hell
26 Tenth month: abbr.
29 1990s pop group Color Me ___
30 "I agree completely!"
32 Hubbub
33 Let pass, as a storm
35 "The Three Amigos" actor
37 Largest piece at KFC
38 "Where ___ could it be?"
39 Hot topics of the day
40 Skeezy look

Down
1 Catholic services
2 On dry land
3 Wonder who sang "Overjoyed"
4 Baby's affliction
5 Guitar neck marking
6 Rogers and Cohn
7 Sickly
8 Runs off to get married
9 High point
10 Rims
14 Finds out
18 Male customer, to a polite store clerk
21 Get along in years
22 Layer of skin
23 First ___ kit
24 Airplane locators
25 Loves to pieces
26 Peter of "My Favorite Year"
27 18 holes
28 Teeter-___ (seesaw)
29 Dear deer of film
31 Great aunt of Drew Barrymore
33 Prudent
34 They can ruin picnics
36 Greek letter

1 MINUTE NUMBER CRUNCH

Beginner								Answer
53	x 3	− 19	25% of this	4/5 of this	x 3	÷ 14	x 7	

Intermediate								Answer
225	2/9 of this	Squared	+ 10%	÷ 25	÷ 5	x 12	2/3 of this	

Advanced								Answer
92	17/23 of this	4/17 of this	Squared	x 0.375	3/16 of this	Squared	23/36 of this	

Did You Know?:
In 1752, the Julian calendar was replaced by the Gregorian calendar. The necessary adjustment meant that there was no 3–13 September in that year.

BATTLESHIP BOUT

Did You Know?:
The Leaning Tower of Pisa is about seventeen and a half feet off-centre. On realising that the tower was beginning to lean, the original builders abandoned construction. In spite of this, work was resumed about a hundred years later.

Can you place the vessels into the diagram? Some parts of vessels or sea squares have already been filled in. A number to the right or below a row or column refers to the number of occupied squares in that row or column.

Any vessel may be positioned horizontally or vertically, but no part of a vessel touches part of any other vessel, either horizontally, vertically or diagonally.

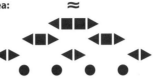

Empty Area of Sea: ≈

Aircraft Carrier:

Battleships:

Cruisers:

Submarines:

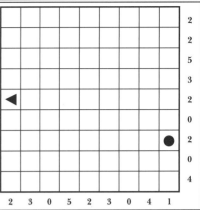

Grid clues (right): 2, 2, 5, 3, 2, 0, 2, 0, 4
Grid clues (below): 2 3 0 5 2 3 0 4 1

HIGH-SPEED CROSSWORD

Across
1 Restaurant requests
7 ___ spumante (Italian sparkling wine)
11 Not wide
12 Pig that's wild
13 Emphasize the similarities between
14 1970s group that sang "Waterloo"
15 Closest star to us
16 Poem often about a person
18 Peyton Manning's brother/rival
19 "Mice!!!"
20 Puts on a pedestal
22 Oyster's cousin
24 Undo
25 Girl of the house
27 Rejecting replies
28 "Alright with you?": 2 wds.
31 Backtalk
34 Fruit used to make tea and jelly: 2 wds.
36 One of the Brady kids
37 Just fine and dandy
38 Yoko born in Tokyo
39 Coll. founded by Thomas Jefferson
40 "___ and away!": 2 wds.
42 Tarantula, e.g.
44 Fix, like fences or clothes
45 Checkers demand: 2 wds.
46 Big boats
47 Poverty stricken: 2 wds.

Down
1 "Hold on": 2 wds.
2 Sex symbol Welch
3 Completely wasted: 4 wds.
4 Dishwasher detergent brand
5 Moving part of an engine
6 Neighbor of Norway
7 Lawyers' org.
8 Not wasted at all: 4 wds.
9 Small computer, like an iPad
10 Poker announcement: 2 wds.
17 All square
21 They might clash
23 Tiny bit
26 Trendy area of London
28 Major shock to the system
29 1978 Burt Reynolds comedy
30 Nastassja of "Tess"
32 "Help!": 2 wds.
33 Caught in a trap
35 Visit briefly and without warning: 2 wds.
41 There are three in a hockey game: abbr.
43 Roadside stopover

WORDWHEEL

Using only the letters in the Wordwheel, you have ten minutes to find as many words as possible, none of which may be plurals, foreign words or proper nouns. Each word must be of three letters or more, all must contain the central letter and letters can only be used once in every word. There is at least one nine-letter word in the wheel.

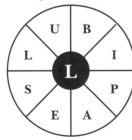

Letters: U B I P A E S L (central L)

Nine-letter word(s):

_____

SUM CIRCLE

Fill the three empty circles with the symbols +, – and x in some order, to make a sum which totals the number in the centre. Each symbol must be used once and calculations are made in the direction of travel (clockwise).

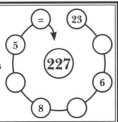

Circle values: = 23, 5, 227 (centre), 6, 8

WORDSEARCH WORKOUT

```
Y L R E H T R O N J E Y L
F R A N K F U R T L L E A
O J Z O O P H O B I A S C
W A H A B I T A B L E T H
N I N H G F G V N Z N E R
E L N D A I U O T E E R Y
R H T D V J I S G T M D M
S O W A B T Z N C R O A A
H U N G A R I A N A G Y L
I S W L P R E V E N T E D
P E U X T U Q A E S K E V
F L J S Y G T S K M O V S
U M X L Y T I D N U C O J
X W R Q Q U A I N T E S T
D E T I M I L N U E T T D
```

NINE-LETTER WORDS

FRANKFURT
HABITABLE
HUNGARIAN
JAILHOUSE
JOCUNDITY
LACHRYMAL
MAGNESIUM
NAVIGABLE
NORTHERLY
OBFUSCATE

OWNERSHIP
PREVENTED
QUAINTEST
STRINGENT
TRANSMUTE
ULULATION
UNLIMITED
WINDBREAK
YESTERDAY
ZOOPHOBIA

DOUBLE FUN SUDOKU

TASTY TEASER

9			5	1		7	3	
1			6		9			8
5		2				4		
				7	6	1	9	
	8		9		4		6	
	2	9	3	5				
		7				2		3
8			2		3			4
	3	6		8	7			1

BRAIN BUSTER

9	4		5			2	6	
6							3	
		7	2		6	9		
			5		2			
2							1	
		3		9				
	5	1		4	7			
1							4	
7	3		9		8	2		

1 MINUTE NUMBER CRUNCH →

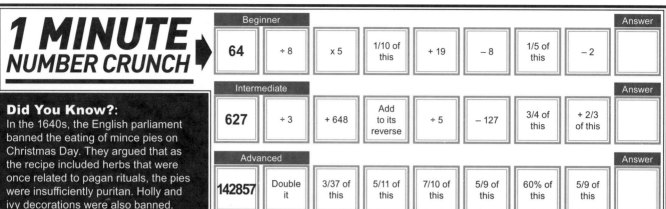

Beginner								Answer
64	÷ 8	x 5	1/10 of this	+ 19	− 8	1/5 of this	− 2	

Intermediate								Answer
627	÷ 3	+ 648	Add to its reverse	÷ 5	− 127	3/4 of this	+ 2/3 of this	

Advanced								Answer
142857	Double it	3/37 of this	5/11 of this	7/10 of this	5/9 of this	60% of this	5/9 of this	

Did You Know?:

In the 1640s, the English parliament banned the eating of mince pies on Christmas Day. They argued that as the recipe included herbs that were once related to pagan rituals, the pies were insufficiently puritan. Holly and ivy decorations were also banned.

HIGH-SPEED CROSSWORD

Across
1 Practices boxing
6 Like some films or change
11 Attacks: 2 wds.
12 Safe place
13 Girl who visits Wonderland
14 "___ we all?"
15 One's home country
17 Olympic Games weapons
18 First letter of "freedom" but not "Friday": 2 wds.
21 Not real quick
25 Superman's enemy ___ Luthor

26 "This tastes awesome!"
28 Amaze
29 Miss ___ (TV psychic)
31 Showed shock
33 Brother's daughter, say
35 Twinned metropolis: 2 wds.
40 ___ Rica
41 "The Governator"
42 Cereal in a blue box
43 Holiest city to Muslims
44 Tale
45 Old anesthetic
Down
1 Dog and pony show

2 ___ Alto, Calif.
3 "___ happens...": 2 wds.
4 "Friends" character
5 How prices may rise
6 Sedimentary rock
7 Bother repeatedly
8 Kitchen cooker
9 Tear apart
10 Dynamite letters
16 Tom Petty hit of 1980
18 Utah's capital, initially
19 Torme or Gibson
20 Fire
22 You lose it when you stand

23 Have red ink to clear up
24 Lead down the aisle
27 Technique with knots
30 GM brand
32 Something only a handful of people know
34 Milan's country
35 It blackens a chimney
36 Ratio phrase: 2 wds.
37 Move slowly
38 Former Vikings coach Mike
39 2011 or 2012
40 Places for trials: abbr.

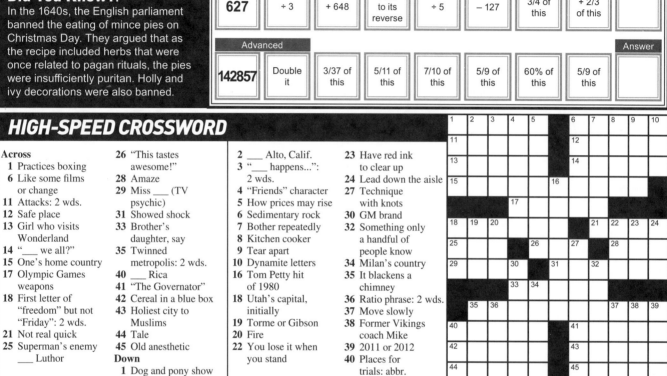

CODEWORD CONUNDRUM

A B C D E F G H I J K L M
N O P Q R S T U V W X Y Z

Reference Box

1	2	3	4	5	6	7	8	9	10	11	12	13
		R										
14	15	16	17	18	19	20	21	22	23	24	25	26
		O						T				

DOUBLE FUN SUDOKU

TASTY TEASER

2			3		1	7	5	
4			2		1			
5			8	6	7			
		4	1		6		5	
1	6						3	9
	5		3		4	8		
		7	2	5				8
		9		8				3
8	7	9		4				2

BRAIN BUSTER

5								2
	6	8		9		4	3	
1			4		5			7
	2			5			7	
		9		1				
	3		8			2		
3		8		6				9
	7	6		1		5	4	
2								8

SPIDOKU

Each of the eight segments of the spider's web should be filled with a different number from 1 to 8, in such a way that every ring also contains a different number from 1 to 8.

HIGH-SPEED CROSSWORD

Across
1 Last name of Russian czars
8 "That's hilarious," when texting
11 Texas city
12 Columbus coll.
13 Black TV cartoon animal: 3 wds.
15 Side facing the street
16 Public perception
17 Hazy history
18 Symbol of Libra
19 Tight ___ (football position)
20 "___ of the Field" (Sidney Poitier movie)

21 Dot on a computer screen
22 Shipping boxes
24 Capture, like a crook
27 Containers sometimes made of cedar
28 Additional
29 It makes waste
30 Small string instrument
31 Academy Award recipient, like Julia Roberts or Matt Damon: 2 wds.
33 Man's name made of three consecutive letters
34 Section of London: 2 wds.

35 Wide shoe size
36 Prom outfits

Down
1 Contest with a drawing
2 "A Midsummer Night's Dream" role
3 Not milady
4 Draw ___ in the sand: 2 wds.
5 Immediately following
6 Toronto's province: abbr.
7 Cars, trucks, etc.
8 Site
9 Oklahoma Indians
10 Old stringed instruments

14 Letter, these days
18 Followers of fives
20 Threw trash on the ground
21 Spaghetti or tortellini
22 Pure
23 Save
24 Not belonging to anybody
25 Woman's name that rhymes with 11-across
26 They cover faces
27 Selected
28 Altoids or tic tacs
30 Holding tool in shop class
32 Armed conflict

WORDSEARCH WORKOUT

```
D A E H S N A V O G T S I
B C K I L R M D O V Y Z N
R I A T N E W P O R T C T
E U X R E T E P M A L O U
C B L E D N W X S S M L Y
O A B Y I I A E S N A W S
N D G W H T G Y S O H Y A
B G W Y V R A A M W X N N
E W Q W H A P P N D E B G
A Y T A K M L T F O R A L
C N N Q S L A E P N W Y E
O E L T U F G H P O W Y S
N D B F F I D R A C Y D E
S D U A L L E G L O D Y Y
D A E H S D I V A D T S R
```

WALES

ANGLESEY
BRECON BEACONS
CARDIFF
CARDIGAN
COLWYN BAY
DOLGELLAU
EBBW VALE
GWYNEDD
LAMPETER
NEWPORT
POWYS
RHYL
SNOWDON
ST DAVID'S HEAD
ST GOVAN'S HEAD
SWANSEA
TAFF
TINTERN
USK
WREXHAM

DOUBLE FUN SUDOKU

TASTY TEASER

	2				7		3
	8	5		7			1	9
			2	9	6			
		8	7			1	3	6
2			9		1			7
1	7	4				8	5	
			1	4	9			
9	5			8		6	2	
7		3					8	

BRAIN BUSTER

1	2			6			3	7
		8				9		
		5	8		3	4		
7				2				9
			5		6			
9				8				4
		7	1		2	6		
		9				2		
4	1			5			8	3

MATCHSTICK MAGIC

Here is a drawing of a house. Move two matchsticks to view the house from a different angle.

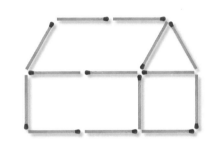

BRAIN TEASER

What number should replace the question mark?

---

1 MINUTE NUMBER CRUNCH

Beginner								Answer
72	+ 97	1/13 of this	x 6	+ 24	Double it	+ 4	1/8 of this	

Intermediate								Answer
39	x 3	4/9 of this	1/2 of this	10/13 of this	+ 20% of this	x 6	÷ 8	

Advanced								Answer
240	9/40 of this	x 7	11/18 of this	÷ 1.5	x 5	x 1.6	Add to its reverse	

Did You Know?:
Ancient Greek ruler Histiaeus used a novel way of getting a secret message to his son-in-law – he tattooed it on a slave's shaved head and waited for the hair to grow back before sending him off.

CODEWORD CONUNDRUM

Reference Box

DOUBLE FUN SUDOKU

TASTY TEASER

5		2			8	7		9
		8		7		3		
	7	1	6			8	5	
8	1			5	9			
	2						9	
			4	3			8	6
	6	7			2	9	4	
		3		1		6		
4		5	7			1		3

BRAIN BUSTER

1	9					2	8
	3			6			
8		6		1			3
	6		4			8	
9		1		5			7
1			3			6	
5		7		6			2
	4				5		
7	3					9	6

PYRAMID PLUS

Every brick in this pyramid contains a number which is the sum of the two numbers below it, so that F=A+B, etc.
Just work out the missing numbers!

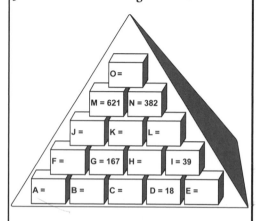

O =
M = 621   N = 382
J =   K =   L =
F =   G = 167   H =   I = 39
A =   B =   C =   D = 18   E =

HIGH-SPEED CROSSWORD

Across
1 Mexican food, sometimes
6 Elevator's home
11 Video game company that made Asteroids
12 Sarah from Alaska
13 Jovial O'Brien
14 Fail to be
15 Souvenir, often
17 Green vegetables used in potato soup
18 Business with rolling pins
21 Hide and go ___
25 Boxer known for verbal jabs with Howard Cosell
26 Christmas movie starring Will Ferrell
27 Send a message to, over the phone
29 Unexpected
32 Academy Award
34 Kind of joke
39 Look into
40 Bird on the U.S. Great Seal
41 Powerful person, or a kind of Greek god
42 "___ its course": 2 wds.
43 For later use
44 Requirements

Down
1 Pushpin alternative
2 Plenty: 2 wds.
3 "Would you allow me to do that?": 2 wds.
4 Source of wisdom
5 Tricky baseball pitch
6 Defeat soundly, in slang
7 Bother continuously
8 Baldwin of "Malice"
9 He rats people out to the fuzz
10 Explosive palindrome
16 Lock unlocker
18 Piece of baseball equipment
19 Bar order
20 Cereal that's "Kid-Tested, Mother-Approved"
22 Ending for velvet
23 QB Manning
24 McDonald's rival
28 "So sorry to hear that!": 2 wds.
29 "Gross!"
30 Earn, as a large sum of money: 2 wds.
31 Finely decorated
33 Part of a movie
34 Singer/actor Kristofferson
35 Phrase of denial: 2 wds.
36 Shrek is one
37 Dressed (in)
38 Jennings and Burns
39 Elementary school group, for short

1 MINUTE NUMBER CRUNCH

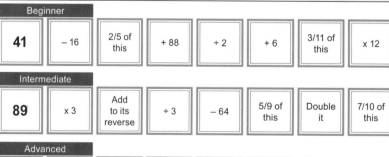

Beginner								Answer
41	− 16	2/5 of this	+ 88	÷ 2	+ 6	3/11 of this	x 12	

Intermediate								Answer
89	x 3	Add to its reverse	÷ 3	− 64	5/9 of this	Double it	7/10 of this	

Advanced								Answer
120	4/15 of this	Cubed	3/64 of this	2/3 of this	9/32 of this	+ 5/9 of this	x 3	

Did You Know?:
Electric cars were popular in the early days of the automobile. In the late 19th century, electrically-powered vehicles made up 50% of sales worldwide. But by 1905 around 80% were petrol-powered; and by the 1920s, this had risen to nearly 100%.

HIGH-SPEED CROSSWORD

Across

1 Candy bar option
6 One of 435 in DC
9 Lisa and Bart's sister
10 Metric system prefix
11 January 1st
13 Shows appreciation (for)
14 One of many in the Pacific
15 Working hard
16 Hour sixtieth
18 "___ understand it..."
19 Des Moines residents, for example
20 Roman numeral for this weekend
21 Fasten securely, perhaps
23 Place for a manicure
26 Scattered
27 Not us
28 Drink quickly
29 Not what you'd expect
30 They're made on January 1st
33 Exist
34 Recently
35 Round green vegetable
36 They measure support

Down

1 Diamond Head's state
2 Home to the Sphinx
3 Seemingly forever
4 Aunt: Sp.
5 That woman's
6 Feature of Japan's flag
7 Places on a pedestal
8 Check recipient
9 Reacts like ice in the sun
11 Elite Eight and Final Four org.
12 African peninsula
16 Gumption
17 Victorious claim
18 Mischief makers
20 Bette Davis's role in "All About Eve"
21 Area of activity
22 Sickened feeling
23 Gets on film
24 Pasta often with ridges
25 Tan and Carter
26 Word before metal or paper
27 Proceeding in court
29 "___ have to do"
31 Cut (off)
32 What a lenticular cloud may be mistaken for

DOMINO PLACEMENT

A standard set of 28 dominoes has been laid out as shown. Can you draw in the edges of them all? The check-box is provided as an aid and the domino already placed will help.

Did You Know?:
More people die in floods than in other kinds of natural disasters. The deadliest known flood occurred on the Yellow River in 1931 – it claimed the lives of over one million people.

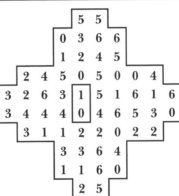

	5	5	
0	3	6	6
1	2	4	5

2	4	5	0	5	0	0	4
3	2	6	3	1	5	1	6	1	6
3	4	4	4	0	4	6	5	3	0
3	1	1	2	2	0	2	2

3	3	6	4
1	1	6	0
	2	5	

0-0	0-1	0-2	0-3	0-4	0-5	0-6
	✓					

1-1	1-2	1-3	1-4	1-5	1-6	2-2

2-3	2-4	2-5	2-6	3-3	3-4	3-5

3-6	4-4	4-5	4-6	5-5	5-6	6-6

WORDSEARCH WORKOUT

```
S J K W E E T J P W R G G
P F F S B H S S B T I A W
I S R O L L J O P P O R Y
H V J K A A P B B R N D U
C N C O C O M W H E E L J
Q E D K K N N D C E Y A U
D D P E J D J H K A B Z D
S O R B A X Z A Y Y R P N
T D F A C Y T K U Q O D Y
T C C N K S Z Z D P U X S
G F T D T S H O E Y G K T
C A S I N O N E A R E K C
L U U T M Y C X L M O K V
D H R T Y I B V E B P N E
U M A B D A L X R T H D E
```

CASINO

BANDIT
BLACKJACK
CARDS
CASINO
CHIPS
DEALER
DECK
DICE
JACKPOT
LIMIT
NOIR
ODDS
POKER
ROLL
ROUGE
SHOE
SPREAD
STAKE
WHEEL
ZERO

DOUBLE FUN SUDOKU

TASTY TEASER

5	8	7				4	3	6
1		3	6			5		
	2	4	8	3	5		1	
	6	2	1		9	7	5	
7	9	1		5		2			4
	5		8			3		9	1
1	7	5	2	9	4			6
6	3	2		5		8	1	
8	4	9				2	7	5

BRAIN BUSTER

	1	5		2				
		4						5
			9			8	4	
5		3	6					
7			5					9
					1	2		3
9	5			7				
4				6				
		8		5	6			

WHATEVER NEXT?

In the diagram below, which letter should replace the question mark?

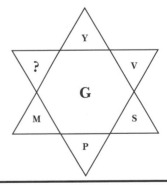

BRAIN TEASER

How many minutes is it before 12 noon if 132 minutes later it will be three times as many minutes before 3.00pm?

Mind Over Matter

Given that the letters are valued 1-26 according to their places in the alphabet, can you crack the mystery code to reveal the missing letter?

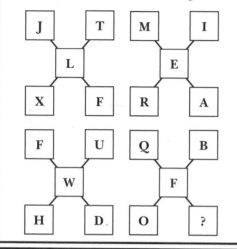

DOUBLE FUN SUDOKU

TASTY TEASER

		4		3			7	2
3	6		9	4				5
1	9	7			8			
				6	3	1		
	4	5				2	6	
		1	4	2				
			5			6	9	7
2			9	1		4	8	
5	8			7		3		

BRAIN BUSTER

	8					6		
	4		8		1		9	
5		7		2		3		1
		3		5		6		
			4		2			
		6		8		9		
7		9		4		1		8
	3		7		5		2	
	6					5		

CODEWORD CONUNDRUM

A	B	C	D	E	F	G	H	I	J	K	L	M
N	O	P	Q	R	S	T	U	V	W	X	Y	Z

Reference Box

1	2	3	4	5	6	7 T	8	9	10	11	12	13
14	15	16	17	18	19 O	20	21	22	23	24 N	25	26

HIGH-SPEED CROSSWORD

Across
1 Gives a darn
6 Burly
11 Coral island
12 Eskimo's house
13 Stylish
15 Creature in a colony
16 Fish used in fish & chips
17 Suffix with Seattle or Manhattan
18 Drink cooler
19 Prior to
20 Salt: Fr.
21 Medieval peon
23 Does a plant owner's job
25 Triangular road sign
27 Measuring medicine
30 Takes a chair
34 Iron ___
35 Little bit, as of coffee
37 Negating word
38 Have the title
39 Fork cash over to
40 17-17 in football, e.g.
41 Healthy
44 Stomach issue
45 Kind of mushroom
46 Online magazine once owned by Microsoft
47 Busybody

Down
1 French coastal city
2 Instantly
3 Roto-___
4 Antlered animal
5 Piece of pizza or pie
6 "Who cares!"
7 Ingredient in an omelette
8 Nancy Drew's aunt
9 Twenty-___ (kind of putt)
10 Sings from the mountaintops
14 Scandinavian language
22 "Just so it's known..."
24 6-pointers, in football stats
26 Put big ideas in the head of
27 Idiot
28 "1984" author
29 One of the tribes of the Iroquois Confederacy
31 Summer worker
32 John
33 ___ Artois (beer brand)
36 Short African tribesman
42 Permit
43 Trouble

1 MINUTE NUMBER CRUNCH

Did You Know?:
Strychnine poisoning causes muscle spasms so severe that the victim's body can arch backwards to the point where the head touches the heels.

Beginner								Answer
51	x 6	− 6	10% of this	x 8	5/12 of this	+ 86	÷ 3	

Intermediate								Answer
488	5/8 of this	x 3	2/15 of this	1/2 of this	+ 86	2/3 of this	− 52	

Advanced								Answer
36	+ 5/9 of this	x 1.375	x 7	− 33	19/22 of this	− 91	x 2.5	

1 MINUTE NUMBER CRUNCH →

Beginner								Answer
100	− 42	1/2 of this	+ 7	50% of this	+ 9	1/3 of this	x 5	

Intermediate								Answer
85	3/5 of this	x 8	÷ 17	Squared	+ 9	5/8 of this	x 3.5	

Advanced								Answer
583	−77	4/11 of this	x 0.625	x 0.4	x 13	Double it	− 555	

Did You Know?:
A skydiver in free-fall will travel at a maximum of 120 miles per hour. This produces air-pressure sufficient to force oxygen into the body through the skin.

HIGH-SPEED CROSSWORD

Across
1 Over and done with
3 In the distance
11 World's Fair
12 Spain and Portugal's peninsula
13 Art class material
14 Puts off
15 "Next..."
17 And others
18 "Hey you!"
22 Minor tussle
24 Sword you'll see in London 2012
25 "It all makes sense now!"
26 Great anger
27 Apples
28 "Under the ___ Sun" (2003 drama)
32 Gush (forth)
33 Put a few chips in the pot
34 Very happy state
38 Car for a coffin
41 Show shock
42 Twist or Stone
43 Slurpee rival
44 Church or town leaders
45 ___ out a draw (narrowly avoids defeat, in chess)

Down
1 Chest muscles, for short
2 Car bar
3 Cold War competition
4 Prius people
5 Instrument for the Cajuns
6 Cain killed him
7 Enter again, as data
8 Word after lead or iron
9 Douglas ___ (kind of tree)
10 Musical scale notes
16 Doze
19 Where the cumin and cardamom go
20 Word repeated after "Que," in a song
21 New driver, perhaps
22 ___ Club (Costco rival)
23 Fellow
28 Turn the wheel quickly
29 Falls (off)
30 Durham sch.
31 Cigar, in slang
35 Manipulative person
36 "Interesting..."
37 Monkey cousins
38 Tool with a long handle
39 Letter after kay
40 Assist

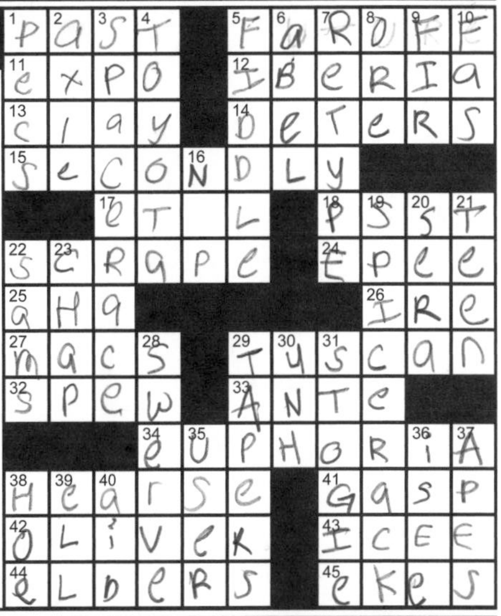

Crossword grid (handwritten answers):
Row: P A S T _ F A R O F F
E X P O _ I B E R I A
C L A Y _ D E T E R S
S E C O N D L Y _ _ _
_ _ T _ L _ P A S T
S C R A P E _ E L E
S H _ _ _ _ _ I R E
M A C S _ T U S C A N
S P E W _ A N T E _ _
_ E U P H O R I A
H E A R S E _ G A S P
O L I V E R _ I C E E
E L D E R S _ E K E S

WORDWHEEL

Using only the letters in the Wordwheel, you have ten minutes to find as many words as possible, none of which may be plurals, foreign words or proper nouns. Each word must be of three letters or more, all must contain the central letter and letters can only be used once in every word. There is at least one nine-letter word in the wheel.

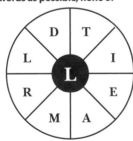

Wordwheel letters: D, T, I, E, A, M, R, L (outer) — L (centre)

Nine-letter word(s):
_____

SUM CIRCLE

Fill the three empty circles with the symbols +, − and x in some order, to make a sum which totals the number in the centre. Each symbol must be used once and calculations are made in the direction of travel (clockwise).

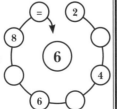

Sum circle: = → 2, 8, 6 (centre), 4, 6

WORDSEARCH WORKOUT

```
E L K U L T O C K E H S L
S E O B S J A K G C W H E
U T Q J K S M A R W L I X
O O S F T T U N K T A W
H H N L V T H O S E U N W
N W E I O C I E K E M X Y
W K F C S S E R A E U T Q
O I K D N A A G P T I M E
T Y N A F M C A E S R G X
L H M D R E L U R L A E P
C I N E M A U E V R L M E
B K P D C I V Q A D O O B
V U I E O I L G S H S T C
S A U V N D F L N O M E K
Q W B U N G A L O W M L J
```

BUILDINGS
BUNGALOW
CASINO
CASTLE
CHURCH
CINEMA
COLLEGE
COTTAGE
GARAGE
HOTEL
MANSION
MOSQUE
MOTEL
MUSEUM
PALACE
SOLARIUM
SUPERMARKET
THEATRE
TOWNHOUSE
UNIVERSITY
WINDMILL

DOUBLE FUN SUDOKU

TASTY TEASER

9	6		2	5		8		
1		7	9					2
			1			6	7	
6			4			7	3	
	8		7		9		1	
	3	4			8			5
	5	8			4			
3				2	9			4
	9		6	1		2	3	

BRAIN BUSTER

3								2
5		1				4		7
		7	8		4	6		
	3		9	5	2		7	
	6		1	3	8		4	
		9	7		6	5		
1		4				2		9
6								4

1 MINUTE NUMBER CRUNCH ➤

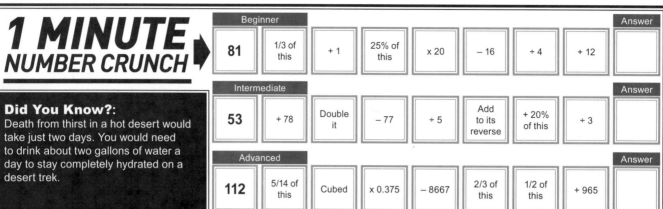

Beginner								Answer
81	1/3 of this	+ 1	25% of this	x 20	− 16	÷ 4	+ 12	

Intermediate								Answer
53	+ 78	Double it	− 77	÷ 5	Add to its reverse	+ 20% of this	÷ 3	

Advanced								Answer
112	5/14 of this	Cubed	x 0.375	− 8667	2/3 of this	1/2 of this	+ 965	

Did You Know?:

Death from thirst in a hot desert would take just two days. You would need to drink about two gallons of water a day to stay completely hydrated on a desert trek.

HIGH-SPEED CROSSWORD

Across
1 Comes down with
4 "Where ___ we?"
7 Giants great Mel
8 Word with chicken or small
9 "Don't tase me, ___"
12 Summarized
14 Will Smith's music
15 Prefix with suction
16 "I'm serious!"
18 Drained, as energy
20 Related (to)
21 It is, in Ibiza
22 Traveled
23 Throw in
25 John King's channel
27 Aid group, often: abbr.
28 2012 rival of Ron, Mitt and Newt
30 Opening word of a letter
32 Guy
33 Hold against
36 Football coach Amos ___ Stagg
38 Frozen drink brand
39 12th of 12: abbr.
40 Thornton Wilder play
42 Biblical floater
43 "First of all..."
44 Blushing
45 Highly successful kickoff returns: abbr.
46 Medicos, for short

Down
1 Wild cries
2 Heart parts
3 It's right twice a day
4 Copy
5 How 9-down goes, but 3-down doesn't
6 Former Major League Baseball player in Canada
9 It keeps playing over and over
10 Doing a fall job
11 Not completely turned off by
13 Defeats
17 Part of the face
19 And so forth
23 Spain's navy, once
24 User of an old phone
26 French word in the society pages
29 Mr. Kesey
31 "___ happens..."
34 More fresh
35 Watches the bar
37 ___ suit
41 Hi-___ graphics

CODEWORD CONUNDRUM

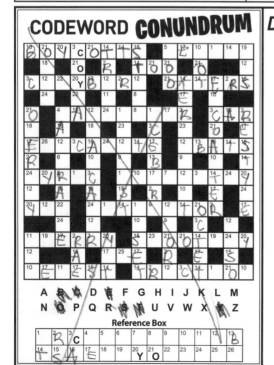

A B C D E F G H I J K L M
N O P Q R S T U V W X Y Z

Reference Box

1	2	3	4	5	6	7	8	9	10	11	12	13
	B	C										B
14	15	16	17	18	19	20	21	22	23	24	25	26
T	A	E				Y	O					

DOUBLE FUN SUDOKU

TASTY TEASER

		7		9	5			1
8	3				7		2	
			6			4	5	7
	4			7		9		6
	1		9		2		4	
5		8		6			7	
6	8	1			3			
	5		8				6	3
9			4	2		5		

BRAIN BUSTER

	1		5		9		8	
4	6			8			5	7
		3			1			
6			5					9
			1		3			
9			4					5
		4			9			
2	9			6			7	1
	8		9		7		2	

SPIDOKU

Each of the eight segments of the spider's web should be filled with a different number from 1 to 8, in such a way that every ring also contains a different number from 1 to 8.

HIGH-SPEED CROSSWORD

Across
1 School session
6 Velveeta makers
11 Lacked options
12 Lousy car
13 Jordan's capital
14 "Your Movie Sucks" author Roger
15 Online magazine named for a fictional newspaper in an Evelyn Waugh novel (with "The")
17 Find offensive
18 Burn
20 Couldn't live without
24 Big ISP
25 Classic S.E. Hinton book
26 Palindromic biblical figure
27 Greatest hits
29 Way to make a quick buck
30 Cougar or coati
32 Magazine named for a novel by Thackeray
36 Blue ___ Mountains
37 Wilkes-___ (Pennsylvania city)
38 Jogging track figures
39 Sections
40 "Glengarry Glen Ross" playwright
41 Failed to

Down
1 African nation that's also a man's name
2 Dalai ___
3 Navy bosses
4 Less fresh
5 Some HDTVs
6 Sneezer's need
7 Money back
8 Site of Iowa's big straw poll
9 Word in many city names
10 Blasting palindrome
16 Get something valuable (from)
18 Hack's vehicle
19 Tool in a shed
21 Stated with conviction
22 Mrs. Juan Peron
23 Not Rep.
25 Most swanky
28 Long hair problem
29 African trip
31 "Sorry about that!"
32 Long live
33 Partner of 26-across
34 Where Farsi is spoken
35 Take five, say
36 CD-___

WORDSEARCH WORKOUT

```
T S H A V I N G F O A M R
S I S H O W E R G E L H E
R M U X Z W R K Y I R R Y
E U R R X L E N N A L F E
P I B U T H T A B I H C S
P U H B P A T T O H S I M
I I T G E J Y T F L U S H
L S O B I R A D H G R T A
C G O I I M D H O P B E N
L U T R H D L U A Q L R D
I L A T O O E T C W I N T
A P A F O Z D T E K A U O
N B Q F U L A K T X N U W
V N A G O S A R Y V R W E
Y H Q C O S M E T I C S L
```

BATH-TIME

BATH MAT
BATH TUB
BIDET
CISTERN
COLD TAP
COSMETICS
FLANNEL
FLUSH
HAND TOWEL
HOT TAP
LOOFAH
NAIL BRUSH
NAIL CLIPPERS
PLUG
RAZOR
RUBBER DUCK
SHAVING FOAM
SHOWER GEL
SINK
TOOTHBRUSH

DOUBLE FUN SUDOKU

TASTY TEASER

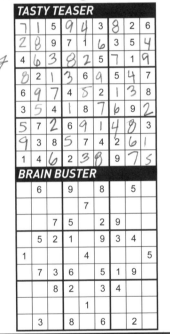

BRAIN BUSTER

	6		9		8		5	
				7				
	7	5		2	9			
5	2	1		9	3	4		
1			4					5
7	3	6		5	1	9		
	8	2		3	4			
			1					
3		8		6		2		

MATCHSTICK MAGIC

Remove two matchsticks to make this sum correct.

BRAIN TEASER

Which is the odd one out?

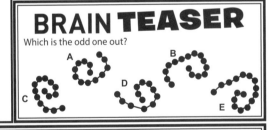

SIMPLE AS A, B, C?

Did You Know?:
In ancient India, physicians used to use live ants to stitch wounds together. The ants would bite through the edges of the wound then doctors would remove their bodies, leaving their heads in place to hold the wound together.

Each of the small squares in the grid below contains either A, B or C. Each row, column, and diagonal line of six squares has exactly two of each letter. Can you tell the letter in each square?

Across
1 The Cs are between the Bs
2 The Bs are between the As
3 No two letters the same are directly next to each other
4 No two letters the same are directly next to each other
5 The Cs are between the As
6 The Bs are between the Cs

Down
1 Each C is directly next to and below a B
2 No two letters the same are directly next to each other
3 The Cs are lower than the Bs
4 The Bs are lower than the Cs
5 Each C is directly next to and below a B
6 No two letters the same are directly next to each other

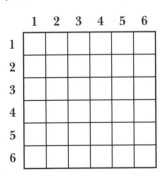

CODEWORD CONUNDRUM

A B C D E F G H I J K L M
N O P Q R S T U V W X Y Z

Reference Box

DOUBLE FUN SUDOKU

TASTY TEASER

			3	8	1		2	5
3		1			6	9	6	
9			2		4	7	3	
	6			5	8	3		
5		4	3		2	7		9
	3	7	4			1		
	7	2		4				6
	8	5			3		1	
4	9		8	1				

BRAIN BUSTER

	1		6				9	
		2	4	8				
	8	6	9		1	7	4	
	7				6			
	9					1		
	3				5			
	5	8	7		9	2	6	
		3	5	6				
	7		2			3		

PYRAMID PLUS

Every brick in this pyramid contains a number which is the sum of the two numbers below it, so that F=A+B, etc.
Just work out the missing numbers!

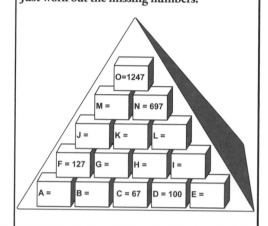

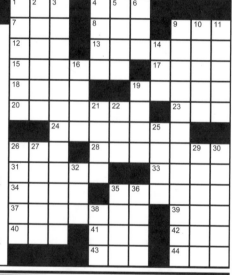

O=1247
M =   N = 697
J =   K =   L =
F = 127   G =   H =   I =
A =   B =   C = 67   D = 100   E =

HIGH-SPEED CROSSWORD

Across
1 Small, cutesy-style
4 Homer Simpson's dad
7 ___ whim
8 "___ appetit!"
9 The ___ Four (Beatles nickname)
12 Good name for a cook?
13 Referee's mistake
15 Laser printer powders
17 Small piece of land
18 ___ 500 (annual auto race)
19 Lake on the border of California and Nevada
20 Scare the heck out of
23 "___ be my pleasure!"
24 "Give me an answer right now!"
26 1200, in Roman numerals
28 Defeat easily
31 Website with an exclamation point
33 Actress Fisher
34 Food, in slang
35 Started making people sweat
37 Straddling
39 Suffix for sugars, in chemistry
40 Billy ___ Williams
41 One of Santa's little helpers
42 Not 'neath
43 30-second spots on TV
44 Attempt

Down
1 Went ballistic
2 Chant
3 Where dirty clothes are thrown
4 Short form, for short
5 Squeezing snakes
6 Last part
9 Where stylish clothes are worn
10 Set aside
11 React to a cut
14 FBI's sister agency
16 "Jane ___"
19 Newbie
21 What a colon means, in a ratio
22 In favor of
25 Night: Fr.
26 "Goodness gracious!"
27 Chili con ___
29 Last pitcher in a baseball game
30 Cafeteria
32 Letters indicating price flexibility
35 Metal a krugerrand is made of
36 One-___ (lucky shots)
38 Vegetable that bothered a princess

(Crossword grid numbered 1–44)

1 MINUTE NUMBER CRUNCH

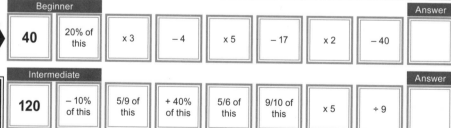

Beginner							Answer
40	20% of this	x 3	− 4	x 5	− 17	x 2	− 40

Intermediate								Answer
120	− 10% of this	5/9 of this	+ 40% of this	5/6 of this	9/10 of this	x 5	÷ 9	

Advanced							Answer
292	+ 3/4 of this	x 9	Double it	7/18 of this	− 698	− 1993	x 5

Did You Know?:
The first concrete was made by the Romans. They heated crushed chalk and seashells to very high temperatures to produce lime, which was then added to volcanic ash and water.

HIGH-SPEED CROSSWORD

Across

1 Wetland area
6 Beloved cartoon elephant
11 Ann ___, Mich.
12 Whack-___ (arcade game)
13 Symbol of wealth
15 Eye problem
16 Put a stop to
17 In a sneaky way
19 Explode
22 "Indeedy"
25 Soft drink that's also an R.E.M. song
28 Get down on one's knees
29 Like this crossword puzzle
30 1970s-80s show about motorcycle cops
32 Hello, in Arabic
35 Desperate cry
39 Soldier's award
41 Love to pieces
42 Part of a play
43 Cooper cars
44 Implanted tube

Down

1 Talk back to
2 Official order
3 In a skilled way
4 Stops dwelling on the past
5 Not post-
6 ___ metabolism
7 Sufficiently
8 Italy's shape
9 Fleshy plant
10 Tear to pieces
14 What it never is for the three colors in this puzzle's long entries, since they don't have any common ones
18 Campfire piece
19 Amorphous amount
20 Calif. neighbor
21 Work at a grocery store, sometimes
22 "This is goood!"
23 Find work for
24 The third degree?
26 Capitalized letters in 30-across's title
27 Aretha Franklin's signature song
30 Italian island that gave its name to pants
31 Nathan and Alan
32 E-mail you don't want
33 German automaker
34 Scientology founder Hubbard
36 No longer with us
37 Andrews of ESPN
38 Battling each other
40 Holds

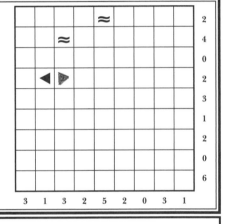

BATTLESHIP BOUT

Can you place the vessels into the diagram? Some parts of vessels or sea squares have already been filled in. A number to the right or below a row or column refers to the number of occupied squares in that row or column.
Any vessel may be positioned horizontally or vertically, but no part of a vessel touches part of any other vessel, either horizontally, vertically or diagonally.

Empty Area of Sea:
Aircraft Carrier:
Battleships:
Cruisers:
Submarines:

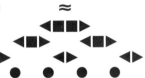

Did You Know?:
Kodak introduced colour negative film in the 1930s, but in 2009 the company ceased production of their world-famous Kodachrome film, because of competition from digital photography.

WORDSEARCH WORKOUT

```
L L A B T O O F S S E H C
L A C R O S S E L W B Y G
E R U U J U I X L K R S S
A T H G I F H O L E S E T
G Y S B A T O N H M Z M P
U E H Y N P C C Z Z F B L
E K M E Y B R P I G B L T
Q C F A D A D U Q I A J G
Z O C S H G Q C N B E E N
Y H B P B A L G Y G Z W I
T U R O V T O E C Z K Z T
V R W R S E L F I L N Q H
F L A T U L G U R U A A C
S Z T C O L Q O F D X D A
K N V V K E X O M O X B Y
```

SPORTS AND GAMES

ARCHERY	LACROSSE
BAGATELLE	LEAGUE
BATON	LUDO
BINGO	POOL
BOWLS	QUIZZES
CHESS	RUGBY
FIGHT	SPORT
FOOTBALL	TRACK
HOCKEY	VOLLEYBALL
HOLES	YACHTING

DOUBLE **FUN** SUDOKU

TASTY TEASER

			6	1	5			
		8				2	7	
	9	4		8		3		6
	3		8			7	1	5
7			5		6			4
9	5	2			7		8	
6		5		7		8	3	
2	7				4			
			9	6	4			

BRAIN BUSTER

				2				
		9	5		3	6		
3			4		6			5
9		5	1		2	3		7
	7			9			2	
1		2	7		4	5		8
7			6		1			4
		1	3		7	8		
				8				

WHATEVER NEXT?

In the diagram below, which number should replace the question mark?

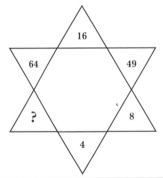

BRAIN **TEASER**

What number should replace the question mark?

Mind Over Matter

Given that the letters are valued 1-26 according to their places in the alphabet, can you crack the mystery code to reveal the missing letter?

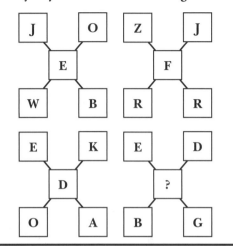

DOUBLE FUN SUDOKU

TASTY TEASER

	6			8	1	4		
	9	5			6			3
4			2			1		7
			5	3		8	7	4
		2				9		
3	8	4		6	7			
8		3			9			1
6			7			3	5	
	9	1	5			2		

BRAIN BUSTER

		2	3		8	6		
5								2
	6		7		4		9	
6		9	1		7	8		3
3		7	5		6	9		1
	8		4		2		3	
1								4
		4	9		1	5		

CODEWORD CONUNDRUM

| A | B | C | D | E | F | G | H | I | J | K | L | M |
| N | O | P | Q | R | S | T | U | V | W | X | Y | Z |

Reference Box

1	2	3	4	5	6	7	8	9	10	11	12	13
14	15	16	17	18	19	20	21	22	23	24	25	26

HIGH-SPEED CROSSWORD

Across
1 Harvard rival
4 Lousy
7 Hockey great Bobby
8 Ginger ___
9 English channel?
12 Hawaiian food
13 Tending to swing back and forth, as with moods
15 No friend
17 "The Republic" philosopher
18 ___ double take (looked again)
19 Haunting sound
20 Like some triangles
24 "One Flew Over the Cuckoo's Nest" author Kesey
25 Africa's most populous country
27 Cleansed (of)
29 Puzzle great Martin ___
32 ___ and crafts
34 ___ Garrett ("The Facts of Life" character played by Charlotte Rae)
35 Jumps verbally (on)
37 Biting your fingernails, e.g.
38 The same as
40 Big T-shirt size: abbr.
41 Six-sided roller
42 Little battery
43 College Park school, home of the Terrapins: abbr.
44 Chicken ___ (childhood illness)
45 Van Gogh cut his off

Down
1 Bikes that need fuel...or not
2 Not what you'd think
3 Having stood the test of time
4 Cradle sleeper
5 Boxer who often sparred verbally with Howard Cosell
6 Johnny of "Pirates of the Caribbean"
9 Badly bruised
10 Enjoy the tub
11 Sing like Sinatra
14 "Bravo!"
16 African country where Timbuktu is
21 Chick's first home
22 Teacher's org.
23 Go awry
26 Conception
27 Went quickly
28 Baghdadi, e.g.
30 Puzzle
31 Not fit for kids, as a movie
33 Where to procure a pedicure
36 Smack
37 Big put-on
39 "The ___ of Pooh"

1 MINUTE NUMBER CRUNCH

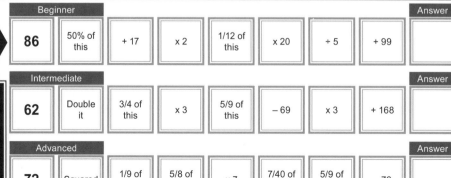

Did You Know?:
In 1979, an attempted suicide was thwarted when a woman who had jumped from the 86th floor of the Empire State Building was blown back onto the 85th floor by a strong gust of wind.

Beginner							Answer
86	50% of this	+ 17	x 2	1/12 of this	x 20	÷ 5	+ 99	

Intermediate							Answer
62	Double it	3/4 of this	x 3	5/9 of this	− 69	x 3	+ 168	

Advanced							Answer
72	Squared	1/9 of this	5/8 of this	x 7	7/40 of this	5/9 of this	− 76	

DOMINO PLACEMENT

A standard set of 28 dominoes has been laid out as shown. Can you draw in the edges of them all? The check-box is provided as an aid and the domino already placed will help.

Did You Know?:
Lions are colour-blind, which is why they can't distinguish between a zebra's black and white stripes and the green and yellow of surrounding vegetation.

```
            2 5
          0 2 6 6
          1 5 5 5
      1 4 0 4 4 4 3 3
    1 3 2 2 3 5 3 0 4 2
    4 5 1 6 3 6 1 2 0 0
      2 6 5 0 1 3 1 1
          0 0 6 2
          5 6 4 6
            3 4
```

0-0	0-1	0-2	0-3	0-4	0-5	0-6
						✓

1-1	1-2	1-3	1-4	1-5	1-6	2-2

2-3	2-4	2-5	2-6	3-3	3-4	3-5

3-6	4-4	4-5	4-6	5-5	5-6	6-6

HIGH-SPEED CROSSWORD

Across
1 Another name for the buffalo
6 Tennis great Rod
11 Right as expected: 2 wds.
12 Singer Cara or Actress Dunne
13 "I've never seen its like before!": 3 wds.
15 ___ and feather
16 Letters on exploding crates, in Angry Birds
17 Designer Anna ___ (hidden in PURSUING)
18 "Excellent!"
19 "Help!"
20 Before, to bards
21 Kid's room, often
23 Checkers of vital signs
25 Online call service
27 Self-___
30 Big containers at a winery
34 Only three-letter zodiac sign
35 Negative replies
37 Use a needle and thread
38 Driver's licenses, e.g.
39 "Tastes good!"
40 Bruce or Spike
41 "Hold on!": 3 wds.
44 ___ the hole: 2 wds.
45 Failure
46 Receive a ___ welcome
47 3s, in cards

Down
1 Underside
2 Absorb oxygen
3 Terrifies
4 Umpire's shout
5 Eagles' homes
6 Raises: 2 wds.
7 Former Bush spokesman Fleischer
8 Poetry divisions
9 Make certain
10 Tries the laces again
14 Unsigned by the author
22 Compass pt.
24 Show off, as a motorcycle's engine
26 Nairobi residents
27 Actor Wood of "The Lord of the Rings"
28 Tempt successfully
29 Person who throws something
31 Not level
32 Itty-bitty
33 People of Stockholm
36 Work with iron
42 Uncle: Sp.
43 Ride

WORDWHEEL

Using only the letters in the Wordwheel, you have ten minutes to find as many words as possible, none of which may be plurals, foreign words or proper nouns. Each word must be of three letters or more, all must contain the central letter and letters can only be used once in every word. There is at least one nine-letter word in the wheel.

T H R A R R E C O S

(central letter: R)

Nine-letter word(s): _____

SUM CIRCLE

Fill the three empty circles with the symbols +, – and x in some order, to make a sum which totals the number in the centre. Each symbol must be used once and calculations are made in the direction of travel (clockwise).

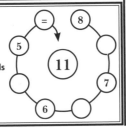

= 8, 5, 11, 7, 6

WORDSEARCH WORKOUT

```
G H T C C Q J B Y C N P L
R S O E V T W K U W A U W
A I P R A M E K I N P C O
T D A E O T U A T X E A B
E N E A T L E J P S C E P
R I T L G D L A Y L U T U
L T E B U H W I S P A Z O
A A V O L O K W N P S T S
L R D W H I S K G G O C E
U G P L C O F F E E P O T
T N Q E E Y P I P Z T I N
A D E S S E R T B O W L N
P U C E E F F O C F X R T
S T W A F I S H F O R K H
A I P I E D I S H A K G T
```

KITCHEN ITEMS
CEREAL BOWL
COFFEE CUP
COFFEE POT
DESSERT BOWL
FISH FORK
GRATER
GRATIN DISH
KETTLE
LADLE
PIE DISH
RAMEKIN
ROLLING PIN
SAUCEPAN
SOUP BOWL
SPATULA
TEA PLATE
TEACUP
TEAPOT
TEASPOON
WHISK

DOUBLE FUN SUDOKU

TASTY TEASER

		4	1	3	7			
		6		2		4	1	9
		5	9		6			
5			3		9		4	
	3	9				8	2	
	4		5		2			7
			7		8	2		
8	1	7		5		6		
			4	6	1	7		

BRAIN BUSTER

	5		2	9	3	1	6	8
		7	8	5	3	2	4	
2	8	3	6	4	1	5	7	9
3	4	7	5	6	8	2	9	1
5	6	2	1	7	9	8	4	3
1	8	8	3	2	4	7	5	6
4	2	5	8	1	6	9	3	7
6	7	1	9	3	2	4	8	5
8	3	9	4	5	7	6	1	2

1 MINUTE NUMBER CRUNCH

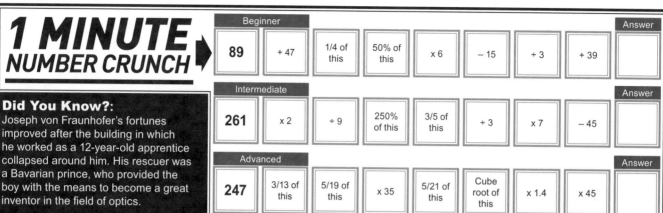

Beginner								Answer
89	+ 47	1/4 of this	50% of this	x 6	− 15	÷ 3	+ 39	

Intermediate								Answer
261	x 2	÷ 9	250% of this	3/5 of this	÷ 3	x 7	− 45	

Advanced								Answer
247	3/13 of this	5/19 of this	x 35	5/21 of this	Cube root of this	x 1.4	x 45	

Did You Know?:
Joseph von Fraunhofer's fortunes improved after the building in which he worked as a 12-year-old apprentice collapsed around him. His rescuer was a Bavarian prince, who provided the boy with the means to become a great inventor in the field of optics.

HIGH-SPEED CROSSWORD

Across
1 Apple drink
6 Picture puzzle
11 Grownup
12 Blow like a volcano
13 Head holders
14 Real nutcase
15 Talks and talks and talks
16 Ted Danson sitcom, or tennis star Boris
17 Born long ago
18 Iguana or pot-bellied pig, to some people
19 Black-and-yellow buzzer
20 Lender who charges too much interest
22 Little labs
23 Made of clay
25 Disgusting, to a kid
27 Address, as a problem
30 Egg ___ (Christmas concoction)
31 Furniture with springs
32 Upper limit, for short
33 Stole from unguarded stores
35 Stronghold
36 Honolulu hello
37 In the area
38 More experienced
39 Great Plains food source
40 Pansy parts
41 Shell out, as cash

Down
1 Words starting a request
2 Dearest principles
3 Kids' game played in a circle
4 Antlered Alaskan animals
5 Some turns on the road: abbr.
6 Put back to zero
7 Country singer Church
8 Variation of 3-down, as played by 4-down?
9 Maintenance
10 Mall tenants
16 Criticized harshly
18 Apiece
21 King: Sp.
22 Photo
24 Magazine with "Spy vs. Spy"
25 Relatives by marriage
26 "Relax!"
28 Gary who wrote the comic strip "The Far Side"
29 Branch out
31 Chicago's NFL team
34 Not us
35 Toss (a coin)
37 "How I Met Your Mother" network

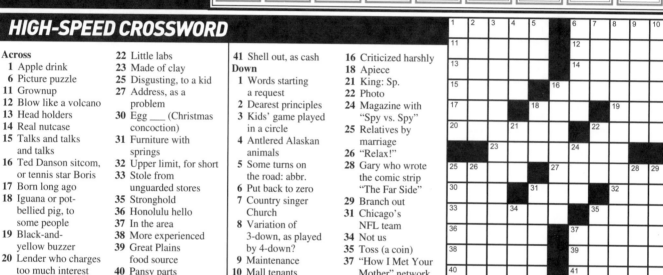

CODEWORD CONUNDRUM

A B C D E F G H I J K L M
N O P Q R S T U V W X Y Z

Reference Box

1	2	3	4	5	6	7	8 K	9	10	11	12	13
14	15	16	17	18	19 I	20	21 N	22	23	24	25	26

DOUBLE FUN SUDOKU

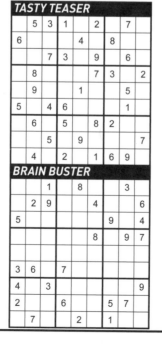

TASTY TEASER

BRAIN BUSTER

SPIDOKU

Each of the eight segments of the spider's web should be filled with a different number from 1 to 8, in such a way that every ring also contains a different number from 1 to 8.

HIGH-SPEED CROSSWORD

Across
1 Kidney-related
6 "Cola Wars" side
11 Concert site
12 Deodorant brand
13 One of Bob Marley's sons, or a cartoon character with a big head
14 Periods of unrest
15 Enthusiasm
16 Puerto ___
17 San Angelo's state
19 Dangerous driving weather
22 Organized the sock drawer
24 Vietnamese soup
25 Roman numeral for 54
26 Little bit (of a drink)
28 12 months old
29 Poem often about a person
30 TV watchdog
32 Japan's money
33 Vietnam's capital
34 Unaccounted for
36 Brigham Young University is there
39 Ocean ___ (big boat)
41 Nimble
42 They had a South American empire
43 Relish
44 Last name that sounds like it hurts
45 Aim the car

Down
1 Give someone a hard time
2 Great Lakes port
3 Gloomy Gus's girlfriend?
4 Fisherman
5 Set (down)
6 The Louvre's city
7 Idle chattering in Monty Python sketches?
8 Smoking gun, e.g.
9 Use a sofa
10 They may include photos
16 Not mainstream
18 Marks a ballot, perhaps
20 "Whoops!"
21 Ending for theater or church
22 Trick
23 Helper
27 Bic or Mont Blanc
31 Snickers bar ingredient
33 Old West "vehicle"
35 Be a good mama cat to your kittens
37 Plant with fleshy leaves
38 Mr., to Germans
39 One of two on the face
40 ___ way (kind of)
41 Rude type

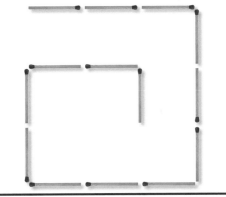

WORDSEARCH WORKOUT

```
D M S U O E G A R U O C L
U I G N I T C A X E P U A
N S G R Y P Y Y U S B C T
C R T I A K M T K J P R Q
O E F N R N Y B V C Z I T
M S T E Z X I T T H O U J
P O T A V E N T S N O R N
R L D U R A B L E T U G R
O U I E M U R E S S K M O
M T V A K O D B E U M P B
I E D T F L I N T Y G L B
S A F F N T L T I L H M U
I V Q P D N O M A I D P T
N K J F A U S T E R E B S
G H R I G O R O U S O J V
```

HARD WORDS
ADAMANT
AUSTERE
BRAVE
COURAGEOUS
DIAMOND
DURABLE
EXACTING
FLINTY
GRANITE
INDURATE
NUMB
RESOLUTE
RIGID
RIGOROUS
ROCKY
SEVERE
SOLID
STOUT
STUBBORN
UNCOMPROMISING

DOUBLE FUN SUDOKU

TASTY TEASER

	7	9					4	3
		3		5			2	6
			8	9		1		5
	6				2			7
	2	1	5		9	3	6	
4			1				8	
3		2		7	8			
6	5			2		4		
8	1				7	9		

BRAIN BUSTER

7			1		4			9
	8		2		6		3	
		5				6		
8		9	6		1	7		5
4		7	3		8	1		2
		2				4		
	7		8		2		9	
3			4		5			6

MATCHSTICK MAGIC

Move two matchsticks to make two squares.

BRAIN **TEASER**

A   B   C   D   E   F   G   H

What letter is two letters to the left of the letter immediately to the right of the letter three letters to the left of the letter three letters to the right of the letter C?

DOMINO
PLACEMENT

Did You Know?:
More energy is used during the eating and digestion process involved in consuming a stick of celery than is gained from the nutritional value of the celery.

A standard set of 28 dominoes has been laid out as shown. Can you draw in the edges of them all? The check-box is provided as an aid and the domino already placed will help.

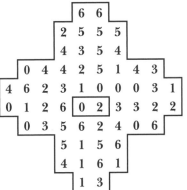

```
            6  6
         2  5  5  5
         4  3  5  4
   0  4  4  2  5  1  4  3
4  6  2  3  1  0  0  0  3  1
0  1  2  6  0  2  3  3  2  2
   0  3  5  6  2  4  0  6
         5  1  5  6
         4  1  6  1
            1  3
```

0-0	0-1	0-2	0-3	0-4	0-5	0-6
		✓				

1-1	1-2	1-3	1-4	1-5	1-6	2-2

2-3	2-4	2-5	2-6	3-3	3-4	3-5

3-6	4-4	4-5	4-6	5-5	5-6	6-6

CODEWORD CONUNDRUM

| 13 | 21 | 22 | 5 | 8 | 11 | | 16 | 25 | 21 | 22 | 2 | 11 | 5 | 8 |
| 21 | | 16 | | 11 | | 3 | | 21 | | 16 | | 17 | | 11 |

A B C D E F G H I J K L M
N O P Q R S T U V W X Y Z

Reference Box

1	2	3	4	5	6	7	8	9	10	11	12	13
14	15	16	17	18	19	20	21	22	23	24	25	26
		A					R				C	

DOUBLE FUN SUDOKU

TASTY TEASER

	2		4		1			
3		4	1			5		6
	6	1			7	9	4	
7	1			2	8			
	3						5	
			3	6			9	1
	8	3	5			4	7	
2		9			4	6		8
		7		9		2		

BRAIN BUSTER

				6		9	8	
5			1					
	6			5	8		2	
			4					7
	8			2			6	
3					5			
	7		9	4		1		
					3			4
	9	2		8				

PYRAMID PLUS

Every brick in this pyramid contains a number which is the sum of the two numbers below it, so that F=A+B, etc.
Just work out the missing numbers!

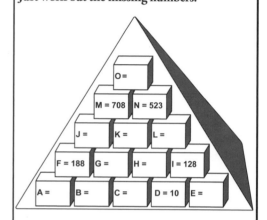

O =
M = 708   N = 523
J =   K =   L =
F = 188   G =   H =   I = 128
A =   B =   C =   D = 10   E =

HIGH-SPEED CROSSWORD

Across
1 Some desktops
4 Arena where the Knicks play, for short
7 "Now I understand!"
8 Every last bit
9 Place for a pea
12 Nameless man, in court: 2 wds.
14 Comic Gasteyer
15 Middle Easterner, often
16 Warning signal
18 Painting on a wall
20 Raise
21 Nutty ___ fruitcake: 2 wds.
22 Georgia known for painting flowers
25 Mona Lisa painter
27 Make believe
29 "Survivor" network
32 Show set on an island
33 Reproductive structure, in biology
35 Makes changes to, as a piece of legislation
38 Financial field, for short
39 ___ and feather
40 Stock analyst's arrow, in good times
42 Critter found in a messy kitchen
43 Ruin
44 High card, in many games
45 Ask nosy questions
46 Neither here ___ there

Down
1 Word before party or bottoms
2 Singing group
3 Big hot place: 2 wds.
4 Magazine with Alfred E. Neuman
5 No neat freak
6 Singing show set in Ohio
9 Big wet place: 2 wds.
10 Light switch choices: 2 wds.
11 "The Divine Comedy" author
13 Heat, Nuggets, etc.
17 Actor Guinness
19 Adore
23 Relatives
24 Winds up
26 Letters on business envelopes
27 Silver: Sp.
28 Like Julius Caesar
30 Untamed horse
31 "Return to ___"
34 Each
36 Pour (out)
37 Practice boxing
41 Attempt

1 MINUTE NUMBER CRUNCH

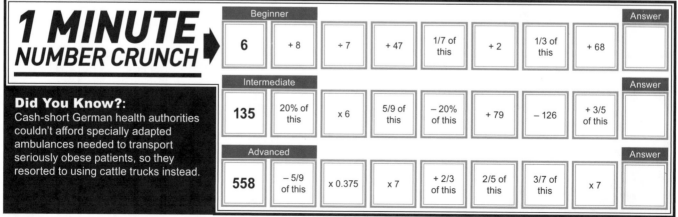

Beginner								Answer
6	+ 8	÷ 7	+ 47	1/7 of this	+ 2	1/3 of this	+ 68	

Intermediate								Answer
135	20% of this	x 6	5/9 of this	− 20% of this	+ 79	− 126	+ 3/5 of this	

Advanced								Answer
558	− 5/9 of this	x 0.375	x 7	+ 2/3 of this	2/5 of this	3/7 of this	x 7	

Did You Know?:
Cash-short German health authorities couldn't afford specially adapted ambulances needed to transport seriously obese patients, so they resorted to using cattle trucks instead.

HIGH-SPEED CROSSWORD

Across
1 Atlas page
4 Fox rival
7 Pop-ups, often
10 "Son ___ gun!"
11 Zodiac sign
12 Compete
13 He shot an apple off his son's head
16 Toledo's lake
17 Dull
18 "You're welcome," to Juan
21 Adorable
22 Designer Wang
24 Ending for mountain or musket
25 Longtime CEO of Apple

28 Farrow of acting or Hamm of soccer
29 "Chestnuts roasting ___ open fire..."
30 Pound or Klein
32 HBO show about a sports agent
36 Money owed
38 Not fooled by
39 An apple famously hit him on the head -- gravity!
42 Baby bear
43 Homer Simpson's dad
44 Ending for some e-mail addresses
45 Secret agent
46 Bad: Fr.

47 "Fantastic Mr. Fox" director Anderson

Down
1 Did the lawn
2 "Hearts ___" (John Ritter sitcom)
3 Sarah from Alaska
4 Boxing great
5 Arthur of "The Golden Girls"
6 Barbershop buy
7 Alphabet City street
8 Gets bigger, as a pupil of the eye
9 Buyer's counterpart
14 Skedaddle
15 Part of XXX or OOO
19 "Whip It" band

20 Stadium
21 Slightly open
25 Assesses
26 Toni Morrison novel
27 Not too hot, like a burner
28 Ambulance workers
31 One day ___ time
33 Being dragged behind
34 Shop
35 "Glee" numbers
37 E-mail from Nigeria, perhaps
40 Jeremy Lin's group, for short
41 Fish that's a general backwards

1 MINUTE NUMBER CRUNCH →

Beginner								Answer
15	x 3	1/9 of this	+ 49	1/9 of this	Squared	+ 20	1/4 of this	

Intermediate								Answer
26	x 8	3/4 of this	÷ 3	x 12	5/8 of this	3/10 of this	÷ 9	

Advanced								Answer
1369	Square root of this	x 11	+ 2047	1/2 of this	+ 2/3 of this	3/5 of this	÷ 3	

Did You Know?:
Pigeons will not perch on an item that contains the metal, gallium. Researchers are looking into spraying statues, etc, with a gallium-based solution to stop the birds fouling them.

WORDSEARCH WORKOUT

```
R O L C I T A M O T U A X
Q T A N A L O G U E E E X
D I G I T A L I J P V B J
D H Q H C T A W T S I R W
I N C H U B T B P D D A T
N N I T V N P T R G U C E
N O I B A T T E R Y Z E K
W J T A F W V E N P T L C
F E E E H E G T R D R E O
X O A K L C Q N J O A T P
R W B V X E Z F I H U N W
K A T R J M K H C R Q T T
K I N E T I C S E S R U N
C H R O N O G R A P H P R
Y Q R E P E A T I N G A A
```

WATCHES

ANALOGUE
AUTOMATIC
BATTERY
BRACELET
CHAIN
CHRONOGRAPH
DIGITAL
DIVE
FOB
HUNTER
KINETIC
LEVER
NURSE'S
PENDANT
POCKET
QUARTZ
REPEATING
RING WATCH
SKELETON
WRISTWATCH

DOUBLE FUN SUDOKU

TASTY TEASER

8	7	3				9	6	5
1			5	8				4
		6	7		8			
2				8	5			
	3		6		4		9	
		9	1					7
		1		5	4			
7			2	3				9
9	6	4				2	5	3

BRAIN BUSTER

	2	4	6			3		
		6					5	8
7			9				2	
	9		7					
2								1
					1		4	
	7			5				6
8	3					5		
		5			7	4	9	

WHATEVER NEXT?

In the diagram below, which number should replace the question mark?

N4

?   V6

7

924   P8

392

BRAIN TEASER

What number should replace the question mark?

Mind Over Matter

Given that the letters are valued 1-26 according to their places in the alphabet, can you crack the mystery code to reveal the missing letter?

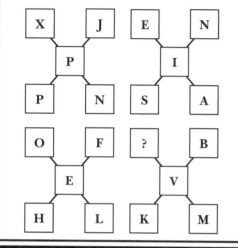

DOUBLE FUN SUDOKU

TASTY TEASER

7					2			
		4	9	5		3		1
	6	9		1		8	4	
	9		4			2	5	8
	1						3	
4	7	8			5		9	
	5	6		3		7	8	
9		2		8	7	6		
		1						5

BRAIN BUSTER

	1		8		5		7	
				4				
		8	7		1	3		
	9	1	5			2	4	6
4				3				2
	2	7	4		6	1	3	
		9	2		7	6		
				9				
	5		6		8		2	

CODEWORD CONUNDRUM

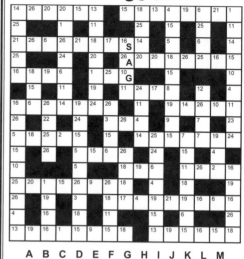

A	B	C	D	E	F	G	H	I	J	K	L	M
N	O	P	Q	R	S	T	U	V	W	X	Y	Z

Reference Box

1	2	3	4	5	6	7	8	9	10	11	12	13
									G			
14	15	16	17	18	19	20	21	22	23	24	25	26
		S										A

HIGH-SPEED CROSSWORD

Across
1 More than hate
6 Beer ingredient
10 Sporty wheels
11 Give off
12 Drinks at Kentucky Derby parties
14 Canadian creature
15 Channel you can watch Jeremy Lin highlights on
16 Sweet serve
17 Japanese grappling
21 Conductor's title
25 "I don't think so"
26 Make smile
27 Rival of Djokovic and Federer
29 Each
30 Internet startups
32 Too-good type
34 "Stop talking in the theater!"
35 Connecticut school
37 Actor Tayback of "Alice"
40 Tropical drink
43 Fleshy plant
44 More than now and again
45 The latest
46 Give a hand to

Down
1 Company that sells anti-Road Runner devices
2 Prepare pasta
3 Gorgeous guy
4 Select
5 Said no to
6 Beatles album with an exclamation point
7 Signs of what's to come
8 Palindromic Dickens kid
9 John and Paul: abbr.
13 Loser, in anti-drug ads
16 Complete jerk
18 Microsoft Word command when you make a mistake
19 Sir's counterpart
20 Severe-looking birds
21 Google ___
22 "So true!"
23 Currency named for a continent
24 Working
28 German shout
31 Capital city where you can spend 23-down
33 At this point
36 A long time
37 Don Corleone of "The Godfather"
38 Clinches, as a victory
39 Word on pennies
40 Dude
41 Bar order
42 Alien's spaceship, maybe

1 MINUTE NUMBER CRUNCH

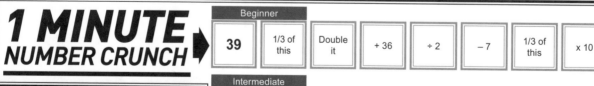

Beginner								Answer
39	1/3 of this	Double it	+ 36	÷ 2	− 7	1/3 of this	x 10	

Intermediate								Answer
494	− 39	÷ 5	+ 66	Double it	− 88	1/2 of this	x 6	

Advanced								Answer
572	Double it	− 0.125 of this	x 11	− 7477	1/2 of this	2/3 of this	5/19 of this	

Did You Know?:
In 1840, a law was passed in Britain that required arsenic sold over the counter in chemists' shops to be coloured with blue dye so that the number of murders by poisoning could be reduced.

BATTLESHIP BOUT

Can you place the vessels into the diagram? Some parts of vessels or sea squares have already been filled in. A number to the right or below a row or column refers to the number of occupied squares in that row or column.

Any vessel may be positioned horizontally or vertically, but no part of a vessel touches part of any other vessel, either horizontally, vertically or diagonally.

Empty Area of Sea: ≈

Aircraft Carrier: ◀▣▣▶

Battleships: ◀▣▶   ◀▣▶

Cruisers: ◀▶   ◀▶   ◀▶

Submarines: ●   ●   ●

Did You Know?:
Almost half of the bones in the human body are contained in the hands and feet. One person in twenty has an extra pair of ribs: the superfluous bones may cause problems and can be removed by surgery.

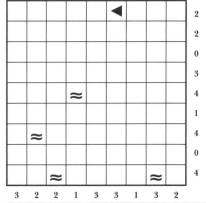

Grid column numbers (bottom): 3 2 2 1 3 3 1 3 2

Grid row numbers (right): 2 2 0 3 4 1 4 0 4

HIGH-SPEED CROSSWORD

Across
1 Late superteacher Escalante
6 Site where "snipers" prowl for bargains
10 Trees used to make wooden matches
12 It's stored in the gallbladder
13 Tony Danza sitcom
15 ___-Americans
16 Full of current events, like a website
19 Hint
23 Snacked on
24 Consecutively
26 Rihanna #1 hit of 2010
29 World ___
30 "___ Miserables"
31 "Portland, Oregon" singer Loretta
32 Mindless creature
34 Practice punches
36 Kids' book series
43 Cannes coin
44 Begin a journey
45 Stick around
46 Pores over Poe or Pope

Down
1 Part of the face
2 Tend to one's cigar
3 Wall Street operation, for short
4 Table-like structures in the Southwest
5 Contest submission
6 Low point
7 Life summary
8 Hirt and Hirschfeld
9 "What can I do for you?"
11 ___-cha chicken (Chinese menu dish)
14 Ivory's counterpart
16 Casual rejections
17 RFK's wife
18 Exhausted
20 Brown or Marino
21 Brush brand
22 Shakespeare title character
24 Types to
25 One way to go
27 Three-letter metal
28 Get the feeling
32 Less polished
33 Give a talk
35 Extra notes, at the end of a letter
36 NBA great Unseld
37 Pizza ___
38 Throwing number
39 Rogers on a horse
40 Mauna ___, Hawaii
41 Movie that flops
42 Additional pds.

WORDWHEEL

Using only the letters in the Wordwheel, you have ten minutes to find as many words as possible, none of which may be plurals, foreign words or proper nouns. Each word must be of three letters or more, all must contain the central letter and letters can only be used once in every word. There is at least one nine-letter word in the wheel.

Letters: I A D P R E C M (centre A)

Nine-letter word(s):
_____

SUM CIRCLE

Fill the three empty circles with the symbols +, – and x in some order, to make a sum which totals the number in the centre. Each symbol must be used once and calculations are made in the direction of travel (clockwise).

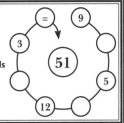

Circle values: = , 9, 5, 12, 3 — centre 51

WORDSEARCH WORKOUT

```
N E V R K Q V E A J A X L
A E L N S S E S E R D G H
I B E Z T D N R E E D J B
I B E T W E E N R E R M A
S I T R H L E G F S E F T
D W N F D G R P E R S O T
E G E D Z E I Z R E S R E
P E G D E C E E A V E E N
R E E N B V J N C O E S D
E E E E L E G A T E E E E
S R D R L P S E T T E E E
S F C E G E M E B K U C C
E J Z N E E M X E J Y S A
D V K Q U M D Q Z C C X E
B O A B S E N T E E H G Y
```

THREE ES
ABERDEEN
ABSENTEE
ADDRESSEE
ATTENDEE
BESEECH
BETWEEN
CAREFREE
DEGREE
DEPRESSED
EERIE
EIGHTEEN
FORESEE
GENTEEL
GREENER
LEGATEE
MELEE
OVERSEER
REDEEM
SETTEE
VENEER

DOUBLE FUN SUDOKU

TASTY TEASER

5			2		9	3		
		3			6	2		8
6		1		8	4			
	4		6	1			8	
	9	2				6	1	
	1			4	2		7	
			7	6		1		5
2		8	5			4		
		7	4		3			6

BRAIN BUSTER

	5						2	
		7	2			6	5	
8			3		5			4
	8	4	9			2	6	1
2	6	1			7	9	8	
6			5		9			1
	1	4		8	3			
	3					7		

1 MINUTE NUMBER CRUNCH

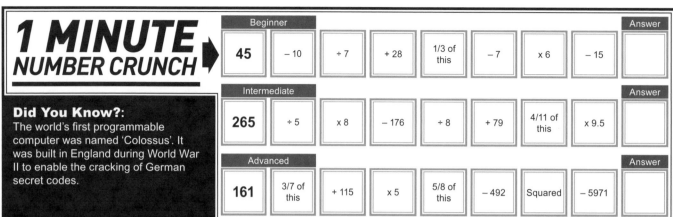

Beginner

| 45 | − 10 | ÷ 7 | + 28 | 1/3 of this | − 7 | x 6 | − 15 | Answer |

Intermediate

| 265 | ÷ 5 | x 8 | − 176 | ÷ 8 | + 79 | 4/11 of this | x 9.5 | Answer |

Advanced

| 161 | 3/7 of this | + 115 | x 5 | 5/8 of this | − 492 | Squared | − 5971 | Answer |

Did You Know?:
The world's first programmable computer was named 'Colossus'. It was built in England during World War II to enable the cracking of German secret codes.

HIGH-SPEED CROSSWORD

Across

1 Some sneakers
6 Elephant's ivory
11 Get rid of, as information on a disk
12 "The game is ___!"
13 Nursery rhyme bird
15 Mono-
16 Earn after expenses
17 Most common word in written English
18 ___ Tin Tin
19 One of four in a deck of cards
20 That girl
21 Battle wound
23 California dunkers
25 Awesome, in slang
27 ____'s holiday (doing on vacation what you do for work)
30 Not in any danger
34 Ending for persist or consist
35 Like a lot
37 Courteney on "Friends"
38 Doc's org.
39 Hotel's cousin
40 Exist
41 "Lookie here!"
44 Just perfect
45 Person's "equator"
46 Examinations
47 Hits flies

Down

1 Big bones
2 Not what you'd expect
3 Sonia Sotomayor, e.g.
4 End of a cigarette
5 Beatles song "I've Just ___ Face"
6 Gang up on
7 Saucer in the sky
8 Make better
9 Permitted
10 Heads of cattle
14 In a relaxed position
22 Dashboard abbr.
24 Sends to the canvas
26 Some tires
27 "Get outta here!"
28 Like a messy person's bed
29 Vampire killers
31 National park in Maine
32 Woods
33 Puts forth, as effort
36 Chews (on)
42 "Have some food!"
43 "I don't think so"

CODEWORD CONUNDRUM

A B C D E F G H I J K L M
N O P Q R S T U V W X Y Z

Reference Box

| 1 I | 2 | 3 | 4 | 5 | 6 | 7 | 8 | 9 | 10 | 11 | 12 | 13 |
| 14 | 15 | 16 | 17 | 18 D | 19 | 20 | 21 | 22 | 23 R | 24 | 25 | 26 |

DOUBLE FUN SUDOKU

TASTY TEASER

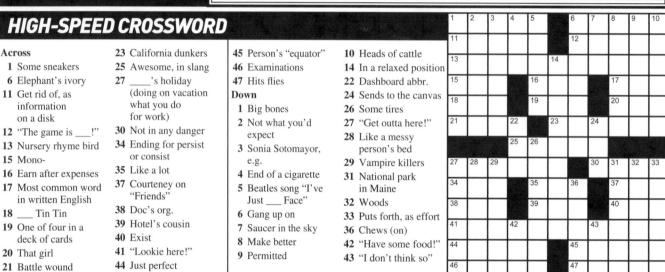

8			4		2			3
		3		7		5		
	7	6		9			2	8
	2	9	8		1	4	7	
1			7		5			2
	5	7	2		9	3	1	
	6	1		5		8	2	
		4		2		1		
7			1		4			6

BRAIN BUSTER

7	9			4		8		
2	8					5		
			5	7				2
3				5				
9		8			5			1
				4				8
6			2	7				
	5					7	4
	3	5			1	9	

SPIDOKU

Each of the eight segments of the spider's web should be filled with a different number from 1 to 8, in such a way that every ring also contains a different number from 1 to 8.

	3		4	
7	8 3	5 2		5
	8 7 2		5
	8 1	3 5	6
6		6	
	7 6	3	
	7 8		

HIGH-SPEED CROSSWORD

Across

1 Homer Simpson exclamations
5 ___ Spring (soap brand)
10 Palin or Ferguson
11 Newspapers, magazines, etc.
12 San Antonio landmark
13 Extremely famous people
14 Bedroom chatter: 2 wds.
16 Hawke of "Training Day"
17 Slithering creature
20 Show up for
24 Be in arrears
25 Enjoyed oysters
26 Cow's sound
27 Birthed anew
29 With no clothing
30 Totally out of cash
32 What a musician reads: 2 wds.
37 Baby kangaroos
38 Make amends (for)
39 "No more for me, thanks": 2 wds.
40 Amber, once
41 Necklace parts, maybe
42 Run like a horse

Down

1 Surreal Spanish painter
2 Taken by mouth
3 Shakespeare title character
4 "Darn it!"
5 Copy
6 Take back, as words
7 "American ___"
8 Bathroom fixture
9 Is in possession of
10 Maple syrup stuff
15 This and that
17 Neither fish ___ fowl
18 Female in a flock
19 Internet
21 Big bird
22 Doze (off)
23 A deer, a female deer
25 Hauls down to the station
28 Toed the line
29 Like "das" words in German
31 Store that once had Blue Light Specials
32 Not all
33 "For ___ jolly good...": 2 wds.
34 Average
35 "What's ___ for me?": 2 wds.
36 100 yrs.
37 Triangular sail

WORDSEARCH WORKOUT

```
T A M E C A L P K F S W T
C L J R L B K X E L O A C
N A N G E D O V T O U T F
D D R O R P A V C W P E X
E E I V O A P L H E B R C
S S W D I P V E U R O J O
S S I D S N S Y P S W U L
E E N Q S I G A B T L G A
R R E T A K B D E O H K Z
T T B U L P C R I T A A Y
P B O R G A B A U S G T S
L O T E E N I T P A H F U
A W T E N A R S C O O S S
T L L N I M D U P R N G A
E V E N W P H M K A Z Q N
```

SETTING A TABLE

BREAD
CARVING DISH
DESSERT BOWL
DESSERT PLATE
FLOWERS
FORK
GRAVY BOAT
KETCHUP
LADLE
LAZY SUSAN
MUSTARD
NAPKIN
PEPPER
PLACE MAT
SOUP BOWL
TEASPOON
TUREEN
WATER JUG
WINE BOTTLE
WINE GLASS

DOUBLE **FUN** SUDOKU

TASTY TEASER

4			3					6
		1	2	8		9		
6	5	9				2	3	8
9					4	1		
	2		6		5		9	
		8	7					3
2	1	7				3	5	9
		4		7	3	6		
5					1			7

BRAIN BUSTER

	1						3	
		2	9		1	8		
4			7		6			5
3	5		1		7		4	8
9	7		2		8		5	6
1			6		3			2
		4	8		9	5		
	6						9	

MATCHSTICK MAGIC

Move one matchstick to make this sum correct.

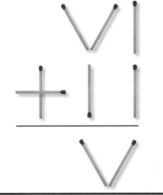

BRAIN **TEASER**

What number should replace the question mark?

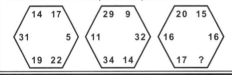

14	17		29	9		20	15
31	5		11	32		16	16
19	22		34	14		17	?

---

1 MINUTE NUMBER CRUNCH

Did You Know?:
Starfish have saved the word from ecological disaster. They eat other sea creatures which, if left to multiply, would destroy the ecosystem of the world's oceans.

Beginner								Answer
37	− 8	x 3	+ 35	50% of this	− 11	x 3	1/5 of this	

Intermediate								Answer
457	Add to its reverse	− 666	÷ 5	x 7	+ 89	2/3 of this	5/8 of this	

Advanced								Answer
161	+ 5/7 of this	+ 2/3 of this	+ 20% of this	− 398	x 4	x 1.875	+ 2/5 of this	

CODEWORD CONUNDRUM

A B C D E F G H I J K L M
N O P Q R S T U V W X Y Z

Reference Box

1 L	2	3	4	5 P	6	7	8	9 I	10	11	12	13
14	15	16	17	18	19	20	21	22	23	24	25	26

DOUBLE FUN SUDOKU

TASTY TEASER

		3	9	6	2			
		5	7		8			
		8		4		3	9	7
	3		5		4			2
	6	7				1	4	
5			6		7		3	
1	9	2		5		8		
			2		1	4		
		3	8	9	2			

BRAIN BUSTER

				1			8
		7	2				3
3	1	9		6			4
	7				3		
5		6			2		1
	3					8	
4			8		9	5	7
7			4	3			
6		5					

PYRAMID PLUS

Every brick in this pyramid contains a number which is the sum of the two numbers below it, so that F=A+B, etc.
Just work out the missing numbers!

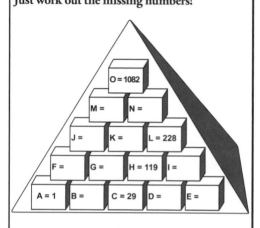

O = 1082
M =   N =
J =   K =   L = 228
F =   G =   H = 119   I =
A = 1   B =   C = 29   D =   E =

HIGH-SPEED CROSSWORD

Across
1 Put one foot in front of the other
5 The San Diego Chicken, e.g.
11 Spoken
12 Video game place
13 Homer Simpson's older daughter
14 Make less messy
15 Connect-the-___ (pencil and paper game)
16 Has the power to
17 Work with acid
19 Get-rich-quick scheme
23 Many different kinds of
26 Pie ___ mode: 2 wds.
27 Put up, as a building
28 Camera company
30 Fix, as an election
31 Material for a cyclist's clothing
33 Grocery store containers
35 Highfalutin'
36 Not her
38 Reverberating sound
41 Evaluate
44 Smear, like paint
45 Sewing kit item
46 "Do ___ others..."
47 Made fun of
48 Townshend or Sampras

Down
1 Auctioneer's shout
2 Threesome
3 Food eaten on a spring holiday: 2 wds.
4 Credit card material
5 Fu ___ (kind of mustache)
6 Section
7 Looks over
8 Meowing pet
9 Kind of poem
10 ___-down (this answer)
18 Simple beds
20 Food eaten on a winter holiday: 2 wds.
21 ___ vera (lotion ingredient)
22 8-down with no tail
23 Action word
24 Opera song for one
25 Damage permanently
29 Wanted in on the poker hand: 2 wds.
32 Sped by, on the highway
34 Backyard structures
37 Small piece of land in the water
39 Jabba the ___ (villain in "Return of the Jedi")
40 Woodwind instrument
41 Tiny crawler
42 Catch a glimpse of
43 Hemingway book "The Old Man and the ___"

(crossword grid, numbered 1–48)

1 MINUTE NUMBER CRUNCH

Beginner								Answer
47	+ 27	1/2 of this	− 16	1/3 of this	x 15	1/5 of this	÷ 3	

Intermediate								Answer
41	+ 92	x 4	3/4 of this	+ 2/3 of this	+ 85	x 1.3	− 489	

Advanced								Answer
59	x 6	+ 2/3 of this	3/10 of this	2/3 of this	x 4	− 319	+ 7/9 of this	

Did You Know?:
Most of the planet's fresh water is stored in a desert. Antarctica is the world's largest desert even though it is the world's coldest place. The average human body contains about ten gallons of water. It also has sufficient iron to make a four-inch nail.

HIGH-SPEED CROSSWORD

Across

1 Mighty trees
5 Purity units, to goldsmiths
11 Made a picture of
12 Roma's country
13 Eat well
14 Silver, tin, etc.
15 "For Pete's ___!"
16 Not just hugs
17 Hawke of Hollywood
18 "Absolutely, general!": 2 wds.
21 Mauna ___ (Hawaiian volcano)
24 Exist
25 iPhone, e.g.
26 Fluid in a pen
28 Be nosy
29 Actress Bynes of "What a Girl Wants"
31 "___ a Song of Bethlehem": 2 wds.
32 Like a mischievous child
36 ___ out a living (barely gets by)
39 Polynesian cocktail: 2 wds.
40 Long-term spy
41 Nicaraguan leader Daniel
42 Part of MIT
43 Male tennis players, sometimes
44 Long period of time

Down

1 Vegas calculations
2 Song for one
3 "One Flew Over the Cuckoo's Nest" author: 2 wds.
4 Candy and such
5 Member of a California reality TV family: 2 wds.
6 Had food at home: 2 wds.
7 "Darn it!"
8 "Woe is me!"
9 Scrabble piece
10 Backtalk
18 Cool and edgy, like Brooklyn kids
19 Talk and talk and talk
20 Make a blunder
21 Movie ape: 2 wds.
22 Wind up
23 Letters before a crook's alias
26 "What ___ going to do?": 2 wds.
30 Blood condition
31 Indian tribe
32 "It's my turn!": 2 wds.
33 Adult female horse
34 Brad of "Thelma & Louise"
35 Thingy
37 Different
38 Becomes hard, as concrete

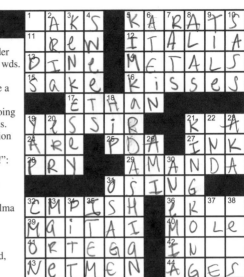

DOMINO PLACEMENT

A standard set of 28 dominoes has been laid out as shown. Can you draw in the edges of them all? The check-box is provided as an aid and the domino already placed will help.

Did You Know?:

The Swiss people hold the world record for eating the most chocolate. Each Swiss averages a consumption of ten kilos (22 pounds) per year. Surprisingly this is twice the amount that the average American consumes.

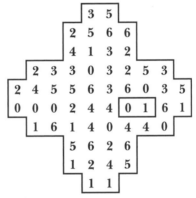

```
                3  5
             2  5  6  6
             4  1  3  2
       2  3  3  0  3  2  5  3
    2  4  5  5  6  3  6  0  3  5
    0  0  0  2  4  4  0  1  6  1
       1  6  1  4  0  4  4  0
             5  6  2  6
             1  2  4  5
                1  1
```

0-0	0-1	0-2	0-3	0-4	0-5	0-6
	✓					

1-1	1-2	1-3	1-4	1-5	1-6	2-2

2-3	2-4	2-5	2-6	3-3	3-4	3-5

3-6	4-4	4-5	4-6	5-5	5-6	6-6

WORDSEARCH WORKOUT

```
N E P R V R K I T R D B W
A D L N E U I T N E I N M
M O V M R P X M R Y E O V
U E O L Y O H I N W W D A
R E R E G R H B R V T O L
A B N I R S R A W F H E E
S K R G A S D E N J L R X
C X T A A D O W M T A E A
G L R R N G O N A I E G A
A E O B I D G C L R H I A
U D L M E H Y E B X F O G
E Z L R F R B B J P J N O
G I F W O O G K U Y J R R
Q T U M L N O I K C C D N
Q M W B M A D S L P K D R
```

LORD OF THE RINGS

ARAGORN
ARWEN
BERGIL
BRANDYBUCK
DWARF
EDORAS
ELF
ELROND
EOMER
EOWYN
EREGION
GIMLI
LOBELIA
MERIADOC
MERRY
ORC
ROHAN
SARUMAN
SHIRE
TROLL

DOUBLE FUN SUDOKU

TASTY TEASER

6			3					9
	4		2	1			7	
1	2	3				8	4	6
	7				9			4
		4	6		8	2		
3			5				1	
4	3	8				7	5	2
	6			5	3		9	
5				7				8

BRAIN BUSTER

	6						8	5
	7				6		2	1
3				8	4			
7			6					
1		9				6		2
					5			9
			8	6				4
8	1		5				9	
4	9						6	

WHATEVER NEXT?

In the diagram below, which letter should replace the question mark?

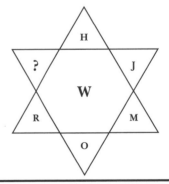

BRAIN TEASER

A   B   C   D   E   F   G   H

What letter is two letters after the letter which is immediately after the letter four letters before the letter which is two letters after the letter E?

Mind Over Matter

Given that the letters are valued 1-26 according to their places in the alphabet, can you crack the mystery code to reveal the missing letter?

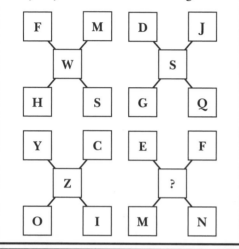

DOUBLE FUN SUDOKU

TASTY TEASER

		6		4		3		
1		5			7	4		6
	3	7	8			9	1	
				6	1		2	3
	8						9	
2	4		9	5				
	7	4			3	2	5	
5		8	2			7		9
		2		7		6		

BRAIN BUSTER

3			6		8			
	7					1	2	
4		8		5		6		
	8	7	9					
				8	5	2		
	5		1			6		7
7	1				4			
		2		9				3

CODEWORD CONUNDRUM

A B C D E F G H I J K L M
N O P Q R S T U V W X Y Z

Reference Box

| 1 | 2 | 3 A | 4 | 5 | 6 | 7 | 8 | 9 | 10 | 11 | 12 | 13 |
| 14 | 15 | 16 | 17 | 18 | 19 | 20 | 21 | 22 B F | 23 | 24 | 25 | 26 |

HIGH-SPEED CROSSWORD

Across
1 Shook hands with
4 City vehicle
7 Palindromic name
8 Greek H
9 "___-Tac-Dough" (Wink Martindale game show)
12 It may include a photo
14 www.rice.___
15 Little devils
16 Toolbox item
18 Springs
20 Apple tablet
21 Cat-eater of TV
22 Dutch beers
25 "Miss Being Mrs." singer Lynn
27 Washington city
29 Basketball hoop
32 Money in Madrid
33 Store number
35 They have one more wheel than bikes
38 Alligator shirt brand
39 Man's name that's also a series of intellectual lectures
40 What you cross flying from America to England
42 "___ et labora"
43 Mooing creature
44 Zero, to soccer players
45 Silly laugh sound
46 Expert

Down
1 Capital of the Philippines
2 Tooth cover
3 City that's home to the NFL's Buccaneers
4 Put money on it
5 State often mentioned in the musical "The Book of Mormon"
6 Grand story
9 City just east of Phoenix
10 Perfect
11 Miss Muffet ate them with whey
13 Mentalist's claim
17 Catcher's ___
19 ___ Lee of baked goods
23 Dudes
24 "___ lively!"
26 "Alright, you win!"
27 ___ music (compose a score for)
28 Less tainted
30 Classic, as an image
31 Interfere
34 Grave letters
36 Work with acid
37 It's just over a foot long?
41 Flock female

1 MINUTE NUMBER CRUNCH

Beginner								Answer
12	1/6 of this	+ 20	Double it	− 30	÷ 7	+ 66	25% of this	

Intermediate								Answer
61	− 15	x 3	x 1.5	÷ 9	+ 57	7/10 of this	x 11	

Advanced								Answer
117	5/9 of this	8/13 of this	÷ 2.5	Squared	+ 0.625	5/16 of this	− 7/10 of this	

Did You Know?:
The last execution in the Tower of London took place in August 1941, when German spy Josef Jakobs was shot by a firing squad. He had parachuted into England earlier that year.

1 MINUTE NUMBER CRUNCH

Beginner								Answer
35	x 3	+ 81	÷ 6	x 9	− 42	+ 3	5/12 of this	

Intermediate								Answer
89	Add to its reverse	Double it	x 1.5	÷ 3	− 78	x 4	+ 47	

Advanced								Answer
11	x 33	− 1/3 of this	x 9	11/18 of this	Add its cube root to this	1/2 of this	x 4	

Did You Know?:
The eyelid muscle is the fastest in the human body. This tiny muscle enables the average person to blink at least 15,000 times a day.

HIGH-SPEED CROSSWORD

Across
1 Washed (down)
6 Remove from memory
11 It's sometimes sprained
12 Female horses
13 Ask a tough trivia question
14 Ancient Peruvians
15 Chum
16 Smart bird
18 Birmingham's state: abbr.
19 Full of fanfare
21 One-seventh of a week
22 2016 Olympics city, for short
23 Food cans, to Brits
24 How things stand in general
27 Creature the Chesapeake Bay is known for
28 Court
29 "___ dead, Jim" ("Star Trek" line)
30 Lunges
34 ___ Wednesday
35 Fine and dandy
36 Head piece
37 Bend (down)
39 Close call
41 Keep away from
42 Violin stroke
43 Put off
44 Histories

Down
1 Metal plates on doors
2 How beer may be served
3 Top part of a skeleton
4 Tree type
5 Bank transaction
6 Poet Dickinson
7 Oversaw
8 2000s CBS show "Joan of ___"
9 Material like an adhesive
10 Ralph Waldo Emerson pieces
17 VIPs, collectively
20 Riyadh resident
23 Old word for you
24 Hit the mat
25 Negotiate, like details
26 Builds, as an appetite
27 Took off after
30 Tail (off)
31 Unions don't like them
32 Card like the Hanged Man
33 Gushes
38 Kind of poem
40 Tax expert, for short

WORDWHEEL

Using only the letters in the Wordwheel, you have ten minutes to find as many words as possible, none of which may be plurals, foreign words or proper nouns. Each word must be of three letters or more, all must contain the central letter and letters can only be used once in every word. There is at least one nine-letter word in the wheel.

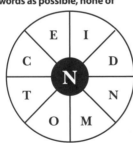

E I
C N D
T N
O M

Nine-letter word(s):
_____

SUM CIRCLE

Fill the three empty circles with the symbols +, – and x in some order, to make a sum which totals the number in the centre. Each symbol must be used once and calculations are made in the direction of travel (clockwise).

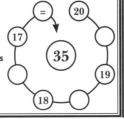

= 20
17
35
19
18

WORDSEARCH WORKOUT

```
U F O D I E Y P Z K W L J
T H E P A S T H X R I B P
Z Z E L A W S D W O R C Y
M Z Q T B A T H E W I F E
Y G N I K N I S W H G S L
N A S N E I L A T U N N O
F Y F A C M N T Y A I I M
G A C A U A E F K L N F E
N S H N Q L S E L Z O F A
I P A R P S D T K Y R O T
L M S E B N E I L Y I C I
I N E M E M O R I E S N N
A H S S W C K Z S H S W G
S S S H T H E F U T U R E
D A F O O T B A L L A G T
```

DREAMS

ALIENS
ANIMALS
CASTLES
CHASES
COFFINS
CROWDS
EATING
FANTASY
FLYING
FOOTBALL
IRONING
MEMORIES
NAKEDNESS
SAILING
SHEEP
SINKING
THE FUTURE
THE PAST
THE WIFE
WORK

DOUBLE FUN SUDOKU

TASTY TEASER

4		8			6	3		9
7				5				8
1	3		4				7	5
	2	5		1	9			
		6				9		
		3	7		2	8		
6	1			2		9	4	
2			4					7
5		4	8		1		2	

BRAIN BUSTER

	5				1			
7			5		4			2
	8		6		1		5	
	6	1	8		9	7	3	
	2	7	1		3	9	6	
	9		7		2		4	
6			3		5			9
		4				8		

1 MINUTE NUMBER CRUNCH →

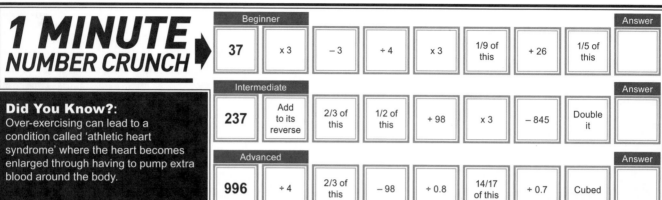

Beginner								Answer
37	x 3	− 3	÷ 4	x 3	1/9 of this	+ 26	1/5 of this	

Intermediate								Answer
237	Add to its reverse	2/3 of this	1/2 of this	+ 98	x 3	− 845	Double it	

Advanced								Answer
996	÷ 4	2/3 of this	− 98	÷ 0.8	14/17 of this	+ 0.7	Cubed	

Did You Know?:

Over-exercising can lead to a condition called 'athletic heart syndrome' where the heart becomes enlarged through having to pump extra blood around the body.

HIGH-SPEED CROSSWORD

Across

1 Mischief makers
5 Chicken houses
10 Not cooked very much, like a steak
11 Firetruck feature
12 Item for getting wrinkles out of clothes
13 Restaurant choices
14 Timetable
16 Month after Sept.
17 Academy Award
21 "Star Wars" director George
23 Vodka brand, for short
24 Pose a question to
25 Apprehend, like a crook
26 Sesame ___
29 Looks over quickly
31 "See what you think!": 2 wds.
32 Make a mistake
33 It shows how much something costs: 2 wds.
37 Hand-manipulated character
40 Herb used with salmon
41 Evaluate
42 Capital of Norway
43 Lions' homes
44 Pierce with a knife

Down

1 Purple flower
2 Painter Chagall
3 What Wayne Gretzky played: 2 wds.
4 One of the five tribes of the Iroquois Confederacy
5 Guitarist Santana
6 Most unusual
7 "___ to a Nightingale"
8 Each
9 Some H.S. students
11 Baseball great Brock or Gehrig
15 Some football positions: abbr.
18 Scammer: 2 wds.
19 Alda of "M*A*S*H"
20 Spare ___ (barbecue dish)
21 Final
22 Computer owner
27 The Big ___ (constellation)
28 Emphasize
29 "Hold on a ___!"
30 Statements of belief
34 That thing's
35 "It's ___ big misunderstanding!": 2 wds.
36 Amorphous amount
37 Buddy
38 Calif. and Conn. are part of it
39 Greek letter

CODEWORD CONUNDRUM

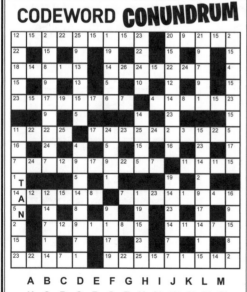

A B C D E F G H I J K L M
N O P Q R S T U V W X Y Z

Reference Box

1	2	3	4	5	6	7	8	9	10	11	12	13
T				**N**								
14	15	16	17	18	19	20	21	22	23	24	25	26
A												

DOUBLE FUN SUDOKU

TASTY TEASER

	8					5		9
			3	6	8			
	7	2		5			1	6
1	5	4	7			2		
8			1		6			5
		7			5	1	9	3
6	2			7		3	8	
			6	4	1			
5		9					7	

BRAIN BUSTER

		3				2		
		2	9		8	1		
5	4						8	9
	6			7			3	
	7	5		3	4			
	5			4			2	
9	1					7	3	
		8	1		9	6		
		6			5			

SPIDOKU

Each of the eight segments of the spider's web should be filled with a different number from 1 to 8, in such a way that every ring also contains a different number from 1 to 8.

HIGH-SPEED CROSSWORD

Across
1 Lack of war
6 Assistants
11 Edgar ___ Poe
12 Child's coughing
13 Coins often given away: 2 wds.
15 Professor's helpers: abbr.
16 West of Old Hollywood
17 Male doll
18 Inquire
19 State south of Mich.
20 Finale
21 Wetter than wet
23 Pro votes
24 Up to now: 2 wds.
26 "Hey, you!"
29 French port on the English Channel
33 Charged particle
34 Pet you may brush
35 Longtime NBC show
36 Gunk
37 Mono-
38 First word of countless book titles
39 Umpire's shout before "You're out!": 2 wds.
42 Not here
43 German WWI menace
44 Approving replies
45 Blog entries

Down
1 Tortellini, rigatoni, etc.
2 Texas city on the border with Mexico: 2 wds.
3 Anchorage's state
4 Jaguar or Jeep
5 Foes
6 Suffered from soreness
7 Tax shelter
8 Shrek's buddy
9 Oregon city, or a man's name
10 Throws around, as money
14 Christmas treat: 2 wds.
22 Kit ___ (candy bar)
23 Ocean that Portugal is on: abbr.
25 Accept flattery eagerly: 3 wds.
26 Where you'll hear oinks
27 Be calming
28 Sleeping sounds
30 Houston's baseball team
31 Ready to reproduce, like dogs: 2 wds.
32 Comes down hard from the sky
34 Green vegetables, casually
40 Wrath
41 "Entourage" channel

WORDSEARCH WORKOUT

W	O	N	E	Z	T	E	E	E	Y	M	N	L
E	U	M	Y	R	C	C	A	T	R	J	P	T
I	A	C	A	N	A	K	X	N	F	N	K	R
G	G	C	A	F	O	O	T	I	N	G	O	D
H	K	L	K	D	N	H	Y	E	Z	T	T	R
T	A	Q	S	G	V	T	R	C	V	E	Y	D
B	B	D	C	M	R	P	P	C	C	Q	I	B
W	E	S	H	E	E	P	R	A	N	G	K	N
B	G	X	P	F	C	O	L	S	N	E	Z	S
I	A	O	G	H	O	P	E	I	J	S	L	K
P	R	S	H	A	P	E	T	D	N	U	T	F
P	U	N	K	R	F	Y	B	V	O	A	R	A
H	O	M	E	W	O	R	K	S	U	C	I	I
B	C	Y	T	I	T	N	E	D	I	X	B	T
C	D	W	N	O	I	T	I	S	O	P	E	H

'LOST' WORDS
BALANCE
CAUSE
COURAGE
DIGNITY
FACE
FAITH
FOOTING
GAME
HOMEWORK
HOPE
IDENTITY
PLACE
POSITION
PROPERTY
SHAPE
SHEEP
SOULS
TRACK
TRIBE
WEIGHT

DOUBLE **FUN** SUDOKU

TASTY TEASER

9				2	1			6
	7				8		3	
1	2	8				5	7	9
	8				4			2
		9	5		7	1		
6			3				9	
8	9	5				6	1	4
	4		6				5	
7			8	4				3

BRAIN BUSTER

		8				9	4	
	3	6			5	8		
1					8		5	
		5				3		
7								2
	6				7			
	2		3					5
		9	1			6	2	
4	8					1		

MATCHSTICK MAGIC

Move four matchsticks to make ten squares.

BRAIN **TEASER**

What is the largest rectangle that can be cut from this piece of timber, in one piece?

SIMPLE AS A, B, C?

Did You Know?:
The 'Spruce Goose' was the largest aircraft ever to fly. Built at the instigation of US millionaire Howard Hughes, the plane had a wingspan of 320 feet. It took to the air in 1947, flew for about a mile and was never flown again.

Each of the small squares in the grid below contains either A, B or C. Each row, column, and diagonal line of six squares has exactly two of each letter. Can you tell the letter in each square?

Across
1 The Bs are between the Cs
2 The As are between the Bs
3 The Cs are next to each other
4 Each B is directly next to and right of an A
5 The Bs are further right than the As
6 The As are next to each other

Down
1 The As are next to each other
2 The As are next to each other
3 Each C is directly next to and below a B
4 The As are lower than the Bs
5 The As are between the Cs
6 The Cs are lower than the As

CODEWORD CONUNDRUM

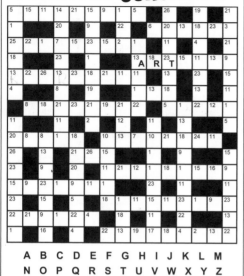

| A | B | C | D | E | F | G | H | I | J | K | L | M |
| N | O | P | Q | R | S | T | U | V | W | X | Y | Z |

Reference Box

1	2	3	4	5	6	7	8	9	10	11	12	13
												A
14	15	16	17	18	19	20	21	22	23	24	25	26
			R					**T**			

DOUBLE FUN SUDOKU

TASTY TEASER

7	6		9		8			3
	9		4		5			6
		2		7			4	
8			6			4	3	
4				8				7
	1	9			2			5
	5			3		6		
6			1		7		2	
2			8		9		1	4

BRAIN BUSTER

1		5		7		8		3
	8	6				9	2	
	1		7		5		6	
		2				5		
	7		2		9		3	
	5	7				4	8	
9		1		3		7		6

PYRAMID PLUS

Every brick in this pyramid contains a number which is the sum of the two numbers below it, so that F=A+B, etc.
Just work out the missing numbers!

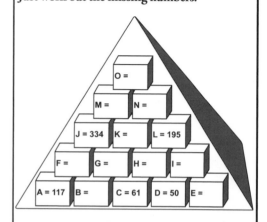

O =

M =   N =

J = 334   K =   L = 195

F =   G =   H =   I =

A = 117   B =   C = 61   D = 50   E =

HIGH-SPEED CROSSWORD

Across
1 It makes a guitar louder
4 Relaxed sighs
7 Jeep or Jetta
8 Big cat in the sky
9 Logo abbrs.
12 Reflexive pronoun
14 Edgy
15 Babe or Baby follower
16 "You and what army?"
18 Archibald and Thurmond of the NBA Hall of Fame
20 Inter ___
21 Shrewd
22 Foyer feature
25 Ready to drink, like a beer
27 Fine
29 Tree that sounds like a sheep
32 They can eject managers
33 Be bright
35 Ups the stakes
38 Cuzco builder
39 Greed is one
40 Chewy candy
42 Yukon creature
43 English 101 word
44 Ending for ranch or Canyon
45 Title TV psychopath, casually
46 Place to study

Down
1 Oaks of the future
2 Owner's guidebook
3 1986 Molly Ringwald movie
4 Lager's cousin
5 Steering wheel
6 Living room piece
9 1986 Chris de Burgh song that hit #3
10 Imitate
11 Vocalize
13 Pronoun for a boat
17 Malone or Marx
19 Poet/songwriter Silverstein
23 Part of a play
24 Tops and balls and such
26 Mama of music
27 "European carryall," in a "Seinfeld" episode
28 Clicked communication
30 "Play more!"
31 One of six in Clue
34 Wasn't out in the open
36 "My goodness!"
37 "Absotively posilutely!"
41 Tex-___ food

1 MINUTE NUMBER CRUNCH

Beginner								Answer
51	÷ 3	+ 22	1/3 of this	x 4	÷ 13	Squared	+ 9	

Intermediate								Answer
127	x 3	+ 69	x 1.2	7/9 of this	+ 21	Square root of this	+ 2/7 of this	

Advanced								Answer
256	÷ 0.5	Cube root of this	x 1.75	x 2.5	Squared	6/49 of this	68% of this	

Did You Know?:
During the course of each day you lose a few millimetres in height. This is due to gravity compressing the bones of your spine. Your spine stretches again as you lie flat in bed.

HIGH-SPEED CROSSWORD

Across
1 Low point
4 Tablet
7 Baltic or Bering
8 Sports ___ (athletic gear for women)
9 Go down a black diamond, e.g.
12 Nightclub type
14 Magician's rabbit's home
15 Gemstone that can be almost any color
16 Mrs., in Mexico
18 Basmati and jasmine
20 October birthstone
21 Drink in a pot
22 Is OK with
25 Stuffed pasta
27 Hard to believe
29 The Knicks, the Celtics, et al.
32 Foot or meter
33 Heavenly harpist
35 Andre who won Wimbledon in 1992
38 The Bruins' sch.
39 Broccoli or spinach, for short
40 No gods
42 Prior to
43 Be indebted
44 Seoul's country: abbr.
45 Path through the mountains
46 Airline until 2001

Down
1 Accompany
2 Type of cap
3 Vehicle you can push your infant in, on the sidewalk
4 Hipster beer, for short
5 Greek god of war
6 Rendezvous
9 Vehicle you can push your infant in, in the grocery store
10 Measure of purity, for gold
11 Slanted type, casually
13 Fire
17 Playwright Coward
19 Rescue
23 Espionage org.
24 Pepsi, for one
26 Dance, music, etc.
27 Smooth
28 Felix's last name, on "The Odd Couple"
30 Nobel Prize-winning novelist Saul ___
31 Cold state
34 Filbert or cashew
36 Pollution problem
37 Corny state
41 Agent, briefly

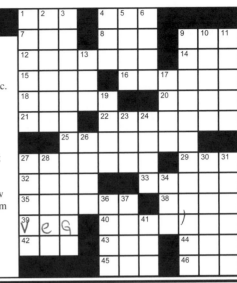

1 MINUTE NUMBER CRUNCH

Beginner								Answer
47	+ 61	1/6 of this	+ 12	x 6	− 6	1/2 of this	1/3 of this	

Intermediate								Answer
42	+ 19	x 9	2/3 of this	÷ 3	+ 11	4/7 of this	x 4	

Advanced								Answer
62	÷ 0.5	x 8	11/16 of this	x 3	5/6 of this	80% of this	x 0.25	

Did You Know?:
The phrase 'Has the cat got your tongue?' comes from the days when the cat-o'-nine-tails was used to inflict punishment. The mere threat of the use of this device was said to render a victim mute with terror, hence the saying.

WORDSEARCH WORKOUT

```
T Q H G Y I C D Y L L O H
B T K L B Y L A A S A G E
W R I K V S C F N V N U I
T L Y L F I I R E E I A F
D C E O L A U R O R W D P
L A V E N D E R I L N I A
K M G M M Y F Y C P I I K
X N H A W C R V L Z G V H
A Y Y Z J A S M I N E L E
W Y E B M M K X C O L P G
S P F E U H V I Y F L P B
D P S L H E C E Z M A A U
J O S C T E V J L C J W U
R P O G L G N G O C Z S B
K Q V Y I Z I V Y I R T C
```

FLOWERY GIRLS' NAMES

ANGELICA
BRYONY
CICELY
DAISY
DAVIDA
FERN
HOLLY
IRIS
IVY
JASMINE
LAVENDER
LILY
MAY
NIGELLA
OLIVE
PANSY
POPPY
ROSEMARY
SAGE
VIOLA

DOUBLE FUN SUDOKU

TASTY TEASER

	6			5	8	4		
	2			9	7			6
1	8	5	4					
	7		3				8	2
	1	9		2	7			
5	6			8		3		
				8	6	3	7	
3			6	2			1	
	5	4	3			9		

BRAIN BUSTER

4	8		6		9	3		
	9				2			
5		9		3		8		
		8		2				
	3				1			
		3		6				
6		4		1		5		
	1				4			
2	5		8		3	7		

WHATEVER NEXT?

In the diagram below, which number should replace the question mark?

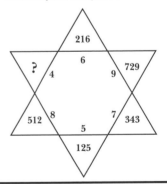

216
6
? 4 9 729
512 8 7 343
5
125

BRAIN TEASER

Simplify and find the value for X.

$$3 \times 7 \times 14 - (8 - 5) - (12 \div 4) = X$$

Mind Over Matter

Given that the letters are valued 1-26 according to their places in the alphabet, can you crack the mystery code to reveal the missing letter?

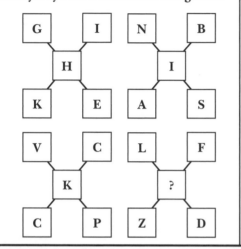

DOUBLE FUN SUDOKU

TASTY TEASER

6		4		1		2		3
	2		6		5			
	3		5		2		7	
7		5	2		4	9		6
	6		1		7		2	
2		8	9		6	7		1
	8		6		5		4	
	1		7		8			
4		6		9		3		7

BRAIN BUSTER

							8	
3		1	8	5		9		7
			9	1				
8				7			1	
7			2		1			4
	4			6				8
				9	6			
4		7		2	3	6		5
	2							

CODEWORD CONUNDRUM

A B C D E F G H I J K L M
N O P Q R S T U V W X Y Z

Reference Box

HIGH-SPEED CROSSWORD

Across
1 Another name for the sun
4 "The Cask of Amontillado" author
7 Despite, in odes
8 100%
9 Bunting tool
12 Former North Carolina senator John
14 Part of some e-mail addresses
15 Peggy and Spike
16 Submit, as a contest entry
18 Rope for cattle
20 Section
21 Elementary school class
22 Not merely angry
25 New York city
27 Astronaut Gus
29 ___-jongg
32 Traveled on
33 Farfalle or gemelli
35 Makes sense
38 Reynolds or Lancaster
39 Two after FDR
40 Big piece of ice
42 Damascus's nation: abbr.
43 It's made of flowers in Hawaii, traditionally
44 Half an African fly
45 Starch eaten in West Africa
46 Runway guess, for short

Down
1 Belgian beer brand
2 "My word!"
3 Contract winner, often
4 It may be 4, for those who shout "Fore!"
5 Former GM make
6 Different
9 Furniture store buy
10 Goodbye, in Grenoble
11 Sushi fish
13 Fool
17 Get good, as with a tackle in football
19 Trade-___ (pros and cons)
23 Disc in the sky
24 Way on or off the interstate
26 Finds a job for
27 Former students
28 Late actor McDowall
30 Not moving
31 Loathing
34 Jackson 5 hit
36 Unpleasant, as a confrontation
37 "Not guilty," for one
41 Rival of Aquafresh

1 MINUTE NUMBER CRUNCH

Did You Know?:
The teddy bear was invented in 1902 by a couple in New York. The success of the toy bear enabled them to start up the Ideal Novelty and Toy Company – a firm that still thrives today.

Beginner							Answer
91	+ 25	1/2 of this	1/2 of this	+ 17	1/2 of this	+ 17	25% of this

Intermediate							Answer
47	x 3	− 75	x 2	5/6 of this	x 0.8	3/4 of this	x 4

Advanced							Answer
39	Squared	7/9 of this	5/7 of this	x 7	− 4738	x 4	+ 9929

DOMINO PLACEMENT

Did You Know?:
In World War II, British soldiers became known as 'Tommies', after an example name that was used to assist in the completion of the enlistment form. The example name was 'Thomas Atkins'.

A standard set of 28 dominoes has been laid out as shown. Can you draw in the edges of them all? The check-box is provided as an aid and the domino already placed will help.

```
                6  6
             3  0  2  1
             1  4  4  1
       3  3  3  6  1  6  4  4
    2  1  5  3  5  5  4  2  3  6
    2  0  2  6  3  0  0  3  4  0
    0  2  5  0  0  1  2  1
             1  2  4  6
             5  6  5  5
                4  5
```

0-0	0-1	0-2	0-3	0-4	0-5	0-6

1-1	1-2	1-3	1-4	1-5	1-6	2-2
			✓			

2-3	2-4	2-5	2-6	3-3	3-4	3-5

3-6	4-4	4-5	4-6	5-5	5-6	6-6

HIGH-SPEED CROSSWORD

Across
1 Parodied
7 Loud landing sound
11 "Conceding that..."
12 Smart and seasoned
13 Drink with an umbrella
14 Sign on a store
15 Bed & breakfasts
16 Letters on some art show works
18 Healthy cereal
21 Four of 52
25 Scenes of competition
27 How to work on your keyboard
29 "All ___!"
30 Win over
31 Pate jelly
32 "The bad cholesterol"
33 Vergil verses, e.g.
37 Agree
40 Mountain climber's tool
42 Complete
43 Irritates repeatedly
44 Peeping pair
45 Tacky art

Down
1 Sorta
2 ___ Williams (co-founder of Blogger and Twitter)
3 Not "ja"
4 Blows up, casually
5 Former USSR rival
6 How to work with your mouse
7 Some dance moves
8 Cool
9 Find a purpose for
10 Lion's house
17 Industrialist Henry
19 From the top
20 City across the continent from NY, NY
21 "Eureka!"
22 Largest island on the Caribbean
23 Genesis man
24 Office items
26 The heavens
28 Like the climate in Tucson
33 Fuel in Ireland
34 Big galoots
35 Honcho
36 Blend together
37 Barack's #2
38 Vine that climbs
39 Scary stinger
41 ___ Omega (major sorority)

WORDWHEEL

Using only the letters in the Wordwheel, you have ten minutes to find as many words as possible, none of which may be plurals, foreign words or proper nouns. Each word must be of three letters or more, all must contain the central letter and letters can only be used once in every word. There is at least one nine-letter word in the wheel.

Nine-letter word(s):
_____

SUM CIRCLE

Fill the three empty circles with the symbols +, – and x in some order, to make a sum which totals the number in the centre. Each symbol must be used once and calculations are made in the direction of travel (clockwise).

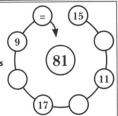

WORDSEARCH WORKOUT

```
E S E E G F G R O O M Q C
U G W N O H A P M Y R O L
I G Y M V G D Y S N C N Q
O L M R E G R P T R N M L
E U L G R T Y E N F O T M
W T W L N G G T E G G A G
G T Y A E A U K H D I U D
Z O G O S S O G R Y F E
F N D P S K D G I D M Y T
E E I D C H A N S A M W N
P N Q E E I L G U I N J U
G D G U T S N O R O B T R
U R U G B X S G H D R A G
C E Y U C I B E Y B X G L
Z D T E G D A G S W K W R
```

G WORDS

GADGET
GAIT
GANTRY
GASPING
GECKO
GEESE
GERM
GIANT
GIFT
GLUE
GLUTTON
GODDESSES
GOVERNESS
GREEDY
GRIMY
GROOM
GROUNDSEL
GRUNTED
GURU
GYPSY

DOUBLE FUN SUDOKU

TASTY TEASER

1	6	4		5			3	
			1	8	2		6	
			4		3		7	
		2	7		5			6
5	9						4	8
6			8		4	7		
	5		2		9			
	2		6	3	1			
	3			7		9	2	1

BRAIN BUSTER

		5			1			
1			8	3				9
3								7
				5			2	8
5	2		3		4		7	6
9	4		7					
4								2
6				1	8			3
		7			8			

1 MINUTE NUMBER CRUNCH →

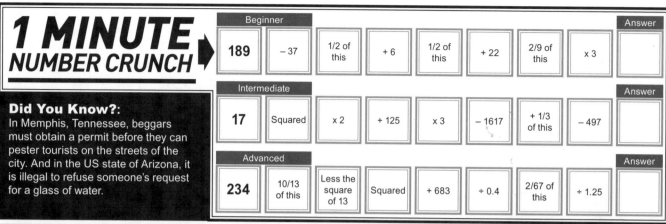

Beginner								Answer
189	− 37	1/2 of this	+ 6	1/2 of this	+ 22	2/9 of this	x 3	

Intermediate								Answer
17	Squared	x 2	+ 125	x 3	− 1617	+ 1/3 of this	− 497	

Advanced								Answer
234	10/13 of this	Less the square of 13	Squared	+ 683	÷ 0.4	2/67 of this	÷ 1.25	

Did You Know?:
In Memphis, Tennessee, beggars must obtain a permit before they can pester tourists on the streets of the city. And in the US state of Arizona, it is illegal to refuse someone's request for a glass of water.

HIGH-SPEED CROSSWORD

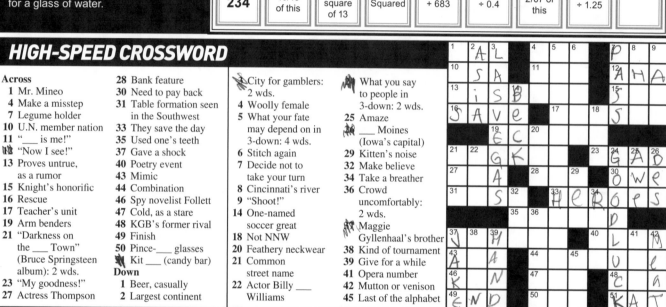

Across
1 Mr. Mineo
4 Make a misstep
7 Legume holder
10 U.N. member nation
11 "___ is me!"
12 "Now I see!"
13 Proves untrue, as a rumor
15 Knight's honorific
16 Rescue
17 Teacher's unit
19 Arm benders
21 "Darkness on the ___ Town" (Bruce Springsteen album): 2 wds.
23 "My goodness!"
27 Actress Thompson
28 Bank feature
30 Need to pay back
31 Table formation seen in the Southwest
33 They save the day
35 Used one's teeth
37 Gave a shock
40 Poetry event
43 Mimic
44 Combination
46 Spy novelist Follett
47 Cold, as a stare
48 KGB's former rival
49 Finish
50 Pince-___ glasses
51 Kit ___ (candy bar)

Down
1 Beer, casually
2 Largest continent
3 City for gamblers: 2 wds.
4 Woolly female
5 What your fate may depend on in 3-down: 4 wds.
6 Stitch again
7 Decide not to take your turn
8 Cincinnati's river
9 "Shoot!"
14 One-named soccer great
18 Not NNW
20 Feathery neckwear
21 Common street name
22 Actor Billy ___ Williams
24 What you say to people in 3-down: 2 wds.
25 Amaze
26 ___ Moines (Iowa's capital)
29 Kitten's noise
32 Make believe
34 Take a breather
36 Crowd uncomfortably: 2 wds.
37 Maggie Gyllenhaal's brother
38 Kind of tournament
39 Give for a while
41 Opera number
42 Mutton or venison
45 Last of the alphabet

CODEWORD CONUNDRUM

A B C D E F G H I J K L M
N O P Q R S T U V W X Y Z

Reference Box

1	2	3	4 O	5	6	7	8	9	10	11	12	13
14	15	16	17	18	19 N	20	21	22	23	24	25	26 I

DOUBLE FUN SUDOKU

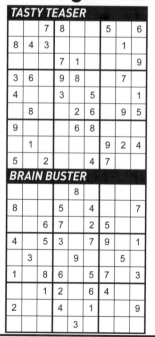

TASTY TEASER

BRAIN BUSTER

SPIDOKU

Each of the eight segments of the spider's web should be filled with a different number from 1 to 8, in such a way that every ring also contains a different number from 1 to 8.

HIGH-SPEED CROSSWORD

Across
1 Shrimp ___
7 Late humor writer Bombeck
11 Andy Warhol's field: 2 wds.
12 Continue: 2 wds.
13 Common compliment: 3 wds.
15 Black, to poets
16 Married woman
17 No longer in style
20 Computer company
22 Scary snake
23 Burning
26 "What an improvement!": 2 wds.
29 Like Superman's actions
30 Dark and depressing, as music
31 Frat party need
32 Jerks
34 ___ talk
36 Space shuttle org.
38 "Can't make any promises": 4 wds.
43 One of the primary colors
44 Herman of movies and TV
45 Word after trash or sandwich
46 River's little cousin

Down
1 Secret agent
2 Dove's sound
3 "The Simpsons" role
4 Guys
5 Investigation
6 "Was ___ harsh?": 2 wds.
7 One of twelve
8 Rent sharers
9 Anchor
10 "No ifs, ___ or buts!"
14 Weapon in the game Clue
17 Route
18 1975 Wimbledon champ Arthur
19 Car part: 2 wds.
21 Diner sandwich
23 First three of 26
24 Idea
25 God of love
27 Foot "finger"
28 Prince album "___ the Times": 2 wds.
32 Up to now: 2 wds.
33 Scary sword
34 ___ Xtra (soft drink)
35 Singing great Fitzgerald
37 Band equipment
39 ___ Moines, Ia.
40 She's a sheep
41 The Red or the Med
42 President pro ___

(Crossword grid with numbered cells 1–46)

WORDSEARCH WORKOUT

```
K A K A W A H I E M Y L H
S U U L A Y S A N R A I L
U H A Z K E Z O W O L F W
Q C C T L L I B E Z D A B
H A A O A Q G D N A W B U
A I O S R E Z A T L Y A S
W U L Y P U R L V Q N L H
A H A C T I A G J N S I W
I F I G A S A D N N W T R
I B K M B P Q N A J R I E
M O A E I U E P T V E G N
A Y A O A O R L O I N E K
M R P G X A A R I D G R G
O I G C T M J P E O O E G
O A L X M K Q E V Q N D R
```

EXTINCT ANIMALS

ADZEBILL
AKIALOA
ATLAS BEAR
 AUROCHS
BALI TIGER
BUSH WREN
CAPE LION
CASPIAN TIGER
DODO
EZO WOLF
GREAT AUK
HAWAII MAMO
HUIA
KAKAWAHIE
LAYSAN RAIL
MOA
PIOPIO
QUAGGA
TARPAN
YALDWYN'S WREN

DOUBLE FUN SUDOKU

TASTY TEASER

BRAIN BUSTER

5	9		7		3		1	6
			1	9	6			
	6					7		
9	2		5		8		6	1
4								9
1	8		6		9		2	4
	5					3		
			2	5	4			
6	4		9		7		5	2

MATCHSTICK MAGIC

Move two matchsticks to make this sum correct.

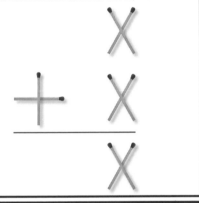

BRAIN TEASER

Three women, Mrs Black, Mrs Red, and Mrs Brown, met in the hairdresser's salon. One of them said "I have black hair and you two have red hair and brown hair, but none of us has the hair colour that matches her name." Mrs Brown responded: "You are quite right."

What colour is Mrs Red's hair?

DOMINO PLACEMENT

Did You Know?:
Although Johannes Gutenberg is generally credited with the invention of the printing press in 1454, he invented neither printing or moveable type. The Chinese were using moveable type in the 11th century, and had forms of block printing in the 9th century.

A standard set of 28 dominoes has been laid out as shown. Can you draw in the edges of them all? The check-box is provided as an aid and the domino already placed will help.

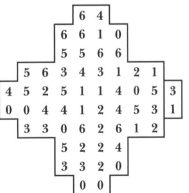

```
            6 4
          6 6 1 0
          5 5 6 6
      5 6 3 4 3 1 2 1
    4 5 2 5 1 1 4 0 5 3
    0 0 4 4 1 2 4 5 3 1
      3 3 0 6 2 6 1 2
          5 2 2 4
          3 3 2 0
            0 0
```

0-0	0-1	0-2	0-3	0-4	0-5	0-6

1-1	1-2	1-3	1-4	1-5	1-6	2-2
		✓				

2-3	2-4	2-5	2-6	3-3	3-4	3-5

3-6	4-4	4-5	4-6	5-5	5-6	6-6

CODEWORD CONUNDRUM

A B C D E F G H I J K L M
N O P Q R S T U V W X Y Z

Reference Box

1	2	3	4	5	6	7	8	9	10	11	12	13
		I		O	R	A						P
14	15	16	17	18	19	20	21	22	23	24	25	26
T					G			E	S	Y		M

DOUBLE FUN SUDOKU

TASTY TEASER

		6			4	1		5
1	8	4	5					
9			2	7		6		
		7		3			9	1
		8	2		9	7		
6	4			1		3		
	3		6	9				8
				1	6	7	3	
4		5	3		2			

BRAIN BUSTER

	9	6		2		8	1	
4	7						9	3
2			5		8			9
	3						5	
6			9		3			1
5	8					6	4	
	4	2		9		1	3	

PYRAMID PLUS

Every brick in this pyramid contains a number which is the sum of the two numbers below it, so that F=A+B, etc.

Just work out the missing numbers!

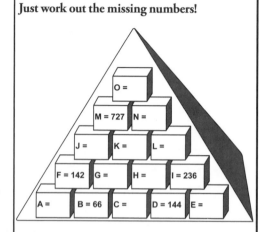

O =
M = 727   N =
J =   K =   L =
F = 142   G =   H =   I = 236
A =   B = 66   C =   D = 144   E =

HIGH-SPEED CROSSWORD

Across
1. Cooper cars
6. Be born, like a chick
11. Illogical
12. Mr. T & pals
13. Drink insertion
14. Kingdom
15. Get it in the goal!: 2 wds.
17. "Hasta la vista, baby"
18. Rotate
21. Light wind
25. Baseball number
26. Top
27. "Who's the Boss?" role
31. Goes down temporarily
32. Perhaps
34. Get it in the goal!: 2 wds.
39. Fracas
40. Claw
41. Tell the server what you want
42. Els of golf
43. Prom purchase
44. Not fresh

Down
1. Loretta Lynn's "___ Being Mrs."
2. Liking
3. Rat (on)
4. One way Coke comes: 3 wds.
5. Mended clothing
6. Safe place
7. "Relax," in the military: 2 wds.
8. Blue shade
9. "Safe!" or "Strike two!"
10. "Makes you wonder..."
16. Spare part?
18. English breakfast, e.g.
19. Kind of vase
20. Cloth for cleaning
22. Mr. Manning
23. 24401 or 29340
24. NYT workers
28. Hosts
29. L.A. squad
30. Sailor's "sure"
31. Leave
33. Data units
34. No Frau
35. Time-tested, in cheesy store names
36. Arm bone
37. Cobra's configuration
38. Body part with a cap
39. Forum administrator, for short

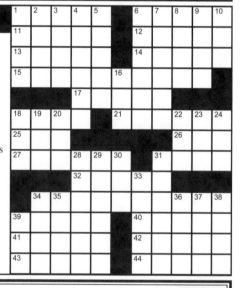

1 MINUTE NUMBER CRUNCH

Did You Know?:
Your hair grows quicker in warm, bright conditions which is why you need a haircut more often in the summertime. The average human has about the same hair coverage as a gorilla; the difference is that gorilla hair is thicker and longer.

Beginner								Answer
27	+ 24	1/3 of this	+ 9	50% of this	− 4	x 8	− 23	

Intermediate								Answer
69	x 2	2/3 of this	÷ 4	+ 137	2/5 of this	Square root of this	Cube root of this	

Advanced								Answer
588	x 2	5/8 of this	11/15 of this	Double it	− 929	x 7	+ 528	

HIGH-SPEED CROSSWORD

Across

1 Missing to the right or left, as a field goal
5 Start of the weekend, if you play it right
11 Object
12 Indicate
13 Tycoon of the 1800s
15 Go in
16 Brady and Hooks
17 The theatrical arts
20 Makes believe
23 Part of a BLT
27 Ghost's shout
28 One of a cat's four
29 Esquire's field of study
30 Black and white vehicle
32 Coal's place
33 In reserve
35 Wheel from Holland
38 "Goodbye, Genevieve!"
42 Kids shoot them at each other
45 At first, second or third
46 Words in a movie
47 Went across a frozen pond
48 Part of Virgo or Aries

Down

1 TV show set in Baltimore, with "The"
2 Lay ___ the line (gamble)
3 Red ink
4 Puts (inside)
5 Four before LBJ
6 Civil War fighter, for short
7 Stuck
8 Explorer of kids' TV
9 Oodles
10 Strong desires
14 Go awry
18 They made Missile Command
19 Do the lawn
20 1-2-3 of 26
21 Dove's sound
22 Defeat
24 He stung like a bee
25 Sit out by the pool
26 Have bills
28 Give a bad review to
31 Fighting
32 Gold, silver and bronze
34 Transportation in the city
35 Cupid, to the Greeks
36 Showy basketball play
37 Swedish quartet
39 ___ to win it
40 Novelist Ferber
41 Computer owner
43 Ending for Canton or Nepal
44 Color in Japan's flag

1 MINUTE NUMBER CRUNCH

Beginner								Answer
25	+ 93	1/2 of this	+ 7	2/11 of this	1/3 of this	+ 28	x 4	

Intermediate								Answer
452	÷ 4	+ 169	x 1.5	7/9 of this	Double it	− 479	x 3	

Advanced								Answer
129	2/3 of this	x 13	Double it	− 25% of this	− 949	5/14 of this	− 2/5 of this	

Did You Know?:
Although 2,600 years ago, mathematician Pythagoras said the Earth was a sphere, and astronomer Aristarchos, 2,300 years ago said the Earth revolved around the Sun, 1,600 years were to pass before they were believed.

WORDSEARCH WORKOUT

```
M F D R Z T X F O M Z C G
C A N X N X U T A D A J Q
O Q O D U W F N G Z N M Y
B B M V T G G A A A O S R
N L L E M O N R P E A R R
U Z A J E U K R P N P X E
T G Z C G Y D U E S N I B
X K L E K N L C C A N D E
P Q J O Z C B D A T M N L
S R H P D R U E N S X I K
B L U E B E R R Y U J R C
F D O N F K A X R M J A U
L Y C H E E H L F A D M H
O L I V E L I M E I N A C
B L C H E R R Y E Q G T V
```

FRUIT AND NUT

ALMOND
BLACKCURRANT
BLUEBERRY
CHERRY
COBNUT
FIG
HUCKLEBERRY
LEMON
LIME
LYCHEE

MANGO
NUTMEG
OLIVE
PEANUT
PEAR
PECAN
PRUNE
REDCURRANT
SATSUMA
TAMARIND

DOUBLE FUN SUDOKU

TASTY TEASER

		8	3	5			9	
	4		7			1	5	
	2	1			8			3
			5	1		2	7	6
		9			8			
1	2	6		4	7			
6		9			3			7
	8	5			4			1
	4			2	3	6		

BRAIN BUSTER

5				4				9
	2		6		9		5	
		4	3		7	2		
3		9				6		1
	8						9	
2		5				3		8
		6	1		4	5		
	1		5		8		7	
9				3				4

WHATEVER NEXT?

In the diagram below, which letter should replace the question mark?

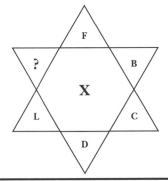

BRAIN TEASER

What should replace the question marks?

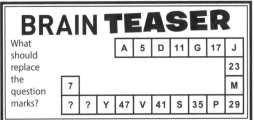

A	5	D	11	G	17	J
						23

| 7 | | | | | | M |
| ? | ? | Y | 47 | V | 41 | S | 35 | P | 29 |

Mind Over Matter

Given that the letters are valued 1-26 according to their places in the alphabet, can you crack the mystery code to reveal the missing letter?

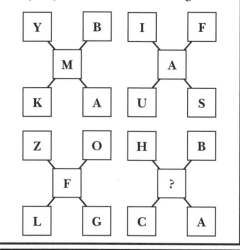

Y		B		I		F
	M				A	
K		A		U		S
Z		O		H		B
	F				?	
L		G		C		A

DOUBLE **FUN** SUDOKU

TASTY TEASER

		6	7		3			5
2				8			6	
		5	9		1	4		7
7	1				5	2		
		4		9		3		
		9	6				4	8
6		3	1		9	8		
	5			3				4
1			4		2	6		

BRAIN BUSTER

	8		1		2		6	
	9	1		5		3	8	
6	5						3	8
9		7			6			4
2	1						5	7
	6	2		3		5	4	
	7		6		9		1	

CODEWORD CONUNDRUM

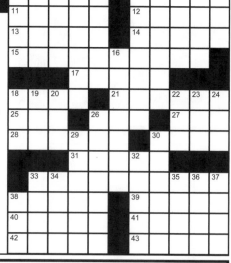

A	B	C	D	E	F	G	H	I	J	K	L	M
N	O	P	Q	R	S	T	U	V	W	X	Y	Z

Reference Box

1	2	3	4	5	6	7	8	9	10	11	12	13
		D										
14	15	16	17	18	19	20	21	22	23	24	25	26
		L							A			

HIGH-SPEED CROSSWORD

Across
1 The Divine ___ (Bette Midler nickname)
6 Tin or tungsten
11 Bring together
12 Run off and get hitched
13 Golf course warnings
14 Bring up, as an issue
15 Taste in a store
17 Simpson, Bonet and Vanderpump
18 Website named for the part of California where it was founded
21 Afternoon snooze
25 "2 funny!"
26 18-across attempt
27 Big beer container
28 Parking lot slots
30 "See ya," in Siena
31 Evoking nostalgia
33 Magazine devoted to keeping life uncluttered
38 Prefix with tasking or talented
39 Say something
40 Mary-Kate or Merlin
41 Creepy
42 John of tractors
43 Unfair putdowns

Down
1 Botch
2 "___ out?" (question to a pet at the door)
3 Be the father, in the Bible
4 ___ Dan ("Deacon Blues" band)
5 Soccer superstar Lionel ___
6 Sea beauty
7 Pass, like time
8 Work hard
9 Church section
10 Blue jeans brand
16 Basketball statistic
18 Ernie of golf
19 Offshoot of jazz
20 Pie ___ mode
22 Go down a black diamond run, e.g.
23 Drink that may be unsweetened
24 In the past
26 Most direct route
29 Meteor indentation
30 Force
32 Gets out of bed
33 Govern
34 Different
35 Country where Machu Picchu is
36 Lion's home
37 ___ out a win (barely defeats)
38 "The ___ Squad"

1 MINUTE NUMBER CRUNCH

Did You Know?:
Austrian composer Gustav Mahler's 3rd symphony is the longest symphony in the standard concert repertoire. Composed between 1893 and 1896, it employs a very large orchestra and chorus and lasts about one hour and forty minutes.

Beginner								Answer
96	− 19	÷ 7	Squared	+ 14	1/5 of this	1/9 of this	x 16	

Intermediate								Answer
17	+ 18	3/7 of this	300% of this	5/9 of this	x 13	120% of this	− 10% of this	

Advanced								Answer
387	5/9 of this	4/5 of this	− 3/4 of this	x 8	+ 7/8 of this	3/5 of this	7/9 of this	

Page 2

1 Minute Number Crunch

Beginner
$75 \times 2 = 150$, $150 - 72 = 78$, $78 \div 3 = 26$, $26 + 18 = 44$, $44 \div 4 \times 3 = 33$, $33 \times 4 = 132$, $132 \div 11 = 12$

Intermediate
$7^3 = 343$, $343 + 7 = 350$, $350 + 35 = 385$, $385 \times 0.4 = 154$, $154 \times 2 = 308$, $308 \times 0.75 = 231$, $231 + 169 = 400$

Advanced
$784 \div 14 \times 9 = 504$, $504 + 196\ (504 \div 18 \times 7) = 700$, 350% of $700 = 2450$, $2450 - 1294 = 1156$, 75% of $1156 = 867$, $867 \div 3 \times 8 = 2312$, $2312 \div 1/4 = 9248$

High-Speed Crossword

L	A	G		O	T	T			
A	V	E		I	R	A		F	I	T
R	A	T	T	L	E	R		A	S	A
E	L	S	E		K	A	P	L	A	N
D	O	T	E	D		O	L	A	Y	
O	N	O		A	M	E	R	I	C	A
	G	E	T	E	V	E	N			
O	N	E	L	A	N	E		G	I	T
R	A	T	E		R	E	A	D	Y	
A	D	H	E	R	E		A	P	O	P
T	I	E		I	N	G	R	A	T	E
E	R	R		D	Y	E		R	O	O
			S	A	M		T	O	N	

Codeword Conundrum

M	A	G	I	C	A	L		C	A	P	A	B	L	E
A		A		L		O		R		E		R		D
M	A	T	R	I	M	O	N	Y		R		E		I
M		E		M		S		S	U	S	P	E	C	T
O		S	U	B	J	E	C	T		U		Z		O
T		G		E			A	M	A	T	E	U	R	
H	O	W	L		R	E	A	L		D		N		
	P		Y	A	K		P		F	E	E		D	
	A		P		D	E	A	L		D	O	O	R	
G	L	I	M	P	S	E		E		G			E	
O		N		R		P	L	E	A	S	E	S		Q
S	A	V	I	O	U	R		X		P		P		U
S		E		A		E	X	P	L	O	S	I	V	E
I		R		C		S		E		O		C		S
P	I	T	C	H	E	S		L	E	N	I	E	N	T

Double Fun Sudoku
Tasty Teaser

8	6	5	7	2	3	9	1	4
2	3	9	1	6	4	5	8	7
1	7	4	5	9	8	6	2	3
6	2	3	8	4	5	1	7	9
7	5	8	9	3	1	4	6	2
9	4	1	6	7	2	8	3	5
4	8	2	3	5	6	7	9	1
5	1	7	2	8	9	3	4	6
3	9	6	4	1	7	2	5	8

Brain Buster

8	1	4	9	2	5	6	3	7
3	9	6	8	7	4	2	1	5
7	5	2	1	6	3	4	8	9
9	7	8	4	1	2	3	5	6
2	3	1	6	5	9	8	7	4
6	4	5	7	3	8	9	2	1
5	8	9	3	4	7	1	6	2
4	6	7	2	8	1	5	9	3
1	2	3	5	9	6	7	4	8

Spidoku

Page 3

High-Speed Crossword

B	A	H		D	E	A			
A	V	A		O	R	R		A	R	I
R	I	T	C	H	I	E		X	E	R
B	A	C	H		C	A	M	E	R	A
E	T	H	E	R		A	B	U	T	
D	E	E		E	A	C	H	O	N	E
			T	A	B	L	O	I	D	
P	E	P	T	A	L	K		Y	D	S
E	L	I	M		E	D	S	E	L	
T	I	E	S	U	P		O	P	R	Y
E	T	C		C	A	L	O	R	I	E
S	E	E		L	I	E		A	D	S
			A	N	D		Y	E	T	

Brain Buster

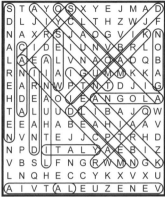

Wordsearch Workout

S	T	A	Y	O	S	X	Y	E	J	M	A	D
D	L	J	I	Y	C	L	T	H	Z	W	J	F
N	A	X	R	S	J	A	O	G	V	I	K	N
A	L	C	I	D	E	I	U	N	V	B	R	O
L	R	A	E	A	L	V	N	A	C	A	D	Q	B
R	E	A	N	I	L	A	I	G	U	M	M	K	A
E	H	T	A	R	N	W	P	T	N	D	J	I	G
H	T	E	D	E	A	O	I	E	A	N	G	O	L	A
E	N	V	N	E	U	U	D	X	L	I	B	A	V
N	P	U	T	E	J	J	C	P	T	R	H	D
V	B	S	L	F	N	G	R	W	M	N	G	K
L	N	Q	H	E	C	C	Y	K	X	V	X	U
A	I	V	T	A	L	E	U	Z	E	N	E	V

Double Fun Sudoku
Tasty Teaser

3	2	1	5	6	9	8	4	7
6	5	7	8	2	4	1	9	3
4	8	9	7	3	1	6	2	5
8	6	4	3	5	7	9	1	2
9	1	5	6	4	2	3	7	8
7	3	2	9	1	8	5	6	4
2	4	6	1	8	3	7	5	9
1	7	3	4	9	5	2	8	6
5	9	8	2	7	6	4	3	1

Brain Buster

4	2	8	6	9	1	3	5	7
1	5	3	8	7	2	4	9	6
9	6	7	5	4	3	2	1	8
3	9	5	2	6	4	7	8	1
6	4	2	1	8	7	5	3	9
8	7	1	3	5	9	6	4	2
5	8	9	7	3	6	1	2	4
2	3	6	4	1	9	7	5	7
7	1	4	9	2	5	8	6	3

Matchstick Magic

The matchsticks which have been moved are outlined.

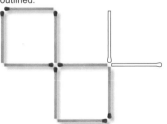

Brain Teaser

36 minutes

Domino Placement

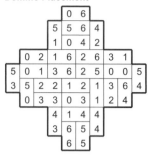

Page 4

Codeword Conundrum

J	O	S	T	L	E		F	A	N	D	A	N	G	O
U		R		D		R		O		E			U	
M	A	G	A	Z	I	N	E		I	N	J	E	C	T
B			G		T		A	I	R		D		S	
O	O	Z	E		I	N	K		A	D	R	I	F	T
	W		D		O		Y	E	T		N		A	
E	N	V	Y	I	N	G		P	E	P	P	E	R	Y
X		I		L		A	W	E		E		S		E
Q	U	E	L	L	E	D		E	L	A	P	S	E	D
U		W		A	S	H		O		E		L		
I	M	P	A	I	R		A	N	Y		T	A	M	P
S		O		L	O	W		A		U		A		A
I	D	I	O	C	Y		S	I	L	E	N	C	E	R
T		N		A		E		T		I			I	T
E	X	T	E	R	I	O	R		Y	E	A	R	L	Y

Double Fun Sudoku

Tasty Teaser

7	9	8	3	4	5	2	1	6
4	3	5	2	6	1	9	7	8
2	6	1	7	9	8	5	4	3
9	7	2	1	8	4	3	6	5
8	4	6	5	3	7	1	9	2
5	1	3	9	2	6	4	8	7
1	2	7	6	5	9	8	3	4
6	5	4	8	1	3	7	2	9
3	8	9	4	7	2	6	5	1

Brain Buster

7	3	9	4	6	8	2	1	5
5	6	1	2	3	9	4	8	7
8	2	4	7	1	5	9	3	6
4	8	7	3	9	6	5	2	1
2	1	5	8	4	7	3	6	9
3	9	6	1	5	2	7	4	8
6	7	3	5	2	1	8	9	4
1	4	8	9	7	3	6	5	2
9	5	2	6	8	4	1	7	3

Pyramid Plus

A=74, B=138, C=55, D=134, E=56, F=212, G=193, H=189, I=190, J=405, K=382, L=379, M=787, N=761, O=1548.

High-Speed Crossword

A	B	E	L		R	I	V	A	L	S
P	E	L	E		O	N	E	S	I	E
E	A	S	E		W	A	N	T	O	N
S	U	E	G	R	A	F	T	O	N	
			R	E	N	E				
D	E	C	A	Y		W	H	A	L	E
I	R	O	N			U	H	O	H	
S	A	N	T	A		E	X	A	M	S
			M	E	L	T				
	S	I	O	U	X	F	A	L	L	S
R	E	S	I	S	T		B	E	A	T
H	E	L	L	E	R		L	I	M	A
O	D	E	S	S	A		E	S	P	N

1 Minute Number Crunch

Beginner

124 − 16 = 108, 108 ÷ 9 = 12, 12 x 7 = 84, 84 + 36 = 120, 120 x 3 = 360, 360 ÷ 20 = 18, 18 x 3 = 54

Intermediate

1973 − 982 = 991, 991 + 39 = 1030, 1030 + 148 = 1178, 1178 ÷ 19 = 62, 62 x 7 = 434, 434 − 48 = 386, 386 ÷ 2 = 193

Advanced

4 to the power of 4 = 256, 256 ÷ 16 x 9 = 144, 144 ÷ 12 x 11 = 132, 132 ÷ 22 x 9 = 54, 54 x 18 = 972, 972 − 677 = 295, 295 + 236 (295 ÷ 5 x 4) = 531

Page 5

High-Speed Crossword

E	D	E	N		C	H	E	S	S	
L	E	G	O		A	U	D	I	O	
F	L	O	W	E	R	G	I	R	L	
		A	S	S	E	T				
P	R	A	Y	S		O	P	A	L	
L	E	G		A	V	E	R	A	G	E
A	L	A		Y	A	M		I	R	A
N	A	M	A	S	T	E		R	E	D
E	X	E	C			R	O	S	E	S
			T	O	U	G	H			
	R	I	N	G	B	E	A	R	E	R
	A	D	O	R	E		R	O	V	E
	P	O	W	E	R		A	M	E	X

1 Minute Number Crunch

Beginner

9 x 8 = 72, 72 + 36 (72 ÷ 2) = 108, 108 − 56 = 52, 52 ÷ 4 = 13, 13 + 94 = 107, 107 − 11 = 96, 96 ÷ 6 = 16

Intermediate

87 + 56 = 143, 143 x 3 = 429, 429 x 2 = 858, 858 − 669 = 189, 189 ÷ 9 x 4 = 84, 84 ÷ 7 x 5 = 60, 220% of 60 = 132

Advanced

20^3 = 8000, 99% of 8000 = 7920, 7920 ÷ 5 x 3 = 4752, 4752 + 891 (4752 ÷ 16 x 3) = 5643, 5643 − 3979 = 1664, 1664 ÷ 32 x 9 = 468, 468 x 7 = 3276

Wordsearch Workout

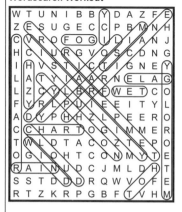

Double Fun Sudoku

Tasty Teaser

5	1	9	2	8	3	6	7	4
4	8	6	1	9	7	5	3	2
3	7	2	4	5	6	8	9	1
2	4	5	3	1	8	7	6	9
7	9	1	5	6	4	3	2	8
6	3	8	7	2	9	4	1	5
1	2	4	6	3	5	9	8	7
9	5	3	8	7	1	2	4	6
8	6	7	9	4	2	1	5	3

Brain Buster

4	8	3	5	6	2	1	9	7
7	9	2	8	3	1	4	6	5
1	5	6	7	9	4	8	3	2
3	7	5	4	2	6	9	8	1
9	4	8	1	7	5	3	2	6
6	2	1	3	8	9	5	7	4
2	1	7	9	5	3	6	4	8
5	6	9	2	4	8	7	1	3
8	3	4	6	1	7	2	5	9

Whatever Next?

369 − Starting at the top, 5−3=2x3=6, 6−3=3x3=9, 9−3=6x3=18, 18−3=15x3=45, 45−3=42x3=126, and 126−3=123x3=369.

Brain Teaser

3 − So that all lines across and down total 10.

Page 6

Mind Over Matter

The value of the letter in the central square is the sum total of the values of the letters in the other squares. Thus the missing value is 22, so the missing letter is V.

Double Fun Sudoku

Tasty Teaser

5	8	4	6	1	7	2	9	3
7	9	3	4	2	8	1	6	5
2	6	1	3	5	9	8	7	4
4	5	9	2	8	3	7	1	6
6	2	8	1	7	4	3	5	9
1	3	7	5	9	6	4	2	8
8	7	2	9	3	5	6	4	1
9	1	6	8	4	2	5	3	7
3	4	5	7	6	1	9	8	2

Brain Buster

3	5	2	6	7	1	4	9	8
7	6	8	4	9	3	1	2	5
9	4	1	2	8	5	7	3	6
5	8	9	1	3	7	6	4	2
4	2	7	5	6	8	3	1	9
1	3	6	9	4	2	5	8	7
8	9	3	7	1	6	2	5	4
2	7	4	3	5	9	8	6	1
6	1	5	8	2	4	9	7	3

Codeword Conundrum

I	N	E	X	A	C	T	L	Y		J	O	I	S	T
M		M		T		A		O		O		D		H
P	I	A	N	O		S	I	G	N	I	F	Y		U
E		N		M		K		A		N		L		N
L	E	A	K	I	E	S	T		S	T	O	L	I	D
		T		C			U		U					E
I	B	I	S		P	A	W	N	B	R	O	K	E	R
N		O		Z		W		D		E		N		E
V	E	N	T	I	L	A	T	O	R		W	O	R	D
I			P		Y			O		W				
S	L	E	E	P	Y		Q	U	I	B	B	L	E	D
I		R		T		P		T		E		E		W
B	A	I	R	S	H	I	P		A	D	D	L	E	
L		S		E		I		E		I		G		L
E	M	E	N	D		S	T	R	I	N	G	E	N	T

High-Speed Crossword

C	H	O	P		S	W	O	O	S	H
L	I	R	A		I	H	A	D	T	O
A	F	E	W		N	I	T	E	R	S
P	I	O	N	E	E	R				
			B	A	R	B	A	R	A	
I	N	A	P	O	D		O	V	E	N
C	O	N	A	N	O	B	R	I	E	N
E	N	D	S		C	A	N	D	L	E
D	E	S	T	R	O	Y				
			A	N	S	W	E	R	S	
M	A	R	G	I	N		H	A	I	L
E	V	E	N	S	O		O	S	L	O
T	E	M	P	E	R		S	T	E	W

1 Minute Number Crunch

Beginner

15 x 5 = 75, 75 ÷ 25 x 7 = 21, 21 + 111 = 132, 132 ÷ 11 x 4 = 48, 48 + 8 (48 ÷ 6) = 56, 56 ÷ 7 = 8, 8 x 9 = 72

Intermediate

12.5% of 64 = 8, 8 x 21 = 168, 168 ÷ 3 x 2 = 112, 75% of 112 = 84, 84 ÷ 7 = 12, 12 x 13 = 156, 156 ÷ 6 x 5 = 130

Advanced

682 + 341 (50% of 682) = 1023, 1023 − 682 (1023 ÷ 3 x 2) = 341, 341 x 11 = 3751, 3751 − 567 = 3184, 125% of 3184 = 3980, 85% of 3980 = 3383, 3383 ÷ 17 = 199

Page 7

Battleship Bout

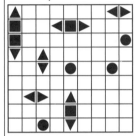

High-Speed Crossword

E	G	G		B	I	T			
N	O	R		A	M	Y		B	A	G
C	L	E	A	N	U	P		E	S	E
A	F	A	R		P	E	N	S	K	E
M	E	T	E	S		O	T	I	S	
P	R	E		I	T	S	G	O	N	E
		S	U	N	R	O	O	F		
J	E	T	S	K	I	S		A	N	A
A	C	H	E		A	B	L	E	R	
P	O	I	S	O	N		A	B	U	T
A	N	T		N	U	R	T	U	R	E
N	O	S		U	K	E		M	A	R
			S	E	T		S	L	Y	

Wordwheel

The nine-letter word is: NEWSPAPER

Wordsearch Workout

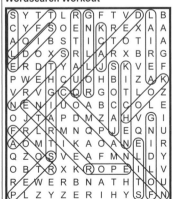

Double Fun Sudoku

Tasty Teaser

3	8	4	9	1	5	6	7	2
6	5	2	7	3	4	9	1	8
1	9	7	8	6	2	4	3	5
9	7	3	1	2	8	5	4	6
5	1	8	4	7	6	2	9	3
4	2	6	3	5	9	7	8	1
8	4	5	2	9	3	1	6	7
2	3	1	6	4	7	8	5	9
7	6	9	5	8	1	3	2	4

Brain Buster

7	2	9	8	6	5	3	4	1
1	6	3	4	9	2	8	7	5
5	8	4	7	3	1	6	2	9
4	9	2	1	8	3	7	5	6
6	5	7	2	4	9	1	3	8
8	3	1	6	5	7	2	9	4
9	7	5	3	1	8	4	6	2
2	1	6	5	7	4	9	8	3
3	4	8	9	2	6	5	1	7

Sum Circle

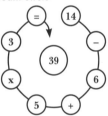

Page 8

1 Minute Number Crunch

Beginner

34 ÷ 2 = 17, 17 x 7 = 119, 119 + 49 = 168, 168 ÷ 8 = 21, 300% of 21 = 63, 63 x 2 = 126, 126 ÷ 9 = 14

Intermediate

72 ÷ 8 x 7 = 63, 63 x 4 = 252, 252 ÷ 3 = 84, 84 ÷ 4 = 21, 21² = 441, 441 x 3 = 1323, 1323 ÷ 9 = 147

Advanced

675 ÷ 5 x 8 = 1080, 1080 ÷ 18 x 5 = 300, 300 + 240 (300 ÷ 5 x 4) = 540, 540 ÷ 9 x 7 = 420, 420 + 126 (420 ÷ 10 x 3) = 546, 546 x 9 = 4914, 4914 ÷ 27 x 7 = 1274

High-Speed Crossword

```
M I L O   J A C K O
A T A D   O T H E R
M E M O R Y L A N E
A M E R I C A
        B E S T M A N
G L A S S   T H E M E
R A C Y     E M I T
A M E N S   W E E D S
M A S C A R A
      W E I G H T S
E A S Y S T R E E T
S W E E T   O R E O
P E E R S   W A S P
```

Codeword Conundrum

```
S U B J U G A T E   B   R   P
Y   A   R   U   O R D E A L
S U R C H A R G E   A   P   A
T   A   N   R E V E L R Y
E X T R U D I N G   E   I   M
M   A   E   O W L   C   A
  C O N Q U E S T   Y E A S T
S   D   R   A   H   M   E
T O P A Z   G Y R A T I N G
R   E   O V A   R   G   E
I   E   O   B O O M E R A N G
C A R A M E L   L   A   R
K   A   I   E F F E C T I V E
E N G I N E   R   S   E   S
N   E   G   C O N S I D E R S
```

Double Fun Sudoku

Tasty Teaser

3	5	4	8	2	1	7	9	6
2	7	8	4	6	9	3	1	5
1	9	6	5	7	3	2	4	8
6	2	5	1	8	4	9	3	7
7	8	1	9	3	6	4	5	2
9	4	3	2	5	7	6	8	1
4	3	2	6	1	8	5	7	9
5	1	7	3	9	2	8	6	4
8	6	9	7	4	5	1	2	3

Brain Buster

2	9	8	6	4	7	5	1	3
5	4	1	9	2	3	7	8	6
3	7	6	5	1	8	9	2	4
9	6	5	3	8	2	4	7	1
8	1	3	7	9	4	6	5	2
7	2	4	1	5	6	8	3	9
4	3	9	8	7	1	2	6	5
1	8	2	4	6	5	3	9	7
6	5	7	2	3	9	1	4	8

Spidoku

Page 9

High-Speed Crossword

```
S A W T O   H A S T A
T R A I N   O N I O N
D I S N E Y W O R L D
  H A N O I   S L Y
I B E   E D E N
M E D U S A   O P A L
A L U M S   D I R G E
C A P P   P A R E R S
  S P A N   S A T
A L E   O L I V E
M I D D L E E A R T H
E M A I L   L I V E R
N A M E S   S L E D S
```

Wordsearch Workout

(word search grid)

Double Fun Sudoku

Tasty Teaser

5	9	7	1	6	8	3	4	2
4	6	2	5	7	3	9	8	1
1	8	3	4	9	2	5	7	6
7	3	8	2	5	9	1	6	4
9	2	4	6	8	1	7	5	3
6	1	5	3	4	7	2	9	8
2	5	6	7	1	4	8	3	9
8	4	1	9	3	5	6	2	7
3	7	9	8	2	6	4	1	5

Brain Buster

4	6	1	8	2	7	5	9	3
9	3	2	4	1	5	7	8	6
8	7	5	9	6	3	1	2	4
3	5	4	1	8	6	2	7	9
6	1	9	3	7	2	8	4	5
7	2	8	5	9	4	3	6	1
2	4	7	6	5	1	9	3	8
5	9	3	2	4	8	6	1	7
1	8	6	7	3	9	4	5	2

Matchstick Magic

The matchsticks which have been removed are outlined.

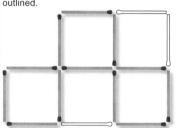

Brain Teaser

Mary 44, Sally 66, Frank 99.

1 Minute Number Crunch

Beginner

99 + 18 (9 + 9) = 117, 117 ÷ 3 = 39, 39 + 13 (39 ÷ 3) = 52, 52 ÷ 2 = 26, 26 + 58 = 84, 84 ÷ 12 = 7, 7 x 5 = 35

Intermediate

829 − 555 = 274, 274 ÷ 2 = 137, 137 + 85 = 222, 222 ÷ 37 = 6, 6^3 = 216, 216 ÷ 9 x 3 = 72, 72 ÷ 8 x 3 = 27

Advanced

94 x 11 = 1034, 1034 ÷ 0.5 = 2068, 2068 + 1551 (2068 ÷ 4 x 3) = 3619, 3619 − 2917 = 702, 702 + 624 (702 ÷ 9 x 8) = 1326, 1326 + 663 (1326 ÷ 2) = 1989, 1989 ÷ 9 x 14 = 3094

Page 10

Codeword Conundrum

Z		R		E	X	H	A	U	S	T	I	B	L	E
E	J	E	C	T		E		U		M		I		
S		C		H	A	N	D	I	C	A	P	P	E	D
T	I	T	L	E		C		H		L		G		
F		A	R		E	M	P	L	O	Y	E	E	S	
U		N	E	E	D		O		I		V		P	
L	A	G		A		N		K		P	A	I	R	
N		U		L	A	S	S	O	E	D		P		E
E	E	L	S		P		T		O		O	V	A	
S		A		P	P	E		Y	O	U	R		D	
S	C	R	A	W	L	E	R	S		R		A		S
	H		S		I		O		B	O	T	C	H	
C	O	N	S	E	Q	U	E	N	C	E		I		E
	K		E		U		I		L	O	O	S	E	
A	E	S	T	H	E	T	I	C	A	L			N	T

Double Fun Sudoku

Tasty Teaser

5	3	8	1	2	7	6	4	9
2	6	9	8	3	4	1	5	7
7	1	4	9	5	6	3	8	2
6	4	2	7	9	1	5	3	8
9	5	3	6	8	2	4	7	1
1	8	7	3	4	5	2	9	6
8	9	5	2	1	3	7	6	4
3	7	1	4	6	9	8	2	5
4	2	6	5	7	8	9	1	3

Brain Buster

6	7	4	2	9	1	3	8	5
2	1	8	3	5	6	4	9	7
5	3	9	7	4	8	6	2	1
9	8	6	5	1	4	2	7	3
1	5	7	9	2	3	8	6	4
4	2	3	8	6	7	5	1	9
7	6	2	1	3	5	9	4	8
8	4	5	6	7	9	1	3	2
3	9	1	4	8	2	7	5	6

Pyramid Plus

A=121, B=69, C=92, D=122, E=129, F=190, G=161, H=214, I=251, J=351, K=375, L=465, M=726, N=840, O=1566.

High-Speed Crossword

B	A	W	L		L	O	R	E	N	
E	R	I	E		A	F	I	R	E	
G	E	R	A	L	D	F	O	R	D	
O	N	E		A	Y	E				
T	A	S	E	R		R	I	V	A	L
			B	A	G		R	A	C	E
A	U	T	O	M	O	B	I	L	E	S
S	K	I	N		D	R	S			
K	E	N	Y	A		O	H	A	R	A
			D	E	N		L	O	M	
C	H	E	V	Y	C	H	A	S	E	
O	U	T	I	E		O	M	E	N	
D	E	A	L	S		T	O	S	S	

1 Minute Number Crunch

Beginner
$8^2 = 64$, 64 - 49 = 15, 15 x 9 = 135, 135 ÷ 15 x 2 = 18, 18 + 67 = 85, 85 + 17 (85 ÷ 5) = 102, 102 ÷ 3 = 34

Intermediate
55 ÷ 11 x 4 = 20, 20 x 1.75 = 35, 35 ÷ 7 x 2 = 10, 400% of 10 = 40, 40 + 47 = 87, 87 ÷ 3 x 2 = 58, 58 ÷ 0.5 = 116

Advanced
459 ÷ 17 x 8 = 216, 216 ÷ 36 x 29 = 174, 174 ÷ 3 x 8 = 464, 62.5% of 464 = 290, 290 + 777 = 1067, 1067 x 4 = 4268, 4268 + 3201 (75% of 4268) = 7469

Page 11

High-Speed Crossword

R	A	G		T	A	B		C	A	R
O	N	O		E	L	I		O	W	E
A	N	I	M	A	L	S		M	E	D
M	A	N	O	R		T	R	I		
		G	N	U		R	A	N	T	O
B	E	B	O	P		O	H	G	O	D
E	V	A				F	E	D		
T	A	C	O	S		C	R	O	S	S
A	N	K	L	E		A	I	R		
		W	E	D		N	O	W	A	Y
S	P	A		A	G	I	T	A	T	E
H	E	R		T	A	N		R	O	N
E	N	D		E	Y	E		D	P	S

Domino Placement

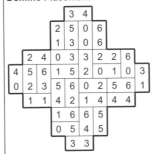

			3	4		
	2	5	0	6		
	1	3	0	6		
2	4	0	3	3	2	6
4	5	6	1	5	2	0	1	0	3
0	2	3	5	6	0	2	5	6	1
1	1	4	2	1	4	4
	1	6	6	5		
	0	5	4	5		
			3	3		

Wordsearch Workout

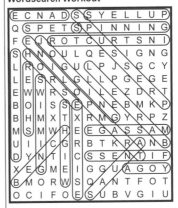

Double Fun Sudoku

Tasty Teaser

7	2	4	9	3	6	8	5	1
9	8	3	7	1	5	6	2	4
1	6	5	8	2	4	9	3	7
5	4	2	1	6	7	3	9	8
3	9	6	4	8	2	1	7	5
8	1	7	3	5	9	2	4	6
2	5	8	6	7	3	4	1	9
4	7	1	2	9	8	5	6	3
6	3	9	5	4	1	7	8	2

Brain Buster

6	3	1	4	7	2	9	8	5
9	5	2	8	6	1	7	4	3
4	8	7	3	5	9	1	6	2
5	1	6	2	4	3	8	7	9
8	4	3	1	9	7	5	2	6
2	7	9	5	8	6	4	3	1
7	6	5	9	3	8	2	1	4
3	2	4	7	1	5	6	9	8
1	9	8	6	2	4	3	5	7

Whatever Next?

G – Assign a number to each letter according to its place in the alphabet, so B=2, D=4, F=6, J=10 and L=12, making a total of 34. The total in the centre is 41, so the missing letter is G (=7).

Brain Teaser

16

Page 12

Mind Over Matter

The sum total of the values of the letters in the bottom squares is subtracted from the sum total of the values of the letters in the top squares. Thus the missing value is 19, so the missing letter is S.

Double Fun Sudoku

Tasty Teaser

4	5	9	7	6	2	1	3	8
6	2	3	4	1	8	7	5	9
1	8	7	9	3	5	4	2	6
7	3	4	1	8	6	2	9	5
2	9	6	5	7	4	8	1	3
5	1	8	3	2	9	6	4	7
3	6	5	8	4	1	9	7	2
8	7	1	2	9	3	5	6	4
9	4	2	6	5	7	3	8	1

Brain Buster

4	2	7	5	3	1	9	6	8
5	6	3	9	7	8	2	1	4
1	9	8	2	6	4	3	7	5
7	8	9	6	4	5	1	3	2
6	4	2	3	1	9	8	5	7
3	5	1	7	8	2	4	9	6
9	3	5	4	2	6	7	8	1
2	1	6	8	9	7	5	4	3
8	7	4	1	5	3	6	2	9

Codeword Conundrum

A	X	I	S		C	L	A	N	G		B	O	S	S
L			E	A	R		O		A		B			A
S	O	U	R		A	C	R	O	S	S		O	W	L
O		V		F		T			P	L	E	A	T	
	S	O	F	T		A	G	U	E			L		
P	I	E		I		M		R		W	H	E	L	P
I		N		S	L	O	G	A	N		X		A	
Q	U	I	L	T		S		V		Y	O	U	N	G
U		O		G	A	Z	E	B	O		D		E	
E	G	R	E	T		I		L		K		E	N	D
	E		A	R	C	H		B	E	N	D			
A	N	T	I	C		Y		A	U		U			B
B	E	E		O	B	J	E	C	T		T	A	M	E
E		A		I		I	N		H	U	T			L
T	A	K	E		G	R	A	Z	E		Y	A	W	L

High-Speed Crossword

W	A	R	S		C	O	I	F	S
A	B	E	T		A	R	N	I	E
S	A	V	A	N	N	A	H	G	A
		P	A	S	T	A			
S	C	A	L	P		O	L	I	V	E
C	A	R	E	S		R	E	N	A	L
R	I	G				O	L	D		
A	R	O	M	A		N	A	I	V	E
M	O	N	E	T		A	B	L	E	R
		L	E	O	N	A				
H	A	V	A	N	A	C	U	B	A	
A	R	I	S	E		U	S	E	R	
M	I	N	E	S		S	A	N	E	

1 Minute Number Crunch

Beginner

22 x 7 = 154, 154 ÷ 2 = 77, 77 ÷ 11 x 4 = 28, 28 + 14 (50% of 28) = 42, 42 − 9 = 33, 33 x 4 = 132, 132 ÷ 11 x 7 = 84

Intermediate

27 x 3 = 81, 81 − 56 = 25, 80% of 25 = 20, 850% of 20 = 170, 170 ÷ 10 x 7 = 119, 119 x 2 = 238, 238 + 823 = 1061

Advanced

96 x 14 = 1344, 1344 + 1008 (1344 ÷ 4 x 3) = 2352, 2352 ÷ 6 x 5 = 1960, 35% of 1960 = 686, 686 + 155 = 841, square root of 841 = 29, 29 x 13 = 377

Page 13

1 Minute Number Crunch

Beginner

1234 x 2 = 2468, 2468 − 999 = 1469, 1469 + 31 = 1500, 90% of 1500 = 1350, 1350 ÷ 5 = 270, 270 ÷ 5 = 54, 54 x 3 = 162

Intermediate

99 ÷ 9 x 5 = 55, 55 ÷ 11 x 5 = 25, square root of 25 = 5, 5 + 1 = 6, 6 + 5 = 11, 11² = 121, 121 x 3 = 363

Advanced

96 x 4 = 384, 384 + 72 (384 ÷ 16 x 3) = 456, 456 ÷ 6 x 5 = 380, 380 − 342 (90% of 380) = 38, 38 + 795 = 833, 833 x 7 = 5831, 5831 − 2978 = 2853

High-Speed Crossword

S	O	L	O		J	O	S	H	E	D
E	R	I	N		U	M	P	I	R	E
N	E	T	S		N	E	A	T	E	N
D	O	T	H		E	N	D			
		L	O	L	A		E	B	A	Y
P	E	E	R	O	U	T		I	P	A
E	P	E	E	S		R	E	G	A	L
C	I	V		S	T	U	M	B	L	E
K	C	A	R		W	E	B	E		
		U	S	E		A	R	T	S	
D	E	A	R	M	E		S	T	E	P
U	M	L	A	U	T		S	H	E	A
G	U	I	L	T	Y		Y	A	M	S

Wordwheel

The nine-letter word is: DISTORTED

Wordsearch Workout

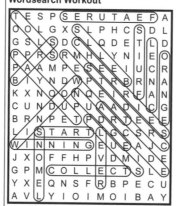

Double Fun Sudoku

Tasty Teaser

1	6	9	7	2	3	8	5	4
8	2	5	4	9	6	1	7	3
4	3	7	5	1	8	2	9	6
5	1	6	9	4	7	3	8	2
7	4	3	8	5	2	9	6	1
2	9	8	6	3	1	7	4	5
9	5	1	2	7	4	6	3	8
6	7	2	3	8	5	4	1	9
3	8	4	1	6	9	5	2	7

Brain Buster

4	6	5	3	8	2	9	1	7
7	2	8	4	1	9	3	5	6
9	3	1	6	7	5	2	4	8
2	7	4	8	9	1	5	6	3
5	8	3	7	6	4	1	2	9
1	9	6	2	5	3	8	7	4
8	1	2	9	4	6	7	3	5
3	4	9	5	2	7	6	8	1
6	5	7	1	3	8	4	9	2

Sum Circle

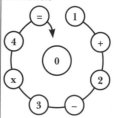

Page 14

1 Minute Number Crunch

Beginner

14 x 6 = 84, 84 ÷ 2 = 42, 42 ÷ 7 = 6, 6 x 2.5 = 15, 500% of 15 = 75, 75 x 3 = 225, 225 ÷ 15 = 15

Intermediate

424 − 128 = 296, 296 ÷ 2 = 148, 148 ÷ 4 = 37, 37 x 7 = 259, 259 + 955 = 1214, 1214 x 2 = 2428, 2428 − 1957 = 471

Advanced

558 + 372 (558 ÷ 3 x 2) = 930, 930 ÷ 10 x 7 = 651, 651 + 465 (651 ÷ 7 x 5) = 1116, 1116 − 248 (1116 ÷ 9 x 2) = 868, 868 − 277 = 591, 591 ÷ 3 x 8 = 1576, 1576 + 591 (1576 ÷ 8 x 3) = 2167

High-Speed Crossword

D	E	C	A	L		A	G	A	P	E
E	R	A	S	E		B	A	N	A	L
M	I	S	S	T	H	E	M	A	R	K
I	N	E		M	O	L	E			
		G	E	M		S	O	F	A	
P	H	R	A	S	E	S		M	E	L
H	O	U	S	E		I	D	E	A	S
I	L	L		E	A	T	I	N	T	O
L	E	E	K		R	U	G			
	I	K	E	A		C	O	O		
S	H	A	N	I	A	T	W	A	I	N
H	E	R	D	S		E	A	G	L	E
E	X	I	S	T		D	R	E	S	S

Codeword Conundrum

S	U	P	E	R		M	A	J	O	R	E	T	T	E
E		Y		I		A		E						R
B	U	L	L	D	O	Z	E	R		V	I	S	T	A
A		O		E		E		D	E	L		S		S
C	A	N	V	A	S		F	I	X	A	T	I	V	E
E		E		N		S		N		L		C		
O	P	T	I	C		Q	U	I	P		D	I	S	C
U		W		E		U		E		B		N		A
S	K	I	D		H	A	I	R		O	U	G	H	T
		T		F		B		E		T				A
S	U	C	C	U	M	B	S		P	A	R	S	E	C
I		H		N		L		W		N		T		L
D	O	Y	E	N		I	M	A	G	I	N	A	R	Y
E		E		N		F		S		S		I		S
S	P	O	T	L	I	G	H	T		T	H	R	U	M

Double Fun Sudoku

Tasty Teaser

8	7	2	5	6	3	9	1	4
6	9	1	8	7	4	3	2	5
4	3	5	9	1	2	6	7	8
3	5	7	2	9	1	4	8	6
1	8	9	7	4	6	2	5	3
2	6	4	3	5	8	7	9	1
9	2	8	6	3	5	1	4	7
7	1	6	4	8	9	5	3	2
5	4	3	1	2	7	8	6	9

Brain Buster

2	3	8	1	7	4	5	6	9
5	9	7	8	6	3	1	2	4
1	6	4	5	2	9	8	7	3
7	8	9	2	4	5	3	1	6
4	5	3	6	9	1	2	8	7
6	1	2	7	3	8	9	4	5
9	4	1	3	8	6	7	5	2
8	2	6	9	5	7	4	3	1
3	7	5	4	1	2	6	9	8

Spidoku

Page 15

High-Speed Crossword

D	E	B	T	S		T	A	R	A	S
O	M	A	H	A		A	R	O	M	A
C	I	T	E	D		K	E	B	A	B
E	L	M		A	W	E		I	Z	E
N	I	A		T	O	O		N	O	R
T	O	N	S		K	N	O	W	N	S
		F	A	R		E	L	I		
S	H	O	W	E	R		E	L	S	E
E	A	R		W	E	T		L	U	X
E	V	E		A	D	O		I	M	P
S	A	V	E	R		A	L	A	M	O
A	N	E	N	D		S	E	M	I	S
W	A	R	E	S		T	A	S	T	E

Wordsearch Workout

Double Fun Sudoku

Tasty Teaser

7	6	8	9	1	3	4	2	5
4	9	2	7	5	6	1	3	8
1	5	3	4	8	2	7	9	6
6	8	1	3	2	5	9	7	4
2	4	9	6	7	8	3	5	1
3	7	5	1	9	4	6	8	2
9	2	6	5	3	1	8	4	7
5	1	7	8	4	9	2	6	3
8	3	4	2	6	7	5	1	9

Brain Buster

3	2	6	7	4	9	8	1	5
5	9	7	1	3	8	4	2	6
4	8	1	6	5	2	9	3	7
1	7	9	2	6	3	5	4	8
2	4	3	8	7	5	1	6	9
8	6	5	9	1	4	3	7	2
6	1	8	3	9	7	2	5	4
7	5	2	4	8	1	6	9	3
9	3	4	5	2	6	7	8	1

Matchstick Magic

The matchsticks which have been removed are outlined.

Brain Teaser

14

Simple as A, B, C

B	A	C	B	C	A
A	B	B	C	C	A
C	C	A	A	B	B
A	B	B	C	A	C
C	C	A	B	A	B
B	A	C	A	B	C

Page 16

Codeword Conundrum

J	E	A	L	O	U	S	L	Y		T	I	M	E	S
U		M		D		U		A		E		E		O
R	A	B	I	D		A	N	N	E	X	E	D		U
O		I		V		K		T		A				N
R	E	G	A	T	H	E	R		F	U	R	L	E	D
		U		Y			Z		R					
T	O	O	L		D	E	L	I	B	E	R	A	T	E
U		U		T		K		N		D		P		S
R	E	S	U	R	G	E	N	C	E		O	P	U	S
B				A		D				M		L		
U	N	B	E	N	T		B	R	E	A	K	I	N	G
L		A		Q		E		O		D		C		I
E		L	A	U	N	D	R	Y		C	H	A	R	D
N		S		I		I		A		A		N		D
T	R	A	W	L		T	E	L	E	P	A	T	H	Y

Double Fun Sudoku

Tasty Teaser

2	6	1	8	9	4	5	3	7
9	7	8	6	3	5	4	1	2
4	3	5	1	2	7	6	9	8
3	1	4	5	7	6	2	8	9
5	8	2	3	4	9	1	7	6
6	9	7	2	8	1	3	5	4
7	2	9	4	1	3	8	6	5
1	4	6	9	5	8	7	2	3
8	5	3	7	6	2	9	4	1

Brain Buster

5	8	7	6	4	1	2	9	3
6	1	3	8	9	2	5	4	7
9	4	2	7	5	3	8	1	6
4	9	6	5	1	7	3	8	2
8	2	5	3	6	9	4	7	1
7	3	1	2	8	4	9	6	5
2	7	4	9	3	6	1	5	8
1	6	8	4	2	5	7	3	9
3	5	9	1	7	8	6	2	4

Pyramid Plus

A=24, B=124, C=68, D=35, E=60, F=148, G=192, H=103, I=95, J=340, K=295, L=198, M=635, N=493, O=1128.

High-Speed Crossword

L	E	O		F	A	B		R	I	P
E	L	F		I	R	E		O	N	E
A	L	F	A	L	F	A		L	A	W
P	A	Y	N	E		M	E	L	D	S
		O	T	T		E	V	E	R	
S	E	U	S	S		D	A	R	E	D
P	A	R						C	A	R
A	R	R	O	W		R	O	O	M	Y
	P	O	L	E		E	R	A		
R	I	C	E	S		M	A	S	S	E
E	E	K		S	T	I	L	T	E	D
A	C	E		O	W	N		E	G	G
P	E	R		N	O	D		R	A	Y

1 Minute Number Crunch

Beginner
88 ÷ 4 x 3 = 66, 66 + 49 = 115, 115 ÷ 5 x 3 = 69, 69 – 42 = 27, 27 + 18 (27 ÷ 3 x 2) = 45, 45 x 4 = 180, 180 ÷ 10 x 3 = 54

Intermediate
394 ÷ 2 = 197, 197 + 88 = 285, 285 ÷ 3 = 95, 120% of 95 = 114, 114 – 77 = 37, 37 x 2 = 74, 74 x 5 = 370

Advanced
7 to the power of 4 = 2401, 2401 x 8 = 19208, 19208 – 6936 = 12272, 12272 ÷ 16 x 5 = 3835, 60% of 3835 = 2301, 2301 – 1534 (2301 ÷ 3 x 2) = 767, 767 x 14 = 10738

Page 17

High-Speed Crossword

P	A	G	E	D		T	I	G	H	T
A	C	E	L	A		E	R	R	O	R
C	I	T	I	Z	E	N	K	A	N	E
E	D	S		Z	E	N		N	E	E
			A	L	L	I	E	D		
A	R	G	U	E		S	A	S	S	Y
L	O	A	D				T	O	K	E
P	E	R	I	L		L	E	N	I	N
	G	O	O	N	I	N				
M	A	O		C	O	T		A	S	P
I	F	Y	O	U	R	E	A	B	L	E
T	E	L	L	S		R	O	B	O	T
T	W	E	E	T		S	K	Y	P	E

1 Minute Number Crunch

Beginner
78 + 15 = 93, 93 ÷ 3 = 31, 31 x 4 = 124, 124 + 20 = 144, 144 ÷ 12 = 12, 12 x 8 = 96, 96 ÷ 2 = 48

Intermediate
291 + 49 = 340, 20% of 340 = 68, 68 ÷ 4 = 17, 17 x 7 = 119, 119 x 2 = 238, 238 – 190 = 48, 48 + 32 = 80

Advanced
342 ÷ 19 x 5 = 90, 170% of 90 = 153, 153 + 119 (153 ÷ 9 x 7) = 272, 272 x 0.625 = 170, 170 ÷ 34 x 5 = 25, 25^3 = 15625, 15625 ÷ 5 x 4 = 12500

Wordsearch Workout

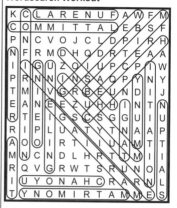

Double Fun Sudoku

Tasty Teaser

8	7	9	6	5	1	3	4	2
5	2	3	7	8	4	1	6	9
1	6	4	3	2	9	5	7	8
3	9	2	4	6	5	8	1	7
7	1	8	2	9	3	6	5	4
4	5	6	8	1	7	2	9	3
2	8	1	9	4	6	7	3	5
9	3	5	1	7	8	4	2	6
6	4	7	5	3	2	9	8	1

Brain Buster

4	6	3	9	7	8	1	2	5
7	5	1	4	2	3	9	6	8
9	8	2	1	6	5	4	7	3
2	1	8	7	3	9	5	4	6
3	9	5	6	8	4	7	1	2
6	4	7	2	5	1	8	3	9
1	7	6	8	9	2	3	5	4
5	2	9	3	4	7	6	8	1
8	3	4	5	1	6	2	9	7

Whatever Next?

12 – The central number is 60 and the lower numbers are 60% of the higher numbers on opposite points of the star.

Brain Teaser

4 x 3 = 12   10 x 6 = 60
8 x 6 = 48
        60

Page 18

Mind Over Matter

The sum total of the values in the top squares equals the value of the central square, as does the sum total of the values in the bottom squares. Thus the missing value is 3, so the missing letter is C.

Double Fun Sudoku

Tasty Teaser

8	1	4	6	9	5	7	2	3
9	5	3	1	7	2	8	6	4
6	7	2	3	8	4	9	1	5
4	9	1	5	6	3	2	8	7
5	6	7	9	2	8	4	3	1
3	2	8	4	1	7	6	5	9
1	4	9	8	5	6	3	7	2
7	3	6	2	4	1	5	9	8
2	8	5	7	3	9	1	4	6

Brain Buster

1	7	6	3	9	8	4	5	2
4	5	8	6	7	2	3	9	1
3	9	2	5	1	4	8	7	6
9	6	5	4	3	1	7	2	8
7	8	3	2	6	9	1	4	5
2	4	1	7	8	5	6	3	9
5	1	9	8	4	7	2	6	3
8	3	7	9	2	6	5	1	4
6	2	4	1	5	3	9	8	7

Codeword Conundrum

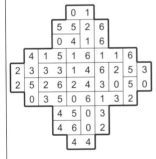

High-Speed Crossword

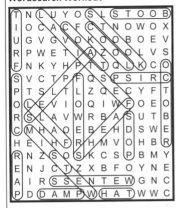

1 Minute Number Crunch

Beginner
232 − 34 = 198, 198 ÷ 2 = 99, 99 ÷ 9 x 5 = 55, 55 ÷ 11 x 4 = 20, 20 + 19 = 39, 39 ÷ 3 x 2 = 26, 26 + 42 = 68

Intermediate
29 x 3 = 87, 87 + 78 = 165, 165 ÷ 11 = 15, 15 + 25 = 40, 40 ÷ 10 x 3 = 12, 12 x 7 = 84, 84 ÷ 3 = 28

Advanced
702 ÷ 39 x 7 = 126, 126 + 224 = 350, 350 ÷ 10 x 7 = 245, 245 ÷ 5 x 3 = 147, 147 ÷ 3 x 2 = 98, 98 x 7 = 686, 686 x 2.5 = 1715

Page 19

Domino Placement

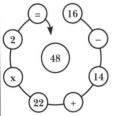

High-Speed Crossword

C	H	I	C			P	A	R	I	S	
H	E	R	A		A	W	A	S	H		
A	M	E	R	I	C	A	N	M	E		
			O	V	E	R					
M	A	D	L	Y		E	N	A	C	T	
O	N	E			Y	O	O	H	O	O	
U	N	I	T	E	D	F	R	O	N	T	
T	I	G	E	R	S			L	E	E	
H	E	N	C	E		C	R	E	S	S	
			C	H	O	O					
	D	E	L	T	A	B	L	U	E	S	
	U	N	I	O	N		E	S	A	U	
	B	E	E	R	S		S	E	R	B	

Wordwheel

The nine-letter word is: OBJECTIVE

Wordsearch Workout

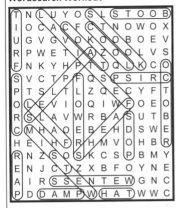

Double Fun Sudoku

Tasty Teaser

6	1	7	8	2	4	5	3	9
5	4	9	1	3	7	6	8	2
8	3	2	9	5	6	1	7	4
7	8	4	5	9	1	2	6	3
1	2	3	7	6	8	9	4	5
9	6	5	2	4	3	8	1	7
2	7	8	3	1	9	4	5	6
4	9	1	6	7	5	3	2	8
3	5	6	4	8	2	7	9	1

Brain Buster

4	2	7	6	8	9	3	5	1
1	9	3	5	7	2	6	4	8
5	6	8	4	1	3	2	7	9
3	8	9	2	4	1	5	6	7
6	7	4	3	5	8	9	1	2
2	1	5	9	6	7	4	8	3
8	3	6	7	9	5	1	2	4
7	5	2	1	3	4	8	9	6
9	4	1	8	2	6	7	3	5

Sum Circle

2, =, 16, −, 14, +, 22, x → centre 48

Page 20

1 Minute Number Crunch

Beginner
29 − 15 = 14, 14 ÷ 2 = 7, 7 + 86 = 93, 93 ÷ 3 = 31, 31 x 5 = 155, 155 − 122 = 33, 33 ÷ 11 = 3

Intermediate
9% of 700 = 63, 63 − 28 = 35, 35 x 4 = 140, 140 + 42 (140 ÷ 10 x 3) = 182, 182 ÷ 2 = 91, 91 − 17 = 74, 74 + 123 = 197

Advanced
22^2 = 484, 484 x 4 = 1936, 1936 ÷ 16 x 5 = 605, 605 ÷ 0.25 = 2420, 2420 − 987 = 1433, 1433 x 2 = 2866, 2866 + 777 = 3643

High-Speed Crossword

J	A	P	A	N		A	M	A	Z	E
A	W	A	R	E		L	E	M	O	N
M	E	L	E	E		A	H	A	N	D
		M	A	D	A	M		R	E	S
O	W	E		L	O	O	S	E		
M	A	T	T	E	L		A	T	O	M
A	N	T	E	S		I	N	T	R	O
N	E	O	N		U	N	D	O	E	S
		S	T	A	R	T		S	O	S
P	A	T		A	L	E	R	O		
O	N	A	I	R		G	O	U	D	A
R	E	T	R	O		R	U	R	A	L
T	W	E	E	N		A	T	S	E	A

Codeword Conundrum

D	E	P	T	H		P	E	S	T	I	L	E	N	T
E		A		A		I		Y		R				A
P	H	R	E	N	E	T	I	C		R	I	S	E	R
A		T		D		H		O		U		W		D
R	O	Y	A	L	S		A	P	O	P	L	E	X	Y
T			E		D		H		T		E			
I	N	F	E	R		O	K	A	Y		E	P	I	C
N		E		S		W		N		A	E			U
G	R	I	P		K	N	O	T		C	A	R	O	B
		G		Z		L		S		C				B
K	I	N	K	A	J	O	U		Q	U	A	R	R	Y
A		E		N		A		A		S		E		H
R	A	D	I	I		D	E	S	P	E	R	A	D	O
M				E		E		H		R		V		L
A	S	S	U	R	E	D	L	Y		S	I	E	V	E

Double Fun Sudoku

Tasty Teaser

7	8	6	9	5	1	3	2	4
5	2	1	3	4	6	8	9	7
4	3	9	8	2	7	1	5	6
9	6	4	5	1	3	2	7	8
8	7	2	6	9	4	5	1	3
3	1	5	7	8	2	4	6	9
6	4	3	2	7	5	9	8	1
2	9	7	1	3	8	6	4	5
1	5	8	4	6	9	7	3	2

Brain Buster

9	5	7	4	3	1	6	8	2
8	1	3	7	2	6	9	4	5
4	2	6	9	8	5	3	1	7
5	3	4	1	7	2	8	6	9
1	9	8	5	6	3	2	7	4
7	6	2	8	9	4	1	5	3
3	7	1	6	4	9	5	2	8
2	4	5	3	1	8	7	9	6
6	8	9	2	5	7	4	3	1

Spidoku

Page 21

High-Speed Crossword

P	A	T		P	A	M		A	B	S
A	R	I		E	G	O		J	O	E
P	U	M		P	I	N		A	R	T
A	G	E			L	E	A	R	N	S
Y	U	L		H	E	Y	S			
A	L	I	K	E		B	A	M		
		A	N	N	A		E	L	A	N
		E	E	L		L	E	G	A	L
		E	T	A	T		A	M	I	
S	A	Y	S	H	I		Z	E	N	
A	D	O		S	K	I		I	T	I
G	A	G		P	E	C		N	A	N
A	M	A		A	N	Y		E	G	G

Wordsearch Workout

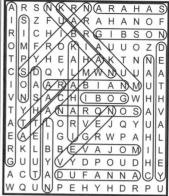

Double Fun Sudoku

Tasty Teaser

6	4	7	5	8	3	1	2	9
2	3	1	7	4	9	6	5	8
9	8	5	1	6	2	7	4	3
5	1	8	2	7	6	3	9	4
4	7	2	3	9	1	8	6	5
3	9	6	4	5	8	2	1	7
1	6	4	8	3	5	9	7	2
7	2	3	9	1	4	5	8	6
8	5	9	6	2	7	4	3	1

Brain Buster

9	4	1	2	5	8	3	7	6
3	8	5	6	7	9	1	4	2
7	6	2	4	1	3	9	5	8
5	3	4	7	8	2	6	9	1
1	2	6	5	9	4	8	3	7
8	9	7	1	3	6	4	2	5
6	1	3	9	2	7	5	8	4
2	5	8	3	4	1	7	6	9
4	7	9	8	6	5	2	1	3

Matchstick Magic

The matchsticks which have been moved are outlined.

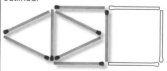

Brain Teaser

6859 − They are cube numbers:
16^3 = 4096
17^3 = 4913
18^3 = 5832
19^3 = 6859

Domino Placement

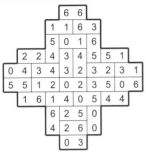

Page 22

Codeword Conundrum

W	A	S	H	B	A	S	I	N		T	A	P	E	R
A		N		L		H		E		A		I		E
G	U	A	N	O		A	V	A	R	I	C	E		P
E		K		N		L		T		L		C		U
S	T	E	A	D	I	L	Y		A	S	P	E	C	T
		B		E		A		P		E				E
S	H	I	N		A	C	Q	U	A	I	N	T	E	D
C		T		Z		A		N		N		E		L
A	M	E	L	I	O	R	A	T	E		A	R	M	Y
R			G		D			U		M				
E	F	F	I	G	Y		J	A	U	N	D	I	C	E
C		E		U		D		L		A		N		P
R		M	A	R	T	I	N	I		B	R	A	V	O
O		U		A		V		A		L		T		X
W	O	R	S	T		A	U	S	T	E	R	E	L	Y

Double Fun Sudoku

Tasty Teaser

1	3	6	8	9	4	5	7	2
4	5	7	2	3	1	6	8	9
9	2	8	5	7	6	3	4	1
3	8	2	7	4	9	1	6	5
6	4	5	1	8	3	2	9	7
7	1	9	6	5	2	4	3	8
2	7	1	3	6	8	9	5	4
5	9	3	4	1	7	8	2	6
8	6	4	9	2	5	7	1	3

Brain Buster

9	2	7	3	8	1	5	6	4
5	6	8	2	9	4	1	7	3
3	4	1	7	6	5	2	8	9
1	3	2	9	4	8	7	5	6
4	7	5	6	3	2	8	9	1
6	8	9	1	5	7	3	4	2
7	9	6	8	1	3	4	2	5
2	1	4	5	7	9	6	3	8
8	5	3	4	2	6	9	1	7

Pyramid Plus

A=22, B=58, C=99, D=75, E=119, F=80, G=157, H=174, I=194, J=237, K=331, L=368, M=568, N=699, O=1267.

High-Speed Crossword

N	A	P	E		E	M	B	L	E	M
E	S	A	U		M	A	L	A	W	I
C	H	U	G		E	L	A	T	E	D
K	Y	L	E		R	I	M			
		A	N	T	I		E	B	A	Y
N	O	D	E	A	L		S	O	L	O
O	R	E		B	L	T		B	A	D
U	S	E	S		A	R	A	B	I	A
N	O	N	O		G	A	R	Y		
			L	E	A		A	F	R	O
B	R	I	D	E	S		B	L	O	W
R	E	V	E	L	S		L	A	M	E
A	V	E	R	S	E		E	Y	E	S

1 Minute Number Crunch

Beginner

71 − 22 = 49, 49 x 2 = 98, 98 + 26 = 124, 50% of 124 = 62, 62 + 19 = 81, 81 ÷ 3 = 27, 27 x 2 = 54

Intermediate

59 x 3 = 177, 177 − 114 = 63, 63 + 21 (63 ÷ 3) = 84, 84 ÷ 12 x 5 = 35, 35 ÷ 7 x 3 = 15, 15 x 13 = 195, 195 + 85 = 280

Advanced

52 ÷ 13 x 7 = 28, 28 x 9 = 252, 252 ÷ 6 = 42, 42^2 = 1764, 1764 − 1323 (1764 ÷ 4 x 3) = 441, 441 ÷ 9 x 5 = 245, 245 + 147 (60% of 245) = 392

Page 23

High-Speed Crossword

L	I	M	B	S		S	C	R	A	M
A	C	U	R	A		C	H	I	L	I
T	H	R	O	W	T	H	I	N	G	S
H	I	D		E	R	E		G	O	S
A	R	E		D	I	M		I	R	E
M	O	R	T		B	E	A	N	E	D
			R	O	U	S	T			
L	A	T	E	N	T		M	O	P	S
O	R	E		E	A	T		V	I	A
A	C	E		S	R	I		E	L	F
T	H	I	R	T	Y	T	H	R	E	E
H	E	N	N	A		L	U	L	U	S
E	D	G	A	R		E	G	Y	P	T

1 Minute Number Crunch

Beginner

36 ÷ 12 = 3, 3 x 20 = 60, 60 + 3 = 63, 63 ÷ 21 = 3, 3 x 19 = 57, 57 + 18 = 75, 75 ÷ 3 = 25

Intermediate

13 x 9 = 117, 117 + 414 = 531, 531 ÷ 9 x 5 = 295, 295 ÷ 5 = 59, 59 + 63 = 122, 122 x 5 = 610, 610 ÷ 10 x 9 = 549

Advanced

26^3 = 17576, 17576 ÷ 8 x 3 = 6591, 6591 + 4394 (6591 ÷ 3 x 2) = 10985, 60% of 10985 = 6591, 6591 − 4607 = 1984, 1984 ÷ 16 x 5 = 620, 620 ÷ 5 x 3 = 372

Wordsearch Workout

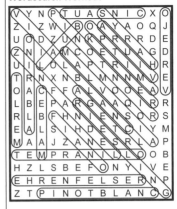

Double Fun Sudoku

Tasty Teaser

8	7	1	4	5	3	2	9	6
3	2	4	7	6	9	5	8	1
6	9	5	1	8	2	3	4	7
7	5	6	2	9	4	8	1	3
2	1	9	8	3	5	7	6	4
4	3	8	6	1	7	9	2	5
1	4	2	5	7	8	6	3	9
5	8	3	9	4	6	1	7	2
9	6	7	3	2	1	4	5	8

Brain Buster

7	2	3	8	4	5	9	1	6
1	9	5	3	6	2	4	7	8
4	8	6	7	1	9	3	2	5
2	3	4	9	8	6	1	5	7
9	6	8	5	7	1	2	3	4
5	1	7	2	3	4	6	8	9
3	4	1	6	5	7	8	9	2
6	7	9	1	2	8	5	4	3
8	5	2	4	9	3	7	6	1

Whatever Next?

P – Assign a number to each letter according to its place in the alphabet. Working clockwise from the top, add the two together, so A+B(1+2)=3, A+E(1+5)=6, C+F(3+6)=9, etc. E=5, so P(16) is needed to make the final figure to 21, and E+P=21.

Brain Teaser

133

Page 24

Mind Over Matter

The sum total of the values of the letters in each diagonal line of three are all equal. Thus the missing value is 16, so the missing letter is P.

Double Fun Sudoku

Tasty Teaser

9	2	8	3	6	5	1	7	4
1	3	7	4	2	8	9	5	6
5	4	6	7	9	1	8	3	2
6	8	4	1	7	2	3	9	5
7	1	5	6	3	9	2	4	8
2	9	3	8	5	4	6	1	7
3	5	2	9	8	7	4	6	1
8	6	1	5	4	3	7	2	9
4	7	9	2	1	6	5	8	3

Brain Buster

2	8	7	3	9	6	1	4	5
9	3	5	1	8	4	6	7	2
1	6	4	2	7	5	3	8	9
5	2	8	7	4	1	9	3	6
4	1	9	8	6	3	5	2	7
6	7	3	9	5	2	4	1	8
3	9	1	5	2	7	8	6	4
7	5	6	4	1	8	2	9	3
8	4	2	6	3	9	7	5	1

Codeword Conundrum

W	H	E	L	P		M	O	T	H	P	R	O	O	F
A		X		E		E		H		E				R
I	N	T	E	R	C	E	D	E		S	E	P	I	A
S		R		V		K		M		E		E		N
T	R	A	V	E	L		E	S	O	T	E	R	I	C
B		R		L		E		A		J				
A	T	O	M	S		U	G	L	Y		Q	U	A	D
N		R		E		X		V		D		R		A
D	I	G	S		P	U	R	E		E	M	E	R	Y
		A		B		R		S		C		L		
A	M	N	I	O	T	I	C		G	E	M	I	N	I
P		Z		N		A		W		M		N		G
P	L	A	Y	S		N	A	I	L	B	R	U	S	H
L				A		C		T		E		R		T
E	M	P	T	I	N	E	S	S		R	E	E	D	S

High-Speed Crossword

N	T	H		F	R	O		S	P	A
I	R	A		E	E	N		H	A	M
P	E	T	E	R	C	O	Y	O	T	E
S	E	S	A	M	E		O	P	E	N
			T	I	D	Y	U	P		
S	E	M	I		E	A	S	E	L	S
E	C	O	N	O		M	A	R	I	E
T	O	N	G	U	E		I	S	L	E
		G	O	T	M	A	D			
A	S	O	F		P	R	I	E	S	T
W	O	L	F	B	L	I	T	Z	E	R
E	L	I		E	O	S		R	E	O
S	E	A		D	Y	E		A	M	Y

1 Minute Number Crunch

Beginner

$36 \div 6 = 6$, $6 \times 17 = 102$, $102 - 86 = 16$, $16 \times 4 = 64$,
$64 \div 16 \times 5 = 20$, $20 + 48 = 68$, $68 \times 2 = 136$

Intermediate

$1215 \div 5 = 243$, $243 \div 27 = 9$, $9 + 5$ $(9 \div 9 \times 5) = 14$,
$14 \div 7 \times 3 = 6$, $6 + 4$ $(6 \div 3 \times 2) = 10$, 950% of $10 = 95$,
$95 + 36 = 131$

Advanced

$13 \times 24 = 312$, $312 \div 12 \times 5 = 130$, $130 + 117$ $(130 \div 10 \times 9) = 247$, $247 \div 13 \times 6 = 114$, $114 + 76$ $(114 \div 3 \times 2) = 190$, $190 \times 4 = 760$, $760 \div 8 \times 3 = 285$

Page 25

Battleship Bout

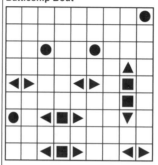

High-Speed Crossword

O	W	L		A	T	E		L	E	G
N	O	I		T	A	R		I	V	E
C	O	S	M	O	K	R	A	M	E	R
E	L	A	I	N	E		P	O	R	E
			L	E	O	N	A			
A	W	O	L		N	O	R	M	A	L
L	E	V	I	S		S	T	A	R	E
A	B	A	C	U	S		F	E	E	D
			E	N	T	E	R			
S	P	I	N		A	L	O	H	A	S
C	A	T	T	Y	R	E	M	A	R	K
A	P	E		E	T	C		L	E	E
R	A	M		E	S	T		L	A	W

Wordwheel

The nine-letter word is: CURRENTLY

Wordsearch Workout

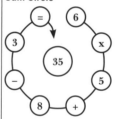

Double Fun Sudoku

Tasty Teaser

9	6	2	3	1	8	7	5	4
1	3	7	5	2	4	9	8	6
4	8	5	7	9	6	2	3	1
6	5	1	4	7	3	8	2	9
3	2	4	9	8	5	1	6	7
8	7	9	2	6	1	5	4	3
7	9	3	6	5	2	4	1	8
2	4	8	1	3	7	6	9	5
5	1	6	8	4	9	3	7	2

Brain Buster

7	9	6	3	4	1	2	5	8
5	8	2	6	9	7	1	4	3
3	1	4	5	2	8	9	6	7
6	7	9	4	1	3	8	2	5
4	3	1	2	8	5	7	9	6
2	5	8	9	7	6	3	1	4
1	4	3	8	5	2	6	7	9
9	6	7	1	3	4	5	8	2
8	2	5	7	6	9	4	3	1

Sum Circle

```
      =        6
   3                x
          35
   −                5
      8        +
```

Page 26

1 Minute Number Crunch

Beginner

$63 - 22 = 41$, $41 \times 2 = 82$, $82 - 16 = 66$, $66 \div 3 = 22$,
$22 + 10 = 32$, $32 \div 4 = 8$, $8 + 88 = 96$

Intermediate

$21 \div 7 \times 3 = 9$, $9 \times 6 = 54$, $54 \div 2 = 27$, $27 \times 7 = 189$,
$189 + 422 = 611$, $611 \times 2 = 1222$, $1222 - 649 = 573$

Advanced

$61 \div 0.5 = 122$, $122 \times 12 = 1464$, $1464 \div 0.6 = 2440$,
$2440 \div 8 \times 3 = 915$, $915 + 244$ $(915 \div 15 \times 4) = 1159$,
$1159 \times 2 = 2318$, $2318 - 978 = 1340$

High-Speed Crossword

I	N	K		A	R	K		A	B	S
R	A	N		B	E	N		F	A	T
A	M	E	R	I	C	A		E	R	A
		E	A	T		P	O	W	E	R
C	O	P	Y		A	S	K			
A	N	A		K	R	A	C	K	E	L
L	E	D		N	B	C		N	A	E
M	I	S	T	O	O	K		I	S	T
			V	C	R		I	C	E	S
F	L	A	S	K		O	A	K		
L	A	X		O	A	T	M	E	A	L
A	C	E		U	N	I		R	B	I
W	E	D		T	Y	S		S	E	T

Codeword Conundrum

S	H	E	I	K	H		E	S	C	A	P	A	D	E
U		M		I		J		L		W		L		N
R	I	P	E	N		U	N	A	D	A	P	T	E	D
V		E		D	U	D		K		I		A		O
E	A	R		E		O	V	E	R	T	H	R	E	W
Y		O		S		O		O				N		
S	C	R	A	T	C	H	Y		D	A	R	I	N	G
	H		L		O		A		E		D		U	
L	A	Z	I	L	Y		G	E	O	D	E	S	I	C
	I		B		P		E		U		U		O	
A	N	T	I	Q	U	A	R	Y		L		P	A	N
M		H		U		C		O	I	L		P		N
I	N	E	X	A	C	T	L	Y		A	B	O	D	E
S		I		F		O		O		R		S		C
S	U	R	E	F	I	R	E		A	D	V	E	N	T

Double Fun Sudoku

Tasty Teaser

4	3	7	1	9	2	8	5	6
9	6	2	8	5	4	3	7	1
5	1	8	3	6	7	2	9	4
1	4	9	7	2	8	5	6	3
6	2	5	4	3	9	1	8	7
8	7	3	5	1	6	9	4	2
2	9	1	6	4	5	7	3	8
3	8	4	9	7	1	6	2	5
7	5	6	2	8	3	4	1	9

Brain Buster

7	1	3	4	6	5	2	9	8
9	2	4	1	8	7	6	3	5
5	8	6	2	3	9	4	7	1
2	3	9	5	7	4	1	8	6
8	6	7	3	2	1	9	5	4
1	4	5	8	9	6	3	2	7
6	9	8	7	1	2	5	4	3
3	5	2	6	4	8	7	1	9
4	7	1	9	5	3	8	6	2

Spidoku

Page 27

High-Speed Crossword

M	A	S	S		P	U	S	H	U	P
A	N	O	N		E	S	T	A	T	E
I	N	F	O		L	E	A	D	E	R
N	E	T		M	O	S	T			
E	X	T	R	A	S		S	H	E	A
		A	U	D	I	T		A	V	A
F	A	C	E	T		O	P	R	A	H
E	G	O		V	O	T	E	D		
W	E	S	T		P	E	N	C	I	L
		I	D	E	S		I	R	A	
C	O	N	M	A	N		I	D	O	S
B	R	E	E	Z	E		M	E	N	S
S	E	E	R	E	D		O	R	S	O

Wordsearch Workout

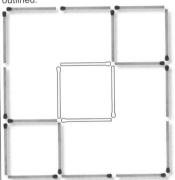

Double Fun Sudoku

Tasty Teaser

4	6	3	7	9	1	2	8	5
2	8	1	6	5	3	7	4	9
7	5	9	4	2	8	6	1	3
6	9	2	1	7	4	5	3	8
1	7	5	8	3	2	9	6	4
3	4	8	9	6	5	1	7	2
5	1	6	3	8	9	4	2	7
9	3	4	2	1	7	8	5	6
8	2	7	5	4	6	3	9	1

Brain Buster

2	4	1	5	6	3	7	9	8
8	3	7	9	1	4	5	2	6
9	6	5	2	7	8	3	4	1
5	9	2	6	3	1	4	8	7
1	8	4	7	2	5	9	6	3
3	7	6	8	4	9	2	1	5
7	1	8	4	5	2	6	3	9
4	5	9	3	8	6	1	7	2
6	2	3	1	9	7	8	5	4

Matchstick Magic

The matchsticks which have been moved are outlined.

Brain Teaser

7% – Single per pair = €3.50
Pack per pair = €3.25
Saving per pair = €0.25

1 Minute Number Crunch

Beginner
104 + 17 = 121, 121 ÷ 11 x 2 = 22, 22 x 4 = 88, 88 – 16 = 72, 72 ÷ 6 x 5 = 60, 60 + 90 = 150, 150 ÷ 3 = 50

Intermediate
390 ÷ 10 x 7 = 273, 273 ÷ 3 x 2 = 182, 182 x 2 = 364, 75% of 364 = 273, 273 – 87 = 186, 186 ÷ 6 = 31, 31 x 12 = 372

Advanced
293 + 739 = 1032, 1032 – 645 (1032 ÷ 8 x 5) = 387, 387 ÷ 9 x 2 = 86, 86 x 7 = 602, 602 ÷ 14 x 5 = 215, 215 + 129 (215 ÷ 5 x 3) = 344, 275% of 344 = 946

Page 28

Codeword Conundrum

H	A	R	D	S	H	I	P		J	I	N	X	E	D
	B		R		A		L	E	A		A		U	
B	E	D	A	Z	Z	L	E		M	A	P	P	E	D
	T		K		E		A		R		U			
P		N	E	O	L	I	T	H	I	C		T	A	D
I		E		V		M		A		H		R		E
Q	U	I	V	E	R	I	N	G		I	D	E	A	L
U		G		R		T		G		T		F		I
A	C	H	E	D		A	W	A	K	E	N	I	N	G
N		B		R		T		R		C		E		H
T	W	O		A	N	E	C	D	O	T	E	S		T
	U		W		H		U		N		W			
S	H	R	A	N	K		O	M	N	I	V	O	R	E
E		G		I	L	K		C		O		E		
A	P	P	E	N	D		E	V	E	R	Y	O	N	E

Double Fun Sudoku

Tasty Teaser

9	7	8	1	3	6	5	4	2
5	1	3	2	7	4	8	6	9
4	6	2	9	5	8	7	3	1
2	9	5	4	1	7	6	8	3
6	3	1	5	8	9	4	2	7
8	4	7	6	2	3	9	1	5
1	2	9	8	4	5	3	7	6
7	8	6	3	9	2	1	5	4
3	5	4	7	6	1	2	9	8

Brain Buster

8	1	2	7	6	5	9	4	3
4	5	9	2	3	1	8	7	6
3	7	6	8	9	4	2	5	1
2	4	5	3	8	9	6	1	7
9	8	7	5	1	6	3	2	4
1	6	3	4	7	2	5	9	8
5	2	8	6	4	7	1	3	9
7	3	1	9	5	8	4	6	2
6	9	4	1	2	3	7	8	5

Pyramid Plus

A=84, B=77, C=21, D=53, E=6, F=161, G=98, H=74, I=59, J=259, K=172, L=133, M=431, N=305, O=736.

High-Speed Crossword

B	R	E	W	S			A	R	M	S
R	O	Y	A	L		D	E	E	P	
O	N	E	S	I	E		D	A	L	E
		E	N	D	S		O	P	E	N
T	E	X	T		S	U	N	S	E	T
A	V	A		P	A	S	S			
G	E	M		A	Y	E		P	E	W
			A	N	T	S		O	R	E
S	A	L	U	T	E		S	P	E	D
C	L	O	T		S	H	A	Q		
R	O	T	H		T	E	N	U	R	E
U	N	T	O		A	T	I	O	N	
B	E	A	R		D	O	Z	E	S	

1 Minute Number Crunch

Beginner

234 − 6 = 228, 50% of 228 = 114, 114 − 96 = 18, 18 ÷ 9 x 4 = 8, 8^2 = 64, 64 ÷ 4 = 16, 16 x 2 = 32

Intermediate

49 x 2 = 98, 98 − 19 = 79, 79 x 3 = 237, 237 − 109 = 128, 128 ÷ 8 = 16, 16 x 1.5 = 24, 24 ÷ 8 x 5 = 15

Advanced

5 x 5 x 9 = 225, square root of 225 = 15, 15 x 39 = 585, 585 + 260 (585 ÷ 9 x 4) = 845, 845 ÷ 5 = 169, 169 − 77 = 92, 92 x 3.75 = 345

Page 29

High-Speed Crossword

M	A	G	S			A	G	L	O	W
A	N	A	T			G	U	I	D	E
I	N	G	A		P	E	N	C	I	L
D	A	G	G	E	R	S		E	N	D
			I	S	L	A				
O	F	F			I	N	N		J	F	K
W	E	T		S	K	I		O	R	E
E	D	S		E	C	O		K	I	N
			A	B	L	E				
P	U	N		F	L	E	A	B	A	G
A	N	I	M	A	L		N	O	N	O
S	I	N	A	I		D	O	T	O	
S	T	A	R	R			S	K	I	N

Domino Placement

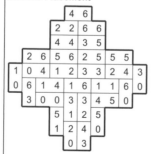

Wordsearch Workout

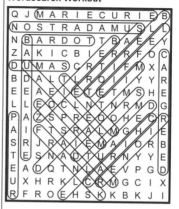

Double Fun Sudoku

Tasty Teaser

5	9	4	2	1	6	3	8	7
1	7	6	3	8	9	5	2	4
8	2	3	5	7	4	6	1	9
2	3	8	7	9	1	4	6	5
6	5	9	8	4	2	1	7	3
7	4	1	6	3	5	8	9	2
4	6	5	1	2	7	9	3	8
9	8	2	4	6	3	7	5	1
3	1	7	9	5	8	2	4	6

Brain Buster

1	6	7	4	5	3	8	9	2
8	4	3	6	2	9	7	1	5
5	9	2	1	7	8	3	6	4
4	2	5	3	9	1	6	7	8
7	8	9	2	4	6	5	3	1
3	1	6	7	8	5	2	4	9
6	3	8	9	1	2	4	5	7
2	7	1	5	3	4	9	8	6
9	5	4	8	6	7	1	2	3

Whatever Next?

B – Assign a number to each letter according to its place in the alphabet, so E=5, L=12, P=16, S=19 and Z=26. Then take the lowest number from the highest in the point directly opposite to give the centre total, so the missing letter is B (=2).

Brain Teaser

Tuesday

Page 30

Mind Over Matter

The sum total of the letters in all five boxes is 60. Thus the missing value is 14, so the missing letter is N.

Double Fun Sudoku

Tasty Teaser

3	6	8	4	2	5	7	9	1
5	4	2	1	9	7	3	6	8
7	1	9	6	3	8	4	5	2
6	8	4	2	5	9	1	3	7
1	2	3	7	8	6	9	4	5
9	5	7	3	1	4	2	8	6
8	9	1	5	7	3	6	2	4
4	7	5	9	6	2	8	1	3
2	3	6	8	4	1	5	7	9

Brain Buster

8	6	2	4	3	7	9	1	5
7	3	1	8	5	9	6	4	2
4	5	9	2	6	1	8	3	7
2	9	3	5	8	4	1	7	6
1	8	4	3	7	6	2	5	9
6	7	5	1	9	2	4	8	3
9	1	8	7	2	5	3	6	4
5	4	6	9	1	3	7	2	8
3	2	7	6	4	8	5	9	1

Codeword Conundrum

```
O V E R W O R K ▪ H I ▪ C
Z ▪ L ▪ U ▪ T U R N E R
E N J O Y M E N T ▪ M ▪ S ▪ E
B ▪ Q ▪ A ▪ I N B O U N D
R E P U G N A N T ▪ U ▪ L ▪ I
A ▪ E ▪ I ▪ L E G ▪ A ▪ T
▪ H A N D S O M E ▪ S P R E E
T ▪ C ▪ E ▪ S ▪ R ▪ D
A N G E L ▪ S T I C K I N G
X ▪ A ▪ O W L ▪ R ▪ N ▪ M
A ▪ I ▪ G ▪ E N D O S C O P Y
T E N S I L E ▪ U ▪ I ▪ R
I ▪ F ▪ C ▪ K I D N A P P E R
O C U L A R ▪ L ▪ G ▪ L ▪ H
N ▪ L ▪ L ▪ B L U E B E L L
```

High-Speed Crossword

```
L I F E S ▪ A S T O
A G E N T ▪ S P A R
B E T T Y W H I T E
S T A R ▪ H E N
▪ I S A ▪ S A G A
A C C E P T S ▪ B O X
W O R S E ▪ A C U T E
E R A ▪ D A K O T A S
D E M O ▪ P E R
▪ L O P ▪ O R E O
C L I N T B L A C K
H A V E ▪ A L P H A
I D E S ▪ N A T T Y
```

1 Minute Number Crunch

Beginner
38 + 212 = 250, 250 ÷ 10 = 25, 25 x 7 = 175, 175 ÷ 5 = 35, 35 x 2 = 70, 70 − 7 = 63, 63 ÷ 9 x 2 = 14

Intermediate
424 − 148 = 276, 276 ÷ 3 x 2 = 184, 184 x 3 = 552, 552 ÷ 4 x 3 = 414, 414 ÷ 9 x 8 = 368, 368 ÷ 2 = 184, 184 + 129 = 313

Advanced
29^3 = 24389, 24389 − 15497 = 8892, 8892 ÷ 4 x 3 = 6669, 6669 ÷ 9 x 5 = 3705, 3705 ÷ 15 x 7 = 1729, 1729 x 2 = 3458, 3458 − 2569 = 889

Page 31

1 Minute Number Crunch

Beginner
25% of 104 = 26, 26 x 2 = 52, 52 + 53 = 105, 105 ÷ 5 = 21, 21 + 19 = 40, 40 ÷ 4 = 10, 10 x 39 = 390

Intermediate
127 + 43 = 170, 170 + 34 (20% of 170) = 204, 204 ÷ 4 = 51, 51 ÷ 3 = 17, 17 + 283 = 300, 31% of 300 = 93, 93 − 67 = 26

Advanced
43 x 7 = 301, 301 + 199 = 500, 69% of 500 = 345, 345 ÷ 15 x 9 = 207, 207 + 23 x 17 = 153, 153 ÷ 9 x 4 = 68, 68 x 7 = 476

High-Speed Crossword

```
P E P ▪ K F C ▪ A P P
O R E ▪ E L L I P S E
T R A C Y A U S T I N
▪ A S T E R
H A S T ▪ A S A P
A R I ▪ H A V E A G O
S T E V E D A L L A S
P I G I R O N ▪ V I E
S E E S ▪ Y E N S
▪ I T S M E
M A T T H O U S T O N
E R A S E R S ▪ A W E
W E B ▪ M E T ▪ D E W
```

Wordwheel

The nine-letter word is: MINUSCULE

Wordsearch Workout

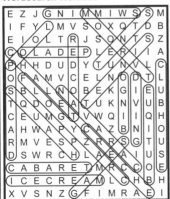

Double Fun Sudoku

Tasty Teaser

8	2	3	5	6	7	9	4	1
4	9	7	2	1	8	3	6	5
5	6	1	3	4	9	2	7	8
6	7	5	4	2	1	8	3	9
9	4	8	7	5	3	6	1	2
3	1	2	8	9	6	7	5	4
2	3	9	1	7	4	5	8	6
1	8	6	9	3	5	4	2	7
7	5	4	6	8	2	1	9	3

Brain Buster

4	8	7	3	2	5	9	1	6
1	6	2	4	7	9	5	3	8
3	5	9	1	8	6	7	2	4
5	2	3	9	1	4	6	8	7
8	7	1	6	5	2	3	4	9
6	9	4	7	3	8	2	5	1
2	4	5	8	9	7	1	6	3
9	1	6	2	4	3	8	7	5
7	3	8	5	6	1	4	9	2

Sum Circle

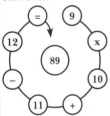

Page 32

1 Minute Number Crunch

Beginner
92 + 18 = 110, 110 ÷ 10 = 11, 11 + 38 = 49, 49 ÷ 7 = 7, 7 + 56 = 63, 63 ÷ 9 x 2 = 14, 14 + 88 = 102

Intermediate
32 x 5 = 160, 160 + 16 = 176, 176 ÷ 4 = 44, 44 ÷ 11 x 5 = 20, 20 x 4.5 = 90, 90 ÷ 5 = 18, 18 x 3 = 54

Advanced
221 x 6 = 1326, 1326 ÷17 x 6 = 468, 468 + 1427 = 1895, 1895 − 379 = 1516, 75% of 1516 = 1137, 1137 x 5 = 5685, 5685 + 2274 (40% of 5685) = 7959

High-Speed Crossword

M	A	Y	A	S		A	G	E	S
A	D	O	B	E		P	E	R	T
D	O	U	B	L	E	P	L	A	Y
		E	L	S	E				
C	L	A	Y		T	A	R	G	E	T
R	A	T			R	I	N	S	E
I	D	E	A		M	O	S	S
S	L	U	R	P		M	E	T
S	E	P	T	I	C		S	E	X	Y
		G	A	G	A				
T	R	I	P	L	E	J	U	M	P
H	E	R	E		M	A	R	I	A
E	V	E	N		S	K	I	L	L

Codeword Conundrum

C	R	A	Y	O	N		P	R	O	J	E	C	T	S
R		V		R		I		O		H				M
E	X	E	R	C	I	S	E	S		I	M	A	G	E
E		R		H		O		L		N				L
P	L	A	T	E	A	U		E	X	T	I	N	C	T
		G		S		T		E					E	
W	H	E	A	T		H	O	P	E	F	U	L	L	Y
A				R		W		R		R			E	
S	U	B	M	A	R	I	N	E		E	X	I	S	T
T		L				D		R		Q		N		
S	E	A	S	I	D	E		R	O	U	T	I	N	E
T		Z		N		A		O		E		T		D
A	L	I	E	N		S	H	R	I	N	K	I	N	G
I		N		E		A				C		A		E
R	E	G	A	R	D	E	D		C	Y	C	L	E	D

Double Fun Sudoku

Tasty Teaser

9	7	5	2	3	8	1	6	4
6	4	2	7	9	1	3	8	5
3	1	8	4	6	5	9	7	2
7	6	4	8	2	9	5	1	3
2	5	3	6	1	7	8	4	9
8	9	1	5	4	3	7	2	6
5	2	7	9	8	4	6	3	1
4	3	9	1	7	6	2	5	8
1	8	6	3	5	2	4	9	7

Brain Buster

2	5	4	1	9	6	3	8	7
7	8	1	4	5	3	2	6	9
3	6	9	7	8	2	4	1	5
1	9	8	3	4	7	5	2	6
5	4	7	6	2	8	9	3	1
6	2	3	5	1	9	7	4	8
8	7	5	2	6	4	1	9	3
4	3	6	9	7	1	8	5	2
9	1	2	8	3	5	6	7	4

Spidoku

Page 33

High-Speed Crossword

U	Z	I
T	A	Z		P	A	R		Z	I	P
A	V	I		A	C	E		S	R	I
E	I	G	H	T	H		L	A	K	E
	A	G	E		A	T	O	Z
S	T	Y	X		R	O	U	S	E	D
P	O	M		B	Y	E		A	V	E
A	R	A	R	A	T		T	G	I	F
	R	I	T	A		H	A	L
Y	E	L	P		Y	O	U	B	E	T
A	R	E		A	L	L		O	Y	L
K	E	Y		S	O	D		R	E	C
		I	R	S

Wordsearch Workout

L	E	I	Y	B	Y	R	R	S	W	V	S	W
E	A	N	I	G	E	R	A	U	B	A	N	X
E	D	Y	I	H	M	S	U	K	C	N	H	M
Q	Y	M	R	G	K	O	X	B	U	C	O	J
Z	U	Q	O	A	N	O	N	N	D	O	J	A
Z	B	E	T	N	G	Y	T	T	S	U	T	S
B	G	O	B	D	T	L	M	N	R	V	S	P
W	O	E	V	E	E	O	A	E	O	E	M	E
N	C	L	P	R	C	F	N	C	S	R	A	R
W	I	W	Z	I	N	U	V	I	K	Q	O	L
M	Q	T	H	U	N	D	E	R	B	A	Y	T
B	L	O	N	D	O	N	U	H	W	P	U	A
V	C	F	A	X	A	F	I	L	A	H	F	L
V	I	C	T	O	R	I	A	W	A	T	T	O
I	C	R	G	C	H	U	R	C	H	I	L	L

Double Fun Sudoku

Tasty Teaser

3	1	8	4	7	9	5	6	2
4	2	9	1	5	6	3	8	7
7	6	5	3	8	2	1	4	9
8	9	4	5	3	1	7	2	6
6	3	2	8	9	7	4	5	1
5	7	1	2	6	4	9	3	8
2	4	3	7	1	8	6	9	5
9	8	7	6	4	5	2	1	3
1	5	6	9	2	3	8	7	4

Brain Buster

7	1	9	6	2	5	3	4	8
5	8	3	4	9	7	2	6	1
4	2	6	8	1	3	5	9	7
8	3	2	9	6	1	4	7	5
1	9	4	7	5	2	6	8	3
6	5	7	3	4	8	9	1	2
9	7	8	2	3	6	1	5	4
3	4	5	1	8	9	7	2	6
2	6	1	5	7	4	8	3	9

Matchstick Magic

The matchsticks which have been moved are outlined.

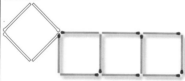

Brain Teaser

E = 36 – Multiply the number of sides by three.

Simple as A, B, C

B	C	A	B	A	C
C	B	B	C	A	A
C	C	A	A	B	B
A	A	C	C	B	B
A	B	B	A	C	C
B	A	C	B	C	A

Page 34

Codeword Conundrum

P	A	R	T	I	C	L	E		Q	U	A	R	T	O
	R		I		A		N		U		L			B
L	U	M	B	A	R		G	L	I	M	P	S	E	S
	M		I		A		U		Z		H			O
E		J	A	Y	W	A	L	K		N	A	S	A	L
X		U		A			F	O	X	Y		U		E
H	O	M	O	N	Y	M		A		M	I	N	U	S
I		B		A		A		L		P		B		C
L	I	L	A	C		R		A	C	H	I	E	V	E
A		E		R	E	S	T		E		A		N	
R	I	D	G	E		H	O	O	D	L	U	M		
A		U		O			I		R		A			
T	E	A	T	O	W	E	L		L	I	B	I	D	O
E				S		E		L		A		Z		
S	W	A	Y	E	D		T	R	A	I	N	E	E	S

Double Fun Sudoku

Tasty Teaser

7	5	9	2	4	6	3	8	1
3	6	2	7	8	1	5	9	4
1	4	8	9	5	3	6	7	2
6	1	4	3	9	7	8	2	5
2	7	5	1	6	8	4	3	9
9	8	3	5	2	4	1	6	7
5	3	6	4	7	2	9	1	8
8	9	7	6	1	5	2	4	3
4	2	1	8	3	9	7	5	6

Brain Buster

8	9	2	7	5	6	3	4	1
3	1	6	2	9	4	7	8	5
4	5	7	8	3	1	6	9	2
7	6	1	9	8	2	5	3	4
9	8	5	4	6	3	2	1	7
2	4	3	5	1	7	9	6	8
6	7	8	3	4	5	1	2	9
1	2	9	6	7	8	4	5	3
5	3	4	1	2	9	8	7	6

Pyramid Plus

A=121, B=25, C=96, D=67, E=126, F=146, G=121, H=163, I=193, J=267, K=284, L=356, M=551, N=640, O=1191.

High-Speed Crossword

W	A	S	H		C	A	D	D	I	E
A	N	T	E		A	R	R	I	V	E
S	T	A	R		R	E	A	D	E	R
P	I	T	T		M	A	C			
		E	Z	R	A		U	P	T	O
E	L	F		E	X	P	L	A	I	N
G	O	A	L	S		E	A	R	L	Y
A	V	I	A	T	O	R		T	E	X
D	E	R	N		R	U	B	Y		
		C	U	D		A	F	A	R	
P	A	Y	O	L	A		R	O	S	A
A	L	U	M	N	I		Q	U	I	P
D	E	M	E	A	N		S	L	A	T

1 Minute Number Crunch

Beginner
57 + 17 = 74, 74 ÷ 2 = 37, 37 + 19 = 56, 56 ÷ 4 = 14, 14 reversed = 41, 41 + 55 = 96, 25% of 96 = 24

Intermediate
23 x 11 = 253, 253 − 192 = 61, 61 x 4 = 244, 244 + 62 = 306, 306 ÷ 3 = 102, 102 ÷ 6 x 5 = 85, 85 + 97 = 182

Advanced
19 x 15 = 285, 285 x 3 = 855, 855 ÷ 19 x 5 = 225, 225 x 14 = 3150, 70% of 3150 = 2205, 2205 ÷ 5 x 3 = 1323, 1323 ÷ 9 x 7 = 1029

Page 35

High-Speed Crossword

M	U	S	C	L	E			M	A	R
A	N	C	H	O	R		F	O	R	E
T	E	R	E	S	A		A	R	I	S
H	A	A	S		S	E	C	E	D	E
I	S	P	S		A	T	S	E	A	
S	E	E	R		E	S	C	O	R	T
			E	A	R	T	H			
O	R	A	C	L	E		E	R	G	S
B	I	G	O	T		C	U	R	E	
T	E	R	R	O	R		K	N	O	T
U	S	E	D		A	T	E	O	U	T
S	E	E	S		P	E	R	U	S	E
E	N	D			T	A	S	T	E	R

Battleship Bout

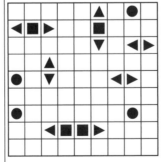

Wordsearch Workout

Double Fun Sudoku

Tasty Teaser

6	8	4	9	2	7	1	3	5
9	2	5	3	8	1	7	4	6
7	3	1	4	5	6	2	8	9
4	1	9	5	3	2	8	6	7
2	7	8	6	1	9	3	5	4
5	6	3	7	4	8	9	2	1
8	9	6	2	7	4	5	1	3
3	4	2	1	9	5	6	7	8
1	5	7	8	6	3	4	9	2

Brain Buster

8	5	1	4	6	7	3	9	2
9	2	3	5	1	8	7	6	4
7	6	4	3	9	2	5	1	8
6	8	2	9	4	5	1	3	7
1	7	5	2	3	6	8	4	9
4	3	9	8	7	1	6	2	5
5	4	7	1	2	3	9	8	6
2	1	6	7	8	9	4	5	3
3	9	8	6	5	4	2	7	1

Whatever Next?

7 – The numbers in the outer points of the star all add up to the central figure.

Brain Teaser

$207 − 72 + 3^2, + 4^2, + 5^2, + 6^2, + 7^2$

Page 36

Mind Over Matter

The value of the letter in the central square is the sum total of the values of the letters in the other squares. Thus the missing value is 24, so the missing letter is X.

Double Fun Sudoku

Tasty Teaser

8	6	7	9	1	4	2	5	3
3	2	9	7	5	8	1	6	4
4	1	5	3	2	6	8	9	7
7	3	8	2	9	5	6	4	1
2	5	4	6	7	1	3	8	9
1	9	6	8	4	3	5	7	2
6	7	3	1	8	9	4	2	5
9	4	1	5	6	2	7	3	8
5	8	2	4	3	7	9	1	6

Brain Buster

7	8	2	6	3	1	4	9	5
3	4	5	9	7	8	6	1	2
9	1	6	4	2	5	3	7	8
6	7	1	3	8	4	2	5	9
8	3	4	2	5	9	1	6	7
5	2	9	7	1	6	8	3	4
4	6	8	5	9	3	7	2	1
2	9	3	1	4	7	5	8	6
1	5	7	8	6	2	9	4	3

Codeword Conundrum

Z	E	A	L	O	T		A		H	I	J	A	C	K
O		L		H	O	N	E	Y		A		H		
N	O	B	O	D	Y		G		E		I		I	
A		I		M		S	E	N	I	L	I	T	Y	
L		N		V	E	N	T		A		N		E	
	Y	O	G	A		O		B		K	O	A	L	A
P			C	A	R	T	O	O	N		N		S	
U	M	B	R	A		M		D		I	N	E	P	T
B		E		N	E	A	R	I	N	G			Y	
L	I	G	H	T		L		C		H	U	S	K	
I		I		W		S	E	C	T		A		M	
C	O	N	Q	U	E	S	T		R		F		E	
	X		U		I		A		A	F	I	E	L	D
	E		I	R	E	N	E	W		S			A	
U	N	I	T	E	D		K		L	E	N	T	I	L

High-Speed Crossword

A	B	B	A		F	A	C	I	A	L
R	O	U	T		E	N	A	C	T	S
M	A	T	H		A	G	R	E	E	D
		T	E	S	T	E	R			
	D	E	N	Y		L	E	F	T	S
R	E	R	A	N		A	L	L	O	T
O	F	F						U	P	A
S	O	L	O	S		T	I	T	A	N
E	G	Y	P	T		A	N	T	Z	
		A	R	R	I	V	E			
U	N	I	Q	U	E		A	R	L	O
R	E	B	U	T	S		I	B	E	T
L	A	M	E	S	T		N	Y	E	T

1 Minute Number Crunch

Beginner
131 − 28 = 103, 103 x 2 = 206, 206 + 39 = 245, 245 ÷ 5 = 49, 49 ÷ 7 x 2 = 14, 14 x 6 = 84, 50% of 84 = 42

Intermediate
1947 x 2 = 3894, 3894 − 1821 = 2073, 2073 ÷ 3 = 691, 691 + 104 = 795, 795 ÷ 15 = 53, 53 x 4 = 212, 212 − 79 = 133

Advanced
330 ÷ 15 x 4 = 88, 88 ÷ 11 x 10 = 80, 80 ÷ 8 x 5 = 50, 50 x 5.5 = 275, 275 ÷ 25 x 7 = 77, 77 + 33 = 110, 110 − 77 (110 ÷ 10 x 7) = 33

Page 37

Domino Placement

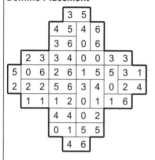

High-Speed Crossword

D	I	S	C	U	S	S		T	E	L
O	N	T	A	R	I	O		A	L	A
C	A	E	S	A	R	S	A	L	A	D
K	N	E	E	L	S		R	E	I	D
E	E	L	S			P	E	N	N	E
D	T	S		P	R	I	N	T	E	R
			S	A	U	N	A			
D	A	S	H	I	N	G		D	O	M
O	T	T	E	R		G	O	R	E	
N	E	R	D		B	E	L	L	E	S
K	A	I	S	E	R	R	O	L	L	S
E	S	P		A	I	R	B	A	S	E
Y	E	S		R	O	S	E	R	E	D

Wordwheel

The nine-letter word is: ARBORETUM

Wordsearch Workout

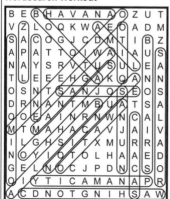

Double Fun Sudoku

Tasty Teaser

4	6	9	3	1	2	5	8	7
1	2	7	8	5	9	3	4	6
5	8	3	4	7	6	1	2	9
7	1	6	2	8	4	9	5	3*
2	9	4	5	6	3	7	1	8
3	5	8	7	9	1	2	6	4
6	4	2	1	3	7	8	9	5
9	3	5	6	2	8	4	7	1
8	7	1	9	4	5	6	3	2

Brain Buster

1	5	4	3	6	9	8	7	2
7	8	9	4	1	2	3	6	5
2	3	6	7	5	8	1	9	4
9	7	5	2	8	1	6	4	3
6	2	3	9	4	5	7	8	1
8	4	1	6	3	7	2	5	9
4	9	2	8	7	3	5	1	6
3	1	7	5	9	6	4	2	8
5	6	8	1	2	4	9	3	7

Sum Circle

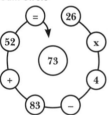

Page 38

1 Minute Number Crunch

Beginner
43 − 15 = 28, 28 ÷ 4 = 7, 7 x 3 = 21, 21 ÷ 7 = 3, 3^2 = 9, 9 + 16 = 25, 25 x 4 = 100

Intermediate
19 + 27 = 46, 46 x 3 = 138, 138 + 831 = 969, 969 ÷ 3 x 2 = 646, 646 − 259 = 387, 387 ÷ 9 x 5 = 215, 215 + 66 = 281

Advanced
425 ÷ 17 x 11 = 275, 275 ÷ 11 x 5 = 125, 125 x 0.4 = 50, 320% of 50 = 160, 160 ÷ 32 x 23 = 115, 115 + 23 x 18 = 90, 90 ÷ 0.3 = 300

High-Speed Crossword

B	R	I	B	E	S			W	I	N
O	B	O	I	S	T		L	A	D	Y
S	I	N	G	T	O		I	R	O	N
		B	E	N	I	G	N	L	Y	
	S	C	R	E	E	C	H			
B	L	U	E		S	E	T	T	E	R
S	A	J	A	K		S	L	O	M	O
S	M	O	K	E	R		U	N	I	T
		F	E	A	R	N	O	T		
A	T	L	A	N	T	I	C			
T	H	I	S		S	C	H	M	O	S
M	O	O	T		O	C	E	A	N	S
S	U	N			N	I	S	S	A	N

Codeword Conundrum

W	I	S	E	C	R	A	C	K		S	Q	U	A	D
I		E		L		U		I		C		R		E
S	H	I	N	E		D	A	N	D	E	L	I	O	N
T		Z		F		I		K		N		N		S
E	J	E	C	T	I	O	N		R	E	V	E	R	E
R		R		O		R		E		A		A		A
I		M		O	B	E	S	E		M		K		
A	C	U	M	E	N		D		N	E	P	H	E	W
	O		A		I	D	I	O	T		I		R	
	M		N		N		E		R		S		E	
L	A	P	D	O	G		R	H	Y	T	H	M	I	C
E		V		C		Y		A		A		K		
A	P	P	R	E	H	E	N	D		S	E	N	N	A
V		E		R		D		R		T		I		G
E	G	R	E	T		E	X	O	N	E	R	A	T	E

Spidoku

Double Fun Sudoku
Tasty Teaser

4	6	3	5	9	2	1	7	8
1	8	2	4	7	6	5	9	3
7	5	9	1	8	3	6	4	2
5	9	6	7	4	8	2	3	1
8	2	4	3	1	9	7	6	5
3	1	7	6	2	5	9	8	4
6	7	1	8	5	4	3	2	9
9	3	8	2	6	1	4	5	7
2	4	5	9	3	7	8	1	6

Brain Buster

5	9	8	4	3	6	2	7	1
3	2	7	9	1	5	4	6	8
6	1	4	2	8	7	9	5	3
4	8	5	1	7	9	6	3	2
9	7	6	3	5	2	1	8	4
2	3	1	8	6	4	5	9	7
8	6	9	7	2	1	3	4	5
7	5	2	6	4	3	8	1	9
1	4	3	5	9	8	7	2	6

Page 39

High-Speed Crossword

S	T	U	D	S		A	N	G	S	T
E	R	N	I	E		F	O	R	T	E
Q	U	E	E	N	O	F	M	E	A	N
U	S	A		D	N	A		E	G	O
E	S	T		S	T	I	N	K	E	R
L	E	E	K		O	R	E			
	S	N	I	P		S	W	A	B	
		T	O	N		S	C	A	M	
M	O	B	S	T	E	R		A	L	E
A	P	E		I	R	A		C	A	R
K	I	N	G	O	F	S	W	I	N	G
E	N	D	O	N		P	E	A	C	E
R	E	S	T	S		Y	E	S	E	S

Wordsearch Workout

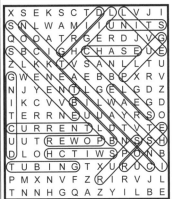

Double Fun Sudoku
Tasty Teaser

3	9	2	6	5	8	4	7	1
5	8	7	4	1	3	6	9	2
4	1	6	2	9	7	8	3	5
2	6	4	9	7	1	5	8	3
1	5	8	3	6	2	9	4	7
9	7	3	5	8	4	1	2	6
8	3	9	1	2	5	7	6	4
6	4	1	7	3	9	2	5	8
7	2	5	8	4	6	3	1	9

Brain Buster

5	8	2	9	7	4	1	3	6
7	1	4	3	6	2	8	9	5
3	6	9	8	1	5	4	7	2
4	2	3	5	9	8	6	1	7
9	7	1	4	2	6	5	8	3
6	5	8	7	3	1	2	4	9
8	4	7	6	5	3	9	2	1
1	3	6	2	4	9	7	5	8
2	9	5	1	8	7	3	6	4

Matchstick Magic

The matchsticks which have been removed are outlined.

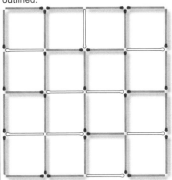

Brain Teaser

90°C

Domino Placement

```
              6 6
          5 5 5 5
          1 0 3 2
      0 2 3 4 0 0 3 2
  3 6 5 1 4 2 6 0 1 3
  2 4 3 4 4 6 5 0 6 3
    1 3 0 6 4 4 0 5
        2 1 4 1
        1 2 6 1
          2 5
```

Page 40

Codeword Conundrum

Double Fun Sudoku

Tasty Teaser

8	9	3	6	5	1	7	2	4
7	2	6	9	8	4	5	3	1
1	5	4	2	7	3	9	8	6
5	7	9	1	6	8	3	4	2
3	6	1	5	4	2	8	7	9
4	8	2	3	9	7	6	1	5
9	3	8	4	1	5	2	6	7
6	1	7	8	2	9	4	5	3
2	4	5	7	3	6	1	9	8

Brain Buster

7	8	6	4	2	9	3	1	5
5	4	9	3	6	1	2	8	7
2	3	1	8	7	5	4	6	9
8	1	5	7	4	6	9	3	2
3	6	7	1	9	2	8	5	4
4	9	2	5	3	8	6	7	1
1	5	3	2	8	4	7	9	6
9	2	8	6	5	7	1	4	3
6	7	4	9	1	3	5	2	8

Pyramid Plus

A=45, B=57, C=143, D=36, E=4, F=102, G=200, H=179, I=40, J=302, K=379, L=219, M=681, N=598, O=1279.

High-Speed Crossword

	F	A	K	E			S	A	B	R	E
	A	G	E	D			P	R	E	E	N
	B	A	N	S		P	A	E	L	L	A
R	S	T		A	R	I		M	A	C	
I	S	U		C	E	N		O	T	T	
C	I	C	A	D	A		O	N	E	S	
			K	I	C	K	O	U	T		
B	O	Y	D		N	U	R	S	E	S	
E	N	D		M	E	S		T	N	T	
A	T	E		O	S	T		A	G	O	
V	I	R	G	O	S		O	K	R	A	
E	M	B	E	R			B	E	A	T	
R	E	Y	E	S			I	S	M	S	

1 Minute Number Crunch

Beginner
22 x 7 = 154, 154 ÷ 14 = 11, 11^2 = 121, 121 + 49 = 170, 170 ÷ 10 = 17, 17 − 8 = 9, 9 x 20 = 180

Intermediate
488 ÷ 8 = 61, 61 − 17 = 44, 44 + 20 (44 ÷ 11 x 5) = 64, cube root of 64 = 4, 4 x 26 = 104, 104 ÷ 4 x 3 = 78, 78 ÷ 3 = 26

Advanced
207 x 6 = 1242, 1242 ÷ 23 x 17 = 918, 918 ÷ 18 x 7 = 357, 357 + 238 (357 ÷ 3 x 2) = 595, 595 ÷ 5 x 4 = 476, 476 ÷ 1.75 = 272, 272 x 9 = 2448

Page 41

High-Speed Crossword

E	V	E	S			D	U	S	T	S	
P	I	N	T		M	A	N	T	R	A	
I	D	E	A		I	N	D	E	E	D	
C	A	R	B	O	N	C	O	P	Y		
			G	L	U	T	E	N			
S	K	I	E	R		D	E	M	O	N	
P	E	Z				O	N	O			
A	R	E	N	A		D	A	N	E	S	
			E	D	G	I	N	G			
	G	O	L	D	E	N	G	O	A	L	
W	O	R	S	E	N		E	L	M	O	
E	N	C	O	R	E		L	I	E	N	
B	E	A	N	S			S	A	N	E	

1 Minute Number Crunch

Beginner
73 + 17 = 90, 90 ÷ 9 x 5 = 50, 50 + 8 = 58, 58 ÷ 2 = 29, 29 reversed = 92, 50% of 92 = 46, 46 + 16 = 62

Intermediate
93 x 3 = 279, 279 ÷ 9 x 5 = 155, 155 − 47 = 108, 108 ÷ 12 x 7 = 63, 63 ÷ 7 = 9, 9 x 75 = 675, 675 + 97 = 772

Advanced
104 ÷ 13 x 8 = 64, square root of 64 = 8, 8 x 72 = 576, 175% of 576 = 1008, 1008 ÷ 12 x 5 = 420, 420 + 378 (420 ÷ 10 x 9) = 798, 798 + 897 = 1695

Wordsearch Workout

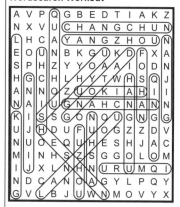

Double Fun Sudoku

Tasty Teaser

5	3	2	9	7	1	6	4	8
6	9	8	5	2	4	3	7	1
4	1	7	6	8	3	9	2	5
8	6	5	1	9	2	7	3	4
3	7	9	8	4	5	2	1	6
2	4	1	3	6	7	8	5	9
9	5	3	2	1	6	4	8	7
7	2	6	4	5	8	1	9	3
1	8	4	7	3	9	5	6	2

Brain Buster

6	3	4	7	5	1	2	8	9
7	1	8	4	9	2	3	6	5
2	9	5	3	8	6	4	1	7
9	5	2	6	7	8	1	4	3
8	4	1	9	3	5	6	7	2
3	6	7	2	1	4	9	5	8
4	8	6	5	2	9	7	3	1
5	7	9	1	6	3	8	2	4
1	2	3	8	4	7	5	9	6

Whatever Next?

K – Assign a number to each letter according to its place in the alphabet, so A=1, B=2, C=3, etc. Adding together the values of the two letters in each point of the star results in the central figure, 17. F=6, so the missing letter is K(=11).

Brain Teaser

8

Left	Right
8 x 5 = 40	6 x 4 = 24
4 x 2 = 8	8 x 3 = 24
48	48

Page 42

Mind Over Matter

The sum total of the values of the letters in the two left squares minus the sum total of the values of the letters in the two right squares equals that of the central square. Thus the missing value is 9, so the missing letter is I.

Double Fun Sudoku

Tasty Teaser

3	2	9	8	7	5	1	4	6
5	7	4	6	9	1	2	3	8
6	1	8	3	4	2	9	7	5
9	6	2	1	3	4	5	8	7
4	3	5	2	8	7	6	1	9
1	8	7	5	6	9	3	2	4
7	5	6	4	2	3	8	9	1
8	4	3	9	1	6	7	5	2
2	9	1	7	5	8	4	6	3

Brain Buster

9	2	1	7	3	5	4	6	8
3	5	6	4	1	8	2	7	9
7	8	4	9	6	2	5	3	1
4	9	3	8	2	7	1	5	6
5	6	2	1	9	4	7	8	3
1	7	8	3	5	6	9	2	4
2	4	5	6	8	9	3	1	7
8	3	9	2	7	1	6	4	5
6	1	7	5	4	3	8	9	2

Codeword Conundrum

B	A	T	H	M	A	T			V	E	R	G	E	R
L		R		A		O	O	Z	E		I			O
E	P	O	X	Y		P		H		S				U
S		V		F	O	A	L		I	R	K	I	N	G
S	P	E	L	L		Z	I	N	C			N		H
	O		O		M		L		D			D		N
S	T	R	A	W		O	B	J	E	C	T	I	V	E
Q		A		E		W		A		G				S
U	N	D	E	R	W	E	A	R		P	I	O	U	S
A		I		H		L		A		S				
B		S		E	L	A	N		C	A	K	E	D	
B	E	H	A	V	E		S	A	R	I		N		W
L			L	D		K			T	R	A	C	E	
E		T		L	A	K	E		O		V		L	
D	E	N	O	T	E			D	A	R	K	E	S	T

High-Speed Crossword

B	O	L	T	S			D	A	M
U	T	A	H	A	N		O	O	Z	E
S	O	W	E	T	O		C	Z	A	R
T	O	Y	S		S	T	E	E	L	E
U	L	E	E		W	A	N	E	S	
P	E	R	V		W	I	N	S	A	T
			E	V	A	N	S			
D	A	B	N	E	Y		E	R	A	S
A	M	U	S	T			L	O	V	E
R	A	R	E	S	T		E	D	E	N
E	Z	R	A		S	A	V	E	R	S
M	O	O	S		E	V	E	N	S	O
E	N	S			E	N	T	E	R	

1 Minute Number Crunch

Beginner

33 − 4 = 29. 29 x 5 = 145, 145 − 15 = 130, 130 x 3 = 390, 390 − 90 = 300, 300 ÷ 6 x 5 = 250, 250 + 14 = 264

Intermediate

89 + 57 = 146, 146 − 29 = 117, 117 ÷ 9 x 5 = 65, 65 ÷ 5 x 4 = 52, 52 x 7 = 364, 364 x .75 = 273, 273 ÷ 3 = 91

Advanced

33 x 25 = 825, 825 ÷ 3 x 2 = 550, 550 ÷ 11 x 9 = 450, 28% of 450 = 126, 126 ÷ 14 x 5 = 45, 45 + 89 = 134, 134 ÷ 0.25 = 536

Page 43

Battleship Bout

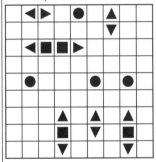

High-Speed Crossword

A	S	H	E	S			A	S	I	S
F	L	A	M	E		A	N	E	R	A
R	O	N	I	N		R	A	D	O	N
I	O	N		D	A	M		O	N	E
C	P	A		S	N	O		N	O	S
A	S	H	E		T	R	U	A	N	T
		M	E	L	I	S	S	A		
B	R	O	K	A	W		A	R	T	S
L	O	N		B	A	A		I	R	E
O	N	T		O	R	B		Z	E	N
O	N	A	I	R		B	L	O	B	S
M	I	N	T	S		R	E	N	E	E
S	E	A	S			S	O	A	K	S

Wordwheel

The nine-letter word is: TRUNCHEON

Wordsearch Workout

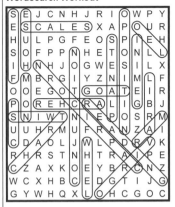

Double Fun Sudoku

Tasty Teaser

5	2	3	6	9	8	1	7	4
6	4	7	3	1	5	2	9	8
1	8	9	7	2	4	5	3	6
2	9	5	8	4	1	7	6	3
7	6	4	5	3	2	9	8	1
3	1	8	9	6	7	4	5	2
4	5	6	1	8	9	3	2	7
9	3	1	2	7	6	8	4	5
8	7	2	4	5	3	6	1	9

Brain Buster

3	5	8	7	1	4	2	6	9
1	7	2	3	6	9	8	5	4
9	4	6	5	2	8	3	1	7
6	1	5	9	3	2	4	7	8
2	8	7	4	5	6	9	3	1
4	9	3	1	8	7	6	2	5
5	2	9	8	7	3	1	4	6
7	6	4	2	9	1	5	8	3
8	3	1	6	4	5	7	9	2

Sum Circle

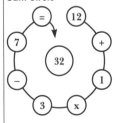

Page 44

1 Minute Number Crunch

Beginner
26 x 6 = 156, 156 ÷ 4 = 39, 39 x 2 = 78, 78 – 16 = 62, 62 ÷ 2 = 31, 31 + 19 = 50, 50 x 6 = 300

Intermediate
340 ÷ 17 = 20, 20 x 2.5 = 50, 50^2 = 2500, 20% of 2500 = 500, 15% of 500 = 75, 75 x 9 = 675, 675 ÷ 3 x 2 = 450

Advanced
55^2 = 3025, 80% of 3025 = 2420, 2420 ÷ 10 x 3 = 726, 726 + 484 (726 ÷ 3 x 2) = 1210, 1210 x 7 = 8470, 8470 – 982 = 7488, 7488 ÷ 18 x 7 = 2912

High-Speed Crossword

S	C	A	L	P		B	E	A	C	H
P	O	L	I	O		E	A	G	L	E
E	L	L	E	R	Y	Q	U	E	E	N
C	O	Y		T	A	U		N	A	N
K	R	I	S		W	I	N	T	R	Y
L	E	N	T		N	E	O			
E	D	G	E	S		T	O	R	T	S
		A	M	T		K	E	E	L	
C	L	A	M	O	R		S	A	R	I
A	I	R		T	E	A		D	E	N
S	T	E	P	H	E	N	K	I	N	G
E	R	N	I	E		N	I	E	C	E
D	E	T	E	R		A	D	D	E	R

Codeword Conundrum

B	A	N	G	L	E		P	R	E	S	U	M	E	S
E		L		R		O		K		E		W		
A	D	J	U	T	A	N	T		S	I	Z	Z	L	E
R		T		S		A	X	E		Z		E		E
D	E	F	T		E	A	T		R	E	C	A	N	T
	L		O		R		O	F	F		N		M	
A	M	O	N	G	S	T		A	S	T	R	I	D	E
Q		P		N		I	N	K		I		N		A
U	N	E	Q	U	A	L		E	S	C	H	E	A	T
A		R		L	E	T		H		I		G		
P	E	A	N	U	T		H	O	E		R	H	E	A
L		T		A	Y	E		A		S			U	
A	T	O	N	E	R		O	B	T	R	U	D	E	D
N		R		V		R		H		T			I	
E	A	S	T	E	R	L	Y		E	X	E	M	P	T

Double Fun Sudoku

Tasty Teaser

5	9	2	4	6	7	8	3	1
3	6	8	1	2	9	7	5	4
1	7	4	5	3	8	6	2	9
6	3	1	8	9	5	2	4	7
7	4	9	2	1	6	3	8	5
8	2	5	7	4	3	1	9	6
2	8	7	9	5	1	4	6	3
4	5	6	3	7	2	9	1	8
9	1	3	6	8	4	5	7	2

Brain Buster

2	5	7	6	4	1	3	9	8
6	9	3	5	7	8	2	4	1
4	1	8	2	3	9	6	7	5
5	6	4	1	2	3	9	8	7
3	8	1	9	6	7	5	2	4
7	2	9	8	5	4	1	6	3
1	3	2	4	8	6	7	5	9
9	4	6	7	1	5	8	3	2
8	7	5	3	9	2	4	1	6

Spidoku

Page 45

High-Speed Crossword

M	A	C	E			O	T	H	E	R
O	P	A	L	S		P	A	Y	M	E
C	A	N	I	T		E	X	P	E	L
H	I	D		R	A	N		E	R	A
A	N	Y	W	A	Y		R	A	P	
		W	H	I	N	E		A	L	S
T	A	R	O	T		A	B	C	D	E
A	L	A		S	T	R	U	T		
P	U	P		I	N	N	I	N	G	
I	M	P		A	P	E		V	I	E
O	N	E	A	L		S	L	I	C	E
C	U	R	V	E		T	O	T	E	S
A	S	S	E	S			P	Y	R	E

Wordsearch Workout

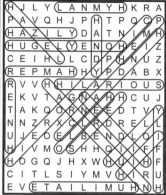

Double Fun Sudoku

Tasty Teaser

1	5	6	9	8	3	7	4	2
4	3	9	7	2	6	8	1	5
7	2	8	5	1	4	3	9	6
3	6	7	1	5	9	4	2	8
9	8	2	3	4	7	6	5	1
5	1	4	2	6	8	9	7	3
2	7	3	8	9	5	1	6	4
8	4	1	6	7	2	5	3	9
6	9	5	4	3	1	2	8	7

Brain Buster

9	6	1	7	3	4	5	8	2
3	5	2	8	6	1	4	9	7
7	8	4	5	9	2	3	1	6
4	1	3	6	2	8	7	5	9
5	2	9	4	7	3	8	6	1
8	7	6	9	1	5	2	4	3
1	5	3	2	4	6	9	7	8
2	4	7	1	8	9	6	3	5
6	9	8	3	5	7	1	2	4

Matchstick Magic

The matchsticks have been placed as follows:

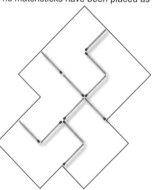

Brain Teaser

2415

1 Minute Number Crunch

Beginner

52 ÷ 4 = 13, 13 x 7 = 91, 91 + 17 = 108, 108 ÷ 9 = 12, 12 + 142 = 154, 50% of 154 = 77, 77 – 38 = 39

Intermediate

501 – 180 = 321, 321 ÷ 3 x 2 = 214, 214 x 2 = 428, 428 + 321 (428 ÷ 4 x 3) = 749, 749 – 627 = 122, 122 + 178 = 300, 22% of 300 = 66

Advanced

77 ÷ 11 x 7 = 49, 49 – 28 (49 ÷ 7 x 4) = 21, 21^3 = 9261, 9261 ÷ 9 = 1029, 1029 ÷ 3 x 2 = 686, 686 x 2 = 1372, 1372 x 7 = 9604

Page 46

Codeword Conundrum

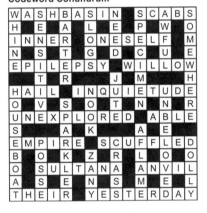

Double Fun Sudoku

Tasty Teaser

3	5	9	7	4	8	1	2	6
1	6	2	9	5	3	7	4	8
4	7	8	1	2	6	5	9	3
5	8	7	4	1	2	3	6	9
6	4	1	3	9	7	8	5	2
9	2	3	6	8	5	4	7	1
7	1	4	8	6	9	2	3	5
2	3	6	5	7	1	9	8	4
8	9	5	2	3	4	6	1	7

Brain Buster

7	3	4	8	6	1	9	5	2
2	6	8	9	5	3	4	7	1
1	9	5	7	2	4	3	6	8
8	7	1	5	9	6	2	4	3
3	4	6	1	8	2	5	9	7
9	5	2	4	3	7	8	1	6
4	2	3	6	1	5	7	8	9
5	1	9	2	7	8	6	3	4
6	8	7	3	4	9	1	2	5

Pyramid Plus

A=50, B=104, C=53, D=111, E=146, F=154, G=157, H=164, I=257, J=311, K=321, L=421, M=632, N=742, O=1374.

High-Speed Crossword

S	L	A	B	S			S	T	A	R
L	I	B	E	L		S	T	O	I	C
A	M	B	L	E		Q	A	N	D	A
M	A	R	I	E	C	U	R	I	E	
		E	T	H	I	C				
A	S	O	F		I	N	H	E	R	E
S	E	W		A	C	T		G	A	Y
H	E	L	E	N	A		S	O	M	E
			A	N	G	S	T			
	M	A	R	I	O	C	U	O	M	O
P	E	N	N	E		A	D	I	E	U
T	O	T	E	S		M	I	L	E	R
A	W	E	D			P	O	S	T	S

1 Minute Number Crunch

Beginner

74 + 47 = 121, 121 ÷ 11 = 11, 11 x 13 = 143, 143 + 9 = 152, 50% of 152 = 76, 76 + 38 = 114, 50% of 114 = 57

Intermediate

39 x 5 = 195, 195 ÷ 3 x 2 = 130, 130 x 1.6 = 208, 208 ÷ 4 x 3 = 156, 156 + 92 = 248, 248 x 3 = 744, 744 + 146 = 890

Advanced

23^2 = 529, 529 + 633 = 1162, 1162 ÷ 0.25 = 4648, 4648 – 1743 (4648 ÷ 8 x 3) = 2905, 2905 x 3 = 8715, 8715 ÷ 15 x 4 = 2324, 2324 ÷ 2 = 1162

Page 47

High-Speed Crossword

B	E	E	R	S			C	O	D	E	D
A	D	D	U	P		A	W	A	K	E	
S	I	G	M	A		S	E	V	E	N	
I	T	A		C	P	A		I	O	U	
N	O	R		I	R	S		D	U	D	
G	R	A	N	N	Y		G	A	T	E	
		L	O	G	I	C	A	L			
S	A	L	T		N	O	B	L	E	S	
A	L	A		I	T	S		A	M	E	
D	U	N		D	O	T		N	B	C	
I	M	P	E	L		U	L	C	E	R	
S	N	O	R	E		M	O	O	R	E	
T	I	E	R	S		E	G	E	S	T	

Domino Placement

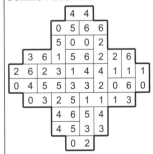

Wordsearch Workout

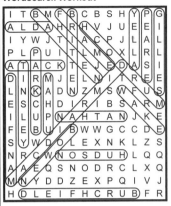

Double Fun Sudoku

Tasty Teaser

2	7	5	1	3	8	6	9	4
8	4	6	9	2	5	7	1	3
1	9	3	4	6	7	8	5	2
4	1	9	6	7	3	5	2	8
3	5	2	8	9	4	1	6	7
6	8	7	2	5	1	4	3	9
5	6	8	3	4	2	9	7	1
7	2	4	5	1	9	3	8	6
9	3	1	7	8	6	2	4	5

Brain Buster

1	2	7	3	5	6	9	8	4
3	5	8	7	9	4	6	1	2
6	9	4	1	2	8	5	7	3
2	3	1	4	7	5	8	9	6
8	7	9	2	6	3	4	5	1
5	4	6	8	1	9	3	2	7
7	8	3	5	4	1	2	6	9
4	6	2	9	8	7	1	3	5
9	1	5	6	3	2	7	4	8

Whatever Next?

M – Assign a number to each letter according to its place in the alphabet, so A=1, B=2, C=3, E=5, H=8 and U=21. Start from the top and move clockwise, adding each number to the next in order to reach the following number, so H + M (13) = U.

Brain Teaser

13 seats – 37 people each paid €51.

Page 48

Mind Over Matter

The value of the letter in each top square is added to the value of the letter in the central square to give the value of the letter in the bottom square diagonally opposite. Thus the missing value is 8, so the missing letter is H.

Double Fun Sudoku

Tasty Teaser

4	5	7	8	6	3	2	1	9
2	6	1	9	7	5	4	8	3
9	3	8	1	4	2	6	7	5
6	7	2	5	3	4	8	9	1
8	9	3	2	1	6	7	5	4
1	4	5	7	9	8	3	2	6
7	1	4	6	8	9	5	3	2
5	8	6	3	2	1	9	4	7
3	2	9	4	5	7	1	6	8

Brain Buster

8	6	2	3	1	5	4	7	9
9	4	7	2	8	6	5	3	1
1	5	3	7	9	4	6	2	8
6	3	8	1	5	7	2	9	4
4	2	9	8	6	3	7	1	5
5	7	1	9	4	2	3	8	6
3	1	6	5	7	9	8	4	2
2	8	4	6	3	1	9	5	7
7	9	5	4	2	8	1	6	3

Codeword Conundrum

S	C	R	E	W	B	A	L	L		J		W		D
U		A		R		Y		K	A	R	A	T	E	
D	E	F	R	A	U	D	E	D		S		R		F
D		T		S			I	M	M	E	N	S	E	
E	X	C	H	E	Q	U	E	R		I		I		N
N		W		U		G	I	N		N		D		D
	V	I	O	L	E	N	C	E		E	A	G	L	E
E		R		R		O		S		T			R	
M	U	M	M	Y		S	Y	M	P	A	T	H	Y	
B		A		A	S	H		L		R			B	
L		T		W		A	R	M	A	D	I	L	L	O
Z		N		I	E	N	S	H	R	I	N	E	D	
O	C	E	A	N	S		O		E		O		L	
N		E		G		P	R	U	D	E	N	T	L	Y

High-Speed Crossword

S	W	I	P	E	D			P	I	G
T	E	R	E	S	A		I	O	W	A
S	T	E	N	C	H		A	L	O	T
			G	O	L	D	M	I	N	E
I	N	O	U	R		E	T	C		
C	A	N	I	T		S	H	E	D	S
E	D	E	N			E	C	R	U	
S	A	A	B	S		T	W	A	I	N
	C	O	T		H	A	R	P	S	
C	A	R	O	U	S	E	L			
A	M	O	K		A	R	R	I	V	E
M	I	S	S		N	E	U	T	E	R
E	D	S			E	S	S	A	Y	S

1 Minute Number Crunch

Beginner
$8^2 = 64$, $64 \div 16 \times 3 = 12$, $12 + 15 = 27$, $27 \times 2 = 54$, $54 - 19 = 35$, $35 \times 2 = 70$, $70 \div 7 \times 6 = 60$

Intermediate
$942 \div 3 = 314$, $314 + 6 = 320$, $320 \div 8 \times 3 = 120$, $120 \div 5 \times 2 = 48$, $48 \div 6 = 8$, $8 \times 1.75 = 14$, $14^2 = 196$

Advanced
$195 \div 13 \times 7 = 105$, $105 + 84 \,(105 \div 5 \times 4) = 189$, $189 \div 7 \times 2 = 54$, $54 - 9 \,(54 \div 6) = 45$, $45 \times 11 = 495$, $495 \div 5 \times 3 = 297$, $297 + 792 = 1089$

Page 49

1 Minute Number Crunch

Beginner
$58 + 19 = 77$, $77 \div 7 \times 4 = 44$, $44 \div 4 = 11$, $11 + 83 = 94$, 50% of $94 = 47$, $47 - 15 = 32$, $32 \div 2 = 16$

Intermediate
$18 \times 3 = 54$, $54 \div 2 = 27$, $27 + 6 \,(27 \div 9 \times 2) = 33$, $33 \times 11 = 363$, $363 \times 2 = 726$, $726 + 242 \,(726 \div 3) = 968$, $968 \div 8 = 121$

Advanced
$64 + 72 = 136$, $136 \div 8 \times 5 = 85$, $85 \times 6 = 510$, $510 \div 17 \times 4 = 120$, $120 \div 0.75 = 160$, $160 \div 32 \times 9 = 45$, $45^2 = 2025$

High-Speed Crossword

E	L	I	N		S	C	A	L	E	S
X	E	N	A		T	Y	R	A	N	T
C	A	S	S	I	U	S	C	L	A	Y
I	S	A	A	C		H	A	M	M	
T	E	N		Y	A	M		L	E	I
E	D	E	N		F	E	M	A	L	E
			I	W	I	L	L			
P	A	T	T	E	R		K	F	C	S
A	L	A		D	E	W		I	R	A
W	K	R	P		I	S	L	E	Y	
P	A	S	S	I	O	N	P	L	A	Y
A	L	A	S	K	A		C	U	T	E
W	I	L	T	E	R		A	P	E	S

Wordwheel

The nine-letter word is: BLASPHEME

Wordsearch Workout

Double Fun Sudoku

Tasty Teaser

2	6	5	1	7	9	4	3	8
3	9	4	8	5	2	7	1	6
1	8	7	3	4	6	5	9	2
9	7	1	5	2	4	8	6	3
6	3	2	9	8	7	1	5	4
5	4	8	6	3	1	9	2	7
8	1	3	4	6	5	2	7	9
7	5	6	2	9	8	3	4	1
4	2	9	7	1	3	6	8	5

Brain Buster

1	5	3	8	9	7	2	6	4
4	2	8	6	5	1	7	3	9
9	7	6	4	2	3	1	5	8
8	6	7	3	4	2	5	9	1
3	4	2	5	1	9	8	7	6
5	9	1	7	8	6	3	4	2
2	1	5	9	3	4	6	8	7
7	8	9	1	6	5	4	2	3
6	3	4	2	7	8	9	1	5

Sum Circle

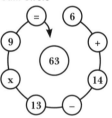

Page 50

1 Minute Number Crunch

Beginner
10% of $150 = 15$, $15 \times 8 = 120$, 50% of $120 = 60$, $60 \div 12 \times 3 = 15$, $15 + 7 = 22$, $22 \div 2 = 11$, $11 \times 10 = 110$

Intermediate
$269 + 47 = 316$, $316 \div 4 = 79$, $79 \times 3 = 237$, $237 - 88 = 149$, $149 + 27 = 176$, $176 \div 8 \times 5 = 110$, $110 + 11 = 121$

Advanced
$84 \div 7 \times 5 = 60$, $60^2 = 3600$, $3600 \div 18 \times 7 = 1400$, $1400 - 578 = 822$, $822 + 1096 = 1918$, $1918 \div 2 = 959$, $959 + 697 = 1656$

High-Speed Crossword

C	L	O	W	N	S			L	A	P
L	A	R	I	A	T			W	I	F	E
I	M	E	L	D	A			O	M	E	N
			D	A	N	B	R	O	W	N
S	P	E	W			S	A	L
C	U	R	I	E			I	D	T	A	G
A		M	I	L	E			T	W	I	N	E
R	A	N	D	R			S	I	M	O	N
	W	I	G			D	E	N	T
L	A	K	E	E	R	I	E
A	X	I	S			O	N	W	A	R	D
L	E	N	T			S	T	E	R	E	O
A	D	D			S	O	B	E	I	T

Codeword Conundrum

O		M		O	P	A	L	E	S	C	E	N	C	E
B	R	I	E	F		V		E		X		A
S		N		F	R	E	Q	U	E	N	T	I	N	G
T	R	E	S	S		R		D		R		A
R		S		H		S	P	E	C	T	A	C	L	E
U		W	O	O	F		A		A		L		L
C	U	E			R		L		S		W	E	R	E
T		E		E	S	C	A	P	E	D		A		C
I	M	P	S		I		V			I		N	O	T
V		E		E	X		E		A	S	K	S		R
E	N	R	A	P	T	U	R	E		M		H		O
	O		Z		I		L		A	V	A	I	L
D	O	C	U	M	E	N	T	A	R	Y		V		Y
	S		R		T		N		E	J	E	C	T
L	E	V	E	L	H	E	A	D	E	D		N		E

Double Fun Sudoku

Tasty Teaser

6	4	8	2	1	9	7	5	3
5	7	2	3	6	8	1	9	4
3	1	9	4	7	5	6	2	8
7	9	3	5	4	2	8	6	1
4	5	6	7	8	1	9	3	2
8	2	1	9	3	6	4	7	5
1	8	5	6	2	7	3	4	9
2	6	4	8	9	3	5	1	7
9	3	7	1	5	4	2	8	6

Brain Buster

8	5	3	2	7	9	6	1	4
4	7	2	1	6	5	8	3	9
6	1	9	3	4	8	5	7	2
3	4	8	7	5	1	2	9	6
1	6	5	4	9	2	7	8	3
2	9	7	6	8	3	4	5	1
7	2	1	8	3	4	9	6	5
9	8	4	5	1	6	3	2	7
5	3	6	9	2	7	1	4	8

Spidoku

Page 51

High-Speed Crossword

T	H	U	M	B	S			D	A	D
V	E	R	I	L	Y			M	I	L	E
S	E	N	S	O	R			A	S	O	F
		S	C	I	E	N	C	E	S
A	R	C	S			A	D	O
V	I	R	U	S			G	N	A	W	S
I	C	A	N	T			E	T	H	E	L
D	E	N	S	E			S	H	O	R	E
		H	A	S			E	Y	E	D
O	P	T	I	M	I	S	M
P	A	W	N			N	O	O	D	L	E
E	R	I	E			G	R	O	V	E	R
N	E	T			S	E	N	D	E	R

Wordsearch Workout

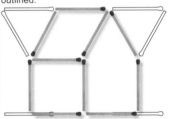

Double Fun Sudoku

Tasty Teaser

6	3	7	4	2	5	1	9	8
5	8	9	6	1	3	7	2	4
4	2	1	7	9	8	6	3	5
1	9	5	3	7	4	2	8	6
8	7	2	9	5	6	3	4	1
3	4	6	1	8	2	9	5	7
2	5	3	8	6	1	4	7	9
9	6	8	2	4	7	5	1	3
7	1	4	5	3	9	8	6	2

Brain Buster

4	9	8	2	1	7	6	3	5
3	5	6	4	8	9	2	7	1
1	2	7	3	6	5	8	9	4
5	8	9	6	4	3	7	1	2
2	3	4	7	9	1	5	8	6
7	6	1	8	5	2	9	4	3
6	4	3	9	2	8	1	5	7
9	7	5	1	3	6	4	2	8
8	1	2	5	7	4	3	6	9

Matchstick Magic

The matchsticks which have been moved are outlined.

Brain Teaser

X – They are every 3rd letter in the alphabet with only straight lines.

A miss E, F

H miss I, K

L miss M, N

T miss V, W

X

Simple as A, B, C

B	B	A	C	C	A
A	C	C	B	B	A
B	B	A	A	C	C
C	A	B	C	A	B
A	C	B	B	A	C
C	A	C	A	B	B

Page 52

Codeword Conundrum

H	I	S	S		U	N	P	I	N		P	O	M	P
U		I	T	S		E		A		P		Y		
F	L	A	X		A	V	E	N	G	E		U	R	
F		T		G		V			C	A	S	T	E	
	B	Y	T	E		E	T	C	H			W		
D	U	E		I		J		R		O	N	I	O	N
I		H		C	H	E	W	E	D		G		E	
S	H	A	N	K		T		M		S	O	N	A	R
C		L		E	S	C	O	R	T		O		V	
O	F	F	E	R		A		R		O	R	O	E	
	L		I	A	M	B		C	A	S	E			
Q	U	A	I	L		R		L		P		P		
U		R		E	R	R	A	T	A		R	A	T	E
I		I		A		W		S	E	A		A		
Z	E	A	L		T	U	L	I	P		T	A	C	K

Double Fun Sudoku

Tasty Teaser

4	3	6	5	1	8	7	2	9
7	5	8	2	9	3	1	4	6
9	2	1	4	7	6	5	3	8
3	8	9	7	6	2	4	5	1
2	4	7	9	5	1	8	6	3
1	6	5	8	3	4	9	7	2
5	7	3	6	8	9	2	1	4
6	9	2	1	4	7	3	8	5
8	1	4	3	2	5	6	9	7

Brain Buster

7	4	9	6	8	2	5	1	3
1	5	6	7	9	3	4	2	8
2	3	8	1	4	5	6	9	7
8	1	5	4	3	7	9	6	2
4	9	7	8	2	6	3	5	1
3	6	2	5	1	9	7	8	4
5	2	1	9	7	4	8	3	6
9	8	4	3	6	1	2	7	5
6	7	3	2	5	8	1	4	9

Pyramid Plus

A=135, B=119, C=147, D=58, E=97, F=254, G=266, H=205, I=155, J=520, K=471, L=360, M=991, N=831, O=1822.

High-Speed Crossword

T	O	N	E		M	A	K	E	I	T
O	P	U	S		A	T	O	N	C	E
T	E	M	P		G	O	R	G	E	D
E	R	E		P	I	L	E			
M	A	R	C	H		L	A	C	E	D
		O	O	O		S	N	A	K	E
P	O	U	T		W	R	E	N		
A	U	N	T	S		W	A	D		
C	R	O	O	N		O	R	G	A	N
		N	O	O	K		A	P	E	
O	R	E	G	O	N		A	M	P	S
B	E	L	I	Z	E		P	E	L	T
S	P	I	N	E	S		U	S	E	S

1 Minute Number Crunch

Beginner
77 ÷ 7 x 3 = 33, 33 x 4 = 132, 132 ÷ 12 x 3 = 33, 33 − 1 = 32, 50% of 32 = 16, 16 x 9 = 144, 144 ÷ 12 x 5 = 60

Intermediate
456 ÷ 3 x 2 = 304, 304 ÷ 4 = 76, 76 x 1.5 = 114, 114 x 3 = 342, 342 ÷ 9 x 5 = 190, 190 − 19 = 171, 171 ÷ 19 x 2 = 18

Advanced
599 ÷ 0.25 = 2396, 2396 x 2 = 4792, 375% of 4792 = 17970, 17970 ÷ 10 x 3 = 5391, 5391 − 2995 (5391 ÷ 9 x 5) = 2396, 2396 x 0.75 = 1797, 1797 − 878 = 919

Page 53

High-Speed Crossword

O	S	C	A	R		F	R	O	Z	E
R	A	L	P	H		L	A	P	E	L
I	H	O	P	E		O	P	E	R	A
G	A	S		T	A	P		N	O	P
I	R	E		T	I	P		Y	E	S
N	A	Y	S		D	E	P	O	S	E
		O	U	R		D	R	U		
S	T	U	P	O	R		O	R	S	O
P	A	R		N	E	C		H	I	P
I	C	E		A	D	O		E	M	U
R	O	Y	A	L		S	L	A	P	S
A	M	E	N	D		M	E	R	L	E
L	A	S	T	S		O	A	T	E	S

1 Minute Number Crunch

Beginner
56 + 13 = 69, 69 ÷ 3 = 23, 23 reversed = 32, 32 − 4 = 28, 28 x 2 = 56, 56 + 4 = 60, 60 ÷ 15 = 4

Intermediate
49 ÷ 7 x 6 = 42, 42 ÷ 3 = 14, 14 x 5 = 70, 70 ÷ 0.2 = 350, 350 ÷ 5 x 4 = 280, 280 ÷ 70 = 4, 4^3 = 64

Advanced
578 ÷ 2 = 289, square root of 289 = 17, 17 + 68 = 85, 80% of 85 = 68, 68 x 1.75 = 119, 119 x 2 = 238, 238 − 109 = 129

Wordsearch Workout

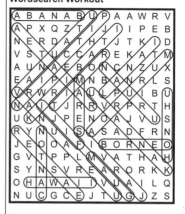

Double Fun Sudoku

Tasty Teaser

2	3	7	9	1	4	5	6	8
1	5	9	8	7	6	3	4	2
6	4	8	2	3	5	1	9	7
5	2	1	3	6	8	9	7	4
9	8	6	7	4	1	2	5	3
4	7	3	5	9	2	6	8	1
8	1	2	4	5	9	7	3	6
3	9	4	6	2	7	8	1	5
7	6	5	1	8	3	4	2	9

Brain Buster

7	9	5	4	3	8	1	2	6
4	3	6	2	5	1	9	8	7
8	2	1	6	9	7	5	4	3
2	5	9	3	1	4	6	7	8
3	6	7	8	2	9	4	1	5
1	4	8	7	6	5	2	3	9
6	1	2	5	7	3	8	9	4
9	8	3	1	4	6	7	5	2
5	7	4	9	8	2	3	6	1

Whatever Next?

N – Clockwise from the top, move 3 places forwards in the alphabet, then 2 back, 5 forwards, 2 back, 7 forwards (N), then 2 back, to L in the centre.

Brain Teaser

48
(6 + 7) x (5 − 2) = 39
(8 + 6) x (4 − 1) = 42
(10 + 2) x (6 − 2) = 48

Page 54

Mind Over Matter

The sum total of the values of the letters in the top squares and central square is equal to the sum total of the values in the bottom squares. Thus the missing value is 17, so the missing letter is Q.

Double Fun Sudoku

Tasty Teaser

4	7	3	2	5	8	6	1	9
8	2	1	6	7	9	3	4	5
5	9	6	1	4	3	7	2	8
2	3	9	4	8	7	1	5	6
1	5	4	3	2	6	9	8	7
6	8	7	5	9	1	2	3	4
7	1	2	8	6	5	4	9	3
3	6	5	9	1	4	8	7	2
9	4	8	7	3	2	5	6	1

Brain Buster

8	5	4	7	6	3	2	1	9
6	3	1	9	2	4	8	7	5
7	2	9	1	8	5	4	6	3
2	1	8	6	7	9	5	3	4
5	6	3	2	4	1	9	8	7
4	9	7	3	5	8	1	2	6
3	4	2	5	1	7	6	9	8
9	8	6	4	3	2	7	5	1
1	7	5	8	9	6	3	4	2

Codeword Conundrum

P	O	A	C	H		A	N	A	L	G	E	S	I	A
A		M		E		C		D		A				C
R	E	A	R	R	A	N	G	E		Z	I	L	C	H
A		S		O		E		Q		E		U		E
L	A	S	S	I	E		Q	U	I	B	B	L	E	D
Y				N		D		A		O		L		
T	H	E	M	E		E	A	T	S		D	A	I	S
I		R		S		J		E		E		B		T
C	H	O	P		W	E	L	L		F	O	Y	E	R
		T		B		C		Y		F				A
S	T	I	L	E	T	T	O		B	U	R	D	E	N
M		C		C		E		B		S		R		G
A	B	A	C	K		D	E	O	X	I	D	I	S	E
S				O		L		L		V		L		S
H	A	C	K	N	E	Y	E	D		E	C	L	A	T

High-Speed Crossword

M	A	J	O	R		R	A	N	U	P
A	L	O	N	E		A	T	O	N	E
K	A	Y	O	S		T	E	R	M	S
E	S	C		E	R	A		M	A	T
I	K	E		T	E	T		A	D	E
T	A	B	S		M	A	N	N	E	R
		R	O	B	O	T	I	C		
S	T	O	N	E	R		P	O	O	H
A	R	T		A	S	P		U	N	O
L	A	H		G	E	L		S	E	N
I	D	E	A	L		A	S	I	D	E
V	E	R	G	E		Z	I	N	G	S
A	S	S	E	S		A	S	S	E	T

1 Minute Number Crunch

Beginner
64 x 2 = 128, 128 + 6 = 134, 134 ÷ 2 = 67, 67 reversed = 76, 76 ÷ 2 = 38, 38 − 2 = 36, 36 ÷ 6 x 5 = 30

Intermediate
120 ÷ 15 x 2 = 16, 16 x 4 = 64, 64 x 2 = 128, 128 ÷ 8 x 5 = 80, 80 x 1.3 = 104, 104 ÷ 4 = 26, 26 x 7 = 182

Advanced
1997 + 666 = 2663, 2663 x 2 = 5326, 5326 − 958 = 4368, 4368 ÷ 3 x 2 = 2912, 2912 ÷ 16 x 5 = 910, 910 ÷ 5 x 3 = 546, 546 − 364 (546 ÷ 3 x 2) = 182

Page 55

Domino Placement

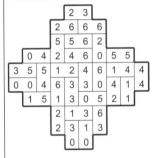

High-Speed Crossword

E	Y	E	S		E	D	I	S	O	N
R	O	V	E		D	A	N	U	B	E
I	D	E	A		I	N	F	L	O	W
C	A	R	R	O	T	C	A	K	E	
			C	O	H	E	N			
I	D	A	H	O		S	T	A	K	E
F	E	W						R	E	V
S	W	E	A	T		S	C	E	N	E
			R	I	S	K	Y			
	P	U	M	P	K	I	N	P	I	E
D	E	N	O	T	E		I	O	W	A
E	S	C	R	O	W		C	L	O	T
L	O	S	S	E	S		S	O	N	S

Wordwheel

The nine-letter word is: AESTHETIC

Wordsearch Workout

Double Fun Sudoku

Tasty Teaser

8	3	5	4	1	6	9	7	2
6	9	7	2	5	8	1	4	3
1	2	4	7	9	3	8	6	5
2	7	6	3	4	9	5	8	1
4	1	3	8	2	5	7	9	6
9	5	8	1	6	7	2	3	4
5	8	1	6	7	4	3	2	9
3	6	2	9	8	1	4	5	7
7	4	9	5	3	2	6	1	8

Brain Buster

5	8	6	3	1	7	9	4	2
1	2	3	4	9	8	6	5	7
4	7	9	2	5	6	8	3	1
9	3	1	7	8	4	5	2	6
6	5	2	9	3	1	7	8	4
7	4	8	5	6	2	3	1	9
3	1	5	6	2	9	4	7	8
2	6	7	8	4	5	1	9	3
8	9	4	1	7	3	2	6	5

Sum Circle

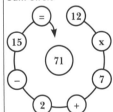

Page 56

1 Minute Number Crunch

Beginner
82 − 39 = 43, 43 x 2 = 86, 86 − 18 = 68, 68 x 2 = 136,
25% of 136 = 34, 34 − 14 = 20, 20 x 70 = 1400

Intermediate
21 ÷ 7 x 2 = 6, 6 + 15 = 21, 21^2 = 441, 441 ÷ 9 x 2 =
98, 98 + 4 = 102, 102 ÷ 17 = 6, 6^3 = 216

Advanced
366 x 5 = 1830, 1830 ÷ 3 x 2 = 1220, 1220 − 366
(1220 ÷ 10 x 3) = 854, 854 − 687 = 167, 167 x 3 = 501,
501 + 835 = 1336, 1336 ÷ 8 x 5 = 835

High-Speed Crossword

T	A	G	G	E	D		C	B	S
E	V	E	R	S	O		G	L	U	T
D	E	N	O	T	E		R	A	T	E
I	R	I	S		S	I	E	S	T	A
U	S	E	S		T	Y	P	E	D
M	E	S	A		M	E	S	S	R	S
			N	O	R	M	A
S	A	V	A	N	T		N	E	A	R
W	R	I	T	E		A	L	T	O
A	C	R	O	S	S		T	U	T	U
M	A	I	M		A	B	O	D	E	S
I	D	L	Y		L	A	M	E	S	T
S	E	E		T	R	Y	S	T	S

Codeword Conundrum

F	A	S	C	I	N	A	T	E		W	A	S	T	E
E		U		R		S		B		H		Q		T
A	M	B	E	R		T	A	B	L	E	A	U		H
S		J		U		E		S		N		A		I
T	R	U	M	P	E	R	Y		H	E	C	T	I	C
		D		T			D		V					A
S	W	I	G		M	A	N	A	G	E	R	I	A	L
N		C		G		V		Z		R		N		L
O	V	E	R	L	O	O	K	E	D		S	E	X	Y
W			E		W			F		L				
F	O	R	M	A	L		A	S	P	I	R	A	N	T
L		A		M		S		E		N		S		H
A		B	L	I	N	K	E	R		I	N	T	E	R
K		B		N		I		V		S		I		E
E	K	I	N	G		T	O	O	T	H	A	C	H	E

Double Fun Sudoku
Tasty Teaser

6	3	7	2	5	1	8	9	4
2	9	8	6	4	7	5	1	3
1	5	4	8	9	3	7	6	2
3	8	5	7	1	9	2	4	6
9	4	6	3	8	2	1	5	7
7	2	1	5	6	4	9	3	8
4	1	2	9	7	6	3	8	5
5	6	3	1	2	8	4	7	9
8	7	9	4	3	5	6	2	1

Brain Buster

2	6	8	4	7	3	1	5	9
9	1	3	6	5	8	2	7	4
5	4	7	1	2	9	8	3	6
1	3	2	5	4	7	9	6	8
6	5	4	9	8	2	7	1	3
7	8	9	3	6	1	5	4	2
8	7	1	2	3	6	4	9	5
4	9	6	8	1	5	3	2	7
3	2	5	7	9	4	6	8	1

Spidoku

Page 57

High-Speed Crossword

J	A	B		A	G	O		H	A	D
U	S	A		L	A	B		A	L	I
S	I	R		P	R	O	G	R	A	M
T	A	R	T		R	E	A	R	S
A	N	Y	W	A	Y		T	Y	K	E
		L	O	C	K		E	R	A	S
A	C	E		T	A	P		E	N	T
L	O	V	E		S	A	G	A
A	C	I	D		P	L	A	S	M	A
	A	N	I	T	A		P	O	O	R
D	I	S	T	U	R	B		N	O	M
U	N	O		B	O	Y		E	R	E
D	E	N		A	V	E		R	E	D

Wordsearch Workout

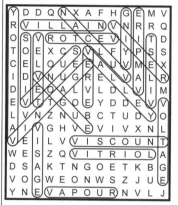

Double Fun Sudoku
Tasty Teaser

4	5	7	1	9	3	2	8	6
1	2	3	6	8	7	4	5	9
6	9	8	5	2	4	1	3	7
3	7	5	2	4	9	6	1	8
8	1	4	3	5	6	7	9	2
9	6	2	7	1	8	5	4	3
5	8	1	9	7	2	3	6	4
7	3	9	4	6	5	8	2	1
2	4	6	8	3	1	9	7	5

Brain Buster

5	6	9	1	8	3	7	4	2
4	7	8	9	6	2	3	5	1
3	1	2	4	7	5	8	9	6
9	3	6	5	1	4	2	7	8
7	5	1	2	3	8	9	6	4
8	2	4	6	9	7	5	1	3
1	8	3	7	5	6	4	2	9
2	9	5	8	4	1	6	3	7
6	4	7	3	2	9	1	8	5

Matchstick Magic

The matchsticks which have been removed are
outlined: those remaining form the digit '9'.

Brain Teaser

6/100 x 5/99 = 1/330

Domino Placement

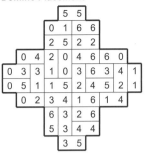

Page 58

Codeword Conundrum

A	K	I	M	B	O		V		F		W	A	F	T
S		M		O		Z	E	N	I	T	H			A
S	M	A	L	L	P	O	X		V		E	M	I	R
E		G		U		N		J	E	S	T			T
T	R	O	U	S	S	E	A	U			S	O	F	A
	E			P			D	U	C	T				R
B	A	C	K	G	A	M	M	O	N		O	N	C	E
	C		N		R		O		I	N		H		
S	H	O	O		S	U	B	A	Q	U	E	O	U	S
Y		W	E	E	P		U			R				
R	E	E	L			O	B	S	E	R	V	A	N	T
I		E	A	R	N		E		I		B			A
N	E	E	D		A		D	A	I	N	T	I	E	R
G		G	A	R	T	E	R		D		D			O
E	P	E	E		E		N		A	S	P	E	C	T

Double Fun Sudoku

Tasty Teaser

6	4	1	3	8	9	5	7	2
9	2	5	4	7	6	8	3	1
8	3	7	5	1	2	6	9	4
1	7	3	9	4	8	2	6	5
2	8	4	6	5	3	7	1	9
5	6	9	1	2	7	4	8	3
4	5	8	7	9	1	3	2	6
3	1	2	8	6	4	9	5	7
7	9	6	2	3	5	1	4	8

Brain Buster

8	7	5	2	4	6	1	3	9
1	6	3	8	9	5	2	7	4
4	2	9	1	7	3	6	5	8
3	1	7	9	6	2	8	4	5
2	4	8	3	5	1	9	6	7
5	9	6	7	8	4	3	1	2
7	3	1	5	2	9	4	8	6
6	8	2	4	3	7	5	9	1
9	5	4	6	1	8	7	2	3

Pyramid Plus

A=138, B=17, C=148, D=13, E=131, F=155, G=165, H=161, I=144, J=320, K=326, L=305, M=646, N=631, O=1277.

High-Speed Crossword

I	M	S		A	M	P		W	H	O
G	E	T		C	O	L		R	A	M
O	N	A		E	V	A		I	B	E
R	U	N	I	T	I	N		T	I	L
		D	I	O	N	S		I	T	E
S	K	I	I	N	G		N	U	T	
A	N	N		E	F	G		G	A	T
V	I	G		O	R	A	C	L	E	
E	G	G		F	R	A	M	E		
T	H	U		A	W	N	I	N	G	S
I	T	A		T	A	G		T	A	T
M	E	R		A	R	E		E	Y	E
E	D	D		L	D	S		R	E	M

1 Minute Number Crunch

Beginner
61 x 3 = 183, 183 + 19 = 202, 202 ÷ 2 = 101, 101 − 66 = 35, 35 ÷ 5 = 7, 7 + 44 = 51, 51 ÷ 3 = 17

Intermediate
48 + 159 = 207, 207 ÷ 9 x 2 = 46, 46 x 2 = 92, 92 − 12 = 80, 25% of 80 = 20, 20² = 400, 75% of 400 = 300

Advanced
Cube root of 50653 = 37, 37 x 111 = 4107, 4107 ÷ 3 = 1369, 1369 − 987 = 382, 382 x 4 = 1528, 1528 − 573 (1528 x 0.375) = 955, 60% of 955 = 573

Page 59

High-Speed Crossword

I	N	C	A	S	E		M	A	A	M
M	A	R	R	O	W		I	F	S	O
P	S	Y	C	H	O		S	E	W	N
E	D	S		O	K	S		W	E	T
L	A	O	S		S	T	A	B	L	E
S	Q	U	A	T		A	T	A	L	L
		R	B	I		R	O	D		
A	N	G	E	L		S	M	A	R	T
M	A	R	R	E	D		S	P	E	W
E	V	A		S	E	A		P	S	I
N	A	P	A		U	N	C	L	E	S
D	J	E	D		C	O	G	E	N	T
S	O	S	O		E	X	I	S	T	S

1 Minute Number Crunch

Beginner
131 + 383 = 514, 514 ÷ 2 = 257, 257 − 55 = 202, 202 ÷ 2 = 101, 101 x 3 = 303, 303 + 17 = 320, 25% of 320 = 80

Intermediate
73 − 37 = 36, square root of 36 = 6, 6 x 13 = 78, 78 ÷ 3 = 26, 26 ÷ 13 x 6 = 12, 12 + 10 (12 ÷ 6 x 5) = 22, 22 x 11 = 242

Advanced
125% of 968 = 1210, 1210 − 869 = 341, 341 + 4572 = 4913, cube root of 4913 = 17, 17 x 8 = 136, 136 ÷ 34 x 7 = 28, 28 ÷ 14 x 9 = 18

Wordsearch Workout

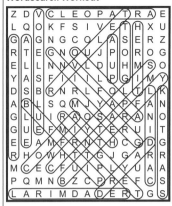

Double Fun Sudoku

Tasty Teaser

2	6	3	9	5	8	4	1	7
4	9	1	7	2	3	5	8	6
8	7	5	4	1	6	3	2	9
7	1	2	8	4	9	6	3	5
3	5	4	1	6	7	2	9	8
9	8	6	5	3	2	1	7	4
1	3	9	6	8	4	7	5	2
5	4	8	2	7	1	9	6	3
6	2	7	3	9	5	8	4	1

Brain Buster

5	6	3	9	2	4	1	7	8
4	8	7	5	3	1	9	6	2
9	1	2	6	8	7	4	3	5
8	4	9	3	1	2	6	5	7
3	7	5	4	6	9	8	2	1
6	2	1	7	5	8	3	9	4
1	9	6	2	4	5	7	8	3
7	5	8	1	9	3	2	4	6
2	3	4	8	7	6	5	1	9

Whatever Next?

F – Start from the top and move clockwise, going back four letters in the alphabet each time, finally moving from J to F, then from F to B.

Brain Teaser

8%
81 + 82 + 77 + 68 = 308
Amongst 100 pupils, this gives 3 losses each, and 4 losses to 8 pupils.

Page 60

Mind Over Matter

The sum total of the values of the letters in the top left and bottom right squares is subtracted from the sum total of the values of the letters in the top right and bottom left squares, giving the value of the letter in the central square. Thus the missing value is 15, so the missing letter is O.

Double Fun Sudoku

Tasty Teaser

6	4	3	2	7	8	9	1	5
9	5	2	4	1	3	8	6	7
7	1	8	5	6	9	2	3	4
2	7	4	8	5	6	3	9	1
8	6	9	1	3	7	5	4	2
1	3	5	9	2	4	6	7	8
3	2	6	7	4	5	1	8	9
4	9	1	3	8	2	7	5	6
5	8	7	6	9	1	4	2	3

Brain Buster

4	1	3	2	5	6	9	8	7
6	5	7	9	8	3	1	2	4
9	8	2	1	4	7	5	3	6
8	4	9	3	7	1	2	6	5
2	6	5	4	9	8	7	1	3
7	3	1	5	6	2	8	4	9
3	2	6	7	1	5	4	9	8
1	7	4	8	3	9	6	5	2
5	9	8	6	2	4	3	7	1

Codeword Conundrum

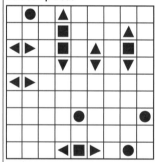

High-Speed Crossword

1 Minute Number Crunch

Beginner
53 x 3 = 159, 159 − 19 = 140, 25% of 140 = 35, 35 ÷ 5 x 4 = 28, 28 x 3 = 84, 84 ÷ 14 = 6, 6 x 7 = 42

Intermediate
225 ÷ 9 x 2 = 50, 50^2 = 2500, 2500 + 250 = 2750, 2750 ÷ 25 = 110, 110 ÷ 5 = 22, 22 x 12 = 264, 264 ÷ 3 x 2 = 176

Advanced
92 ÷ 23 x 17 = 68, 68 ÷ 17 x 4 = 16, 16^2 = 256, 256 x 0.375 = 96, 96 ÷ 16 x 3 = 18, 18^2 = 324, 324 ÷ 36 x 23 = 207

Page 61

Battleship Bout

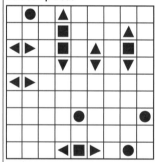

High-Speed Crossword

O	R	D	E	R	S		A	S	T	I
N	A	R	R	O	W		B	O	A	R
E	Q	U	A	T	E		A	B	B	A
S	U	N		O	D	E		E	L	I
E	E	K		R	E	V	E	R	E	S
C	L	A	M		N	E	G	A	T	E
	S	I	S		N	O	S			
T	H	A	T	O	K		S	A	S	S
R	O	S	E	H	I	P		J	A	N
A	O	K		O	N	O		U	V	A
U	P	U	P		S	P	I	D	E	R
M	E	N	D		K	I	N	G	M	E
A	R	K	S		I	N	N	E	E	D

Wordwheel

The nine-letter word is: PLAUSIBLE

Wordsearch Workout

Double Fun Sudoku

Tasty Teaser

9	4	8	5	1	2	7	3	6
1	7	3	6	4	9	5	2	8
5	6	2	7	3	8	4	1	9
3	5	4	8	7	6	1	9	2
7	8	1	9	2	4	3	6	5
6	2	9	3	5	1	8	4	7
4	9	7	1	6	5	2	8	3
8	1	5	2	9	3	6	7	4
2	3	6	4	8	7	9	5	1

Brain Buster

3	9	4	8	5	1	2	6	7
8	6	2	9	4	7	1	3	5
1	5	7	2	3	6	9	8	4
9	3	1	5	6	2	4	7	8
5	2	6	4	7	8	3	1	9
7	4	8	3	1	9	6	5	2
6	8	5	1	2	4	7	9	3
2	1	9	7	8	3	5	4	6
4	7	3	6	9	5	8	2	1

Sum Circle

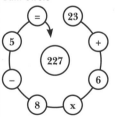

Page 62

1 Minute Number Crunch

Beginner
64 ÷ 8 = 8, 8 x 5 = 40, 40 ÷ 10 = 4, 4 + 19 = 23, 23 − 8 = 15, 15 ÷ 5 = 3, 3 − 2 = 1

Intermediate
627 ÷ 3 = 209, 209 + 648 = 857, 857 + 758 = 1615, 1615 ÷ 5 = 323, 323 − 127 = 196, 196 ÷ 4 x 3 = 147, 147 + 98 (147 ÷ 3 x 2) = 245

Advanced
142857 x 2 = 285714, 285714 ÷ 37 x 3 = 23166, 23166 ÷ 11 x 5 = 10530, 10530 ÷ 10 x 7 = 7371, 7371 ÷ 9 x 5 = 4095, 60% of 4095 = 2457, 2457 ÷ 9 x 5 = 1365

High-Speed Crossword

S	P	A	R	S		S	H	O	R	T
H	A	S	A	T		H	A	V	E	N
A	L	I	C	E		A	R	E	N	T
M	O	T	H	E	R	L	A	N	D	
			E	P	E	E	S			
S	M	A	L	L	F		S	L	O	W
L	E	X		Y	U	M		A	W	E
C	L	E	O		G	A	S	P	E	D
		N	I	E	C	E				
	S	I	S	T	E	R	C	I	T	Y
C	O	S	T	A		A	R	N	I	E
T	O	T	A	L		M	E	C	C	A
S	T	O	R	Y		E	T	H	E	R

Codeword Conundrum

W	A	P	I	T	I		I	M	P	O	R	T	E	R
O		A		I			O		R		A		O	
R	A	R	E	F	Y		B	U	N	G	A	L	O	W
K		S		F		J		L		A		L		D
B	A	N	D	I	C	O	O	T			N	E	E	D	Y
E			I		N		J				I		S	
N	A	P	E		C	O	M	P	O	S	I	T	O	R
C			C		B		R			T				I
H	I	B	E	R	N	A	T	E	D		P	A	N	G
	A		U			F		S		V				H
V	I	N	E	S		W	A	I	S	T	C	O	A	T
I		Q		A		H		X		R		C		E
S	Q	U	A	D	R	O	N		V	I	R	A	G	O
O		E		L		E		L		F		D		U
R	E	T	A	R	D	E	D		Z	E	R	O	E	S

Double Fun Sudoku
Tasty Teaser

2	8	6	4	3	9	1	7	5
4	9	7	2	5	1	3	8	6
5	1	3	8	6	7	9	2	4
9	3	4	1	8	6	2	5	7
1	6	8	5	7	2	4	3	9
7	5	2	3	9	4	8	6	1
3	4	1	7	2	5	6	9	8
6	2	5	9	1	8	7	4	3
8	7	9	6	4	3	5	1	2

Brain Buster

5	4	3	7	6	8	1	9	2
7	6	8	1	9	2	4	3	5
1	9	2	4	3	5	6	8	7
9	2	1	3	5	4	8	7	6
6	8	7	9	2	1	3	5	4
4	3	5	6	8	7	9	2	1
3	5	4	8	7	6	2	1	9
8	7	6	2	1	9	5	4	3
2	1	9	5	4	3	7	6	8

Spidoku

Page 63

High-Speed Crossword

R	O	M	A	N	O	V		L	O	L
A	B	I	L	E	N	E		O	S	U
F	E	L	I	X	T	H	E	C	A	T
F	R	O	N	T		I	M	A	G	E
L	O	R	E		S	C	A	L	E	S
E	N	D		L	I	L	I	E	S	
			P	I	X	E	L			
	C	R	A	T	E	S		N	A	B
C	H	E	S	T	S		M	O	R	E
H	A	S	T	E		V	I	O	L	A
O	S	C	A	R	W	I	N	N	E	R
S	T	U		E	A	S	T	E	N	D
E	E	E		D	R	E	S	S	E	S

Wordsearch Workout

Double Fun Sudoku
Tasty Teaser

4	2	9	8	1	5	7	6	3
6	8	5	4	7	3	2	1	9
3	1	7	2	9	6	4	5	8
5	9	8	7	2	4	1	3	6
2	3	6	9	5	1	8	4	7
1	7	4	6	3	8	5	9	2
8	6	2	1	4	9	3	7	5
9	5	1	3	8	7	6	2	4
7	4	3	5	6	2	9	8	1

Brain Buster

1	2	4	9	6	5	8	3	7
3	7	8	2	1	4	9	5	6
6	9	5	8	7	3	4	1	2
7	8	3	4	2	1	5	6	9
2	4	1	5	9	6	3	7	8
9	5	6	3	8	7	1	2	4
8	3	7	1	4	2	6	9	5
5	6	9	7	3	8	2	4	1
4	1	2	6	5	9	7	8	3

Matchstick Magic

The matchsticks which have been moved are outlined.

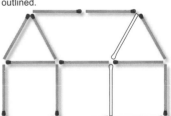

Brain Teaser

4 – The number in the top left sector plus the number in the bottom sector equals the sum of the numbers in the other three sectors.

1 Minute Number Crunch

Beginner
72 + 97 = 169, 169 ÷ 13 = 13, 13 x 6 = 78, 78 + 24 = 102, 102 x 2 = 204, 204 + 4 = 208, 208 ÷ 8 = 26

Intermediate
39 x 3 = 117, 117 ÷ 9 x 4 = 52, 52 ÷ 2 = 26, 26 ÷ 13 x 10 = 20, 20 + 4 (20% of 20) = 24, 24 x 6 = 144, 144 ÷ 8 = 18

Advanced
240 ÷ 40 x 9 = 54, 54 x 7 = 378, 378 ÷ 18 x 11 = 231, 231 ÷ 1.5 = 154, 154 x 5 = 770, 770 x 1.6 = 1232, 1232 + 2321 = 3553

Page 64

Codeword Conundrum

O	R	I	G	I	N		K	E	Y	S	T	O	N	E
M		N		M			C		O		D			L
E	M	A	N	A	T	E		Z		L	A	D	L	E
L		P		G		D	R	E	A	D		B		V
E	X	T	R	E	M	E		M		I	R	A	T	E
T		H		U	N	S	A	F	E		L			N
T	A	R	I	F	F		P		O	R	A	L		
E		N		F	L	O	U	R		P		P		C
	C	O	A	L		O		A	F	R	E	S	H	
W		H		B	E	L	F	R	Y		I		E	
E	A	R	L	Y		E		U	S	E	L	E	S	S
E		O		S	W	A	N	S		N		Q		T
V	E	N	O	M		R		S	O	J	O	U	R	N
I		I		A		N			A		U			U
L	O	C	A	L	I	T	Y		E	Y	E	L	E	T

Double Fun Sudoku
Tasty Teaser

5	3	2	1	4	8	7	6	9
6	4	8	9	7	5	3	1	2
9	7	1	6	2	3	8	5	4
8	1	6	2	5	9	4	3	7
3	2	4	8	6	7	5	9	1
7	5	9	4	3	1	2	8	6
1	6	7	3	8	2	9	4	5
2	9	3	5	1	4	6	7	8
4	8	5	7	9	6	1	2	3

Brain Buster

1	9	6	4	5	3	7	2	8
4	5	3	2	7	8	6	1	9
8	7	2	6	9	1	4	5	3
3	6	7	9	4	2	1	8	5
9	4	8	1	6	5	2	3	7
2	1	5	8	3	7	9	6	4
5	8	9	7	1	6	3	4	2
6	2	4	3	8	9	5	7	1
7	3	1	5	2	4	8	9	6

Pyramid Plus
A=102, B=97, C=70, D=18, E=21, F=199, G=167, H=88, I=39, J=366, K=255, L=127, M=621, N=382, O=1003.

High-Speed Crossword

T	A	C	O	S		S	H	A	F	T
A	T	A	R	I		P	A	L	I	N
C	O	N	A	N		A	R	E	N	T
K	N	I	C	K	K	N	A	C	K	
			L	E	E	K	S			
B	A	K	E	R	Y		S	E	E	K
A	L	I						E	L	F
T	E	X	T		I	R	O	N	I	C
			O	S	C	A	R			
	K	N	O	C	K	K	N	O	C	K
P	R	O	B	E		E	A	G	L	E
T	I	T	A	N		I	T	R	A	N
A	S	I	D	E		N	E	E	D	S

1 Minute Number Crunch

Beginner
41 − 16 = 25, 25 ÷ 5 x 2 = 10, 10 + 88 = 98, 98 ÷ 2 = 49, 49 + 6 = 55, 55 ÷ 11 x 3 = 15, 15 x 12 = 180

Intermediate
89 x 3 = 267, 267 + 762 = 1029, 1029 ÷ 3 = 343, 343 − 64 = 279, 279 ÷ 9 x 5 = 155, 155 x 2 = 310, 310 ÷ 10 x 7 = 217

Advanced
120 ÷ 15 x 4 = 32, 32^3 = 32768, 32768 ÷ 64 x 3 = 1536, 1536 ÷ 3 x 2 = 1024, 1024 ÷ 32 x 9 = 288, 288 + 160 (288 ÷ 9 x 5) = 448, 448 x 3 = 1344

Page 65

High-Speed Crossword

	H	E	A	T	H		R	E	P
	M	A	G	G	I	E		E	X	A
N	E	W	Y	E	A	R	S	D	A	Y
C	L	A	P	S			I	S	L	E
A	T	I	T		M	I	N	U	T	E
A	S	I		I	O	W	A	N	S	
		M	M	X	I	I				
	S	N	A	P	I	N		S	P	A
S	P	A	R	S	E		T	H	E	M
C	H	U	G			I	R	O	N	Y
R	E	S	O	L	U	T	I	O	N	S
A	R	E		O	F	L	A	T	E	
P	E	A		P	O	L	L	S		

Domino Placement

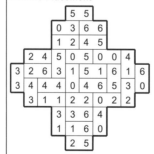

Wordsearch Workout

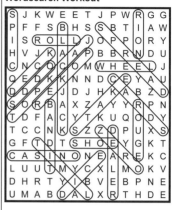

Double Fun Sudoku
Tasty Teaser

5	8	7	9	2	1	4	3	6
9	1	3	6	4	7	5	2	8
4	2	6	8	3	5	9	1	7
3	6	4	1	8	9	7	5	2
7	9	1	5	6	2	3	8	4
2	5	8	4	7	3	6	9	1
1	7	5	2	9	4	8	6	3
6	3	2	7	5	8	1	4	9
8	4	9	3	1	6	2	7	5

Brain Buster

8	4	1	5	3	2	9	7	6
3	7	9	4	6	8	1	2	5
2	6	5	1	9	7	3	8	4
5	8	3	6	2	9	7	4	1
7	1	2	3	5	4	8	6	9
6	9	4	7	8	1	2	5	3
9	5	6	2	7	3	4	1	8
4	2	8	9	1	6	5	3	7
1	3	7	8	4	5	6	9	2

Whatever Next?
J – Start from the top and move clockwise, going back three letters in the alphabet each time, finally moving from M to J, then from J to G.

Brain Teaser
24 minutes

Page 66

Mind Over Matter
The value of the letter in the bottom right is subtracted from the value in the bottom left; this total is subtracted from the sum total of the values in the two top squares, to give the value in the central square. Thus the missing value is 2, so the missing letter is B.

Double Fun Sudoku

Tasty Teaser

8	5	4	1	3	6	9	7	2
3	6	2	9	4	7	8	1	5
1	9	7	2	5	8	4	3	6
9	2	8	7	6	3	1	5	4
7	4	5	8	1	9	2	6	3
6	3	1	4	2	5	7	8	9
4	1	3	5	8	2	6	9	7
2	7	6	3	9	1	5	4	8
5	8	9	6	7	4	3	2	1

Brain Buster

3	8	1	5	7	9	2	6	4
6	4	2	8	3	1	5	9	7
5	9	7	6	2	4	3	8	1
8	1	3	9	5	7	6	4	2
9	7	5	4	6	2	8	1	3
4	2	6	1	8	3	9	7	5
7	5	9	2	4	6	1	3	8
1	3	8	7	9	5	4	2	6
2	6	4	3	1	8	7	5	9

Codeword Conundrum

R	O	T	A	R	Y		A	L	B	A	C	O	R	E
E		E		O		Z		I		D		U		A
P	I	T	O	N		I	N	V	O	I	C	I	N	G
L		A		D	O	N		E		E		J		L
I	O	N		E		C	O	N	J	U	G	A	T	E
E		U		A		C		O		R		R		R
D	I	S	Q	U	I	E	T		I	S	O	B	A	R
	M		U		G		A		N		W		C	
R	A	D	I	A	L		V	I	T	A	L	I	T	Y
	G		C		O		E		B		T		A	
W	O	R	K	H	O	R	S	E		S		C	O	S
H		A		E		O		A	F	T		H		H
I	N	V	I	D	I	O	U	S		A	X	I	O	M
M		E		G		S		Y		I		E		A
S	E	R	P	E	N	T	S		A	N	O	R	A	K

High-Speed Crossword

C	A	R	E	S		B	E	E	F	Y
A	T	O	L	L		I	G	L	O	O
L	O	O	K	I	N	G	G	O	O	D
A	N	T		C	O	D		I	T	E
I	C	E		E	R	E		S	E	L
S	E	R	F		W	A	T	E	R	S
			Y	I	E	L	D			
D	O	S	I	N	G		S	I	T	S
O	R	E		S	I	P		N	O	T
O	W	N		P	A	Y		T	I	E
F	E	E	L	I	N	G	W	E	L	L
U	L	C	E	R		M	O	R	E	L
S	L	A	T	E		Y	E	N	T	A

1 Minute Number Crunch

Beginner
51 x 6 = 306, 306 − 6 = 300, 10% of 300 = 30, 30 x 8 = 240, 240 ÷ 12 x 5 = 100, 100 + 86 = 186, 186 ÷ 3 = 62

Intermediate
488 ÷ 8 x 5 = 305, 305 x 3 = 915, 915 ÷ 15 x 2 = 122, 122 ÷ 2 = 61, 61 + 86 = 147, 147 ÷ 3 x 2 = 98, 98 − 52 = 46

Advanced
36 + 20 (36 ÷ 9 x 5) = 56, 56 x 1.375 = 77, 77 x 7 = 539, 539 − 33 = 506, 506 ÷ 22 x 19 = 437, 437 − 91 = 346, 346 x 2.5 = 865

Page 67

1 Minute Number Crunch

Beginner
100 − 42 = 58, 58 ÷ 2 = 29, 29 + 7 = 36, 50% of 36 = 18, 18 + 9 = 27, 27 ÷ 3 = 9, 9 x 5 = 45

Intermediate
85 ÷ 5 x 3 = 51, 51 x 8 = 408, 408 ÷ 17 = 24, 24^2 = 576, 576 ÷ 9 = 64, 64 ÷ 8 x 5 = 40, 40 x 3.5 = 140

Advanced
583 − 77 = 506, 506 ÷ 11 x 4 = 184, 184 x 0.625 = 115, 115 x 0.4 = 46, 46 x 13 = 598, 598 x 2 = 1196, 1196 − 555 = 641

High-Speed Crossword

P	A	S	T		F	A	R	O	F	F
E	X	P	O		I	B	E	R	I	A
C	L	A	Y		D	E	T	E	R	S
S	E	C	O	N	D	L	Y			
		E	T	A	L		P	S	S	T
S	C	R	A	P	E		E	P	E	E
A	H	A					I	R	E	
M	A	C	S		T	U	S	C	A	N
S	P	E	W		A	N	T	E		
			E	U	P	H	O	R	I	A
H	E	A	R	S	E		G	A	S	P
O	L	I	V	E	R		I	C	E	E
E	L	D	E	R	S		E	K	E	S

Wordwheel

The nine-letter word is: TREADMILL

Wordsearch Workout

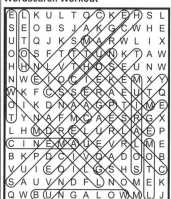

Double Fun Sudoku

Tasty Teaser

9	6	3	2	5	7	8	4	1
1	4	7	9	8	6	3	5	2
8	2	5	1	4	3	6	7	9
6	9	1	4	2	5	7	3	8
5	8	2	7	3	9	4	1	6
7	3	4	6	1	8	2	9	5
2	5	8	3	9	4	1	6	7
3	1	6	5	7	2	9	8	4
4	7	9	8	6	1	5	2	3

Brain Buster

3	4	6	5	7	9	8	1	2
5	8	1	6	2	3	4	9	7
2	9	7	8	1	4	6	5	3
4	3	8	9	5	2	1	7	6
9	1	5	4	6	7	3	2	8
7	6	2	1	3	8	9	4	5
8	2	9	7	4	6	5	3	1
1	7	4	3	8	5	2	6	9
6	5	3	2	9	1	7	8	4

Sum Circle

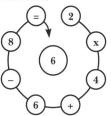

Page 68

1 Minute Number Crunch

Beginner
81 ÷ 3 = 27, 27 + 1 = 28, 25% of 28 = 7, 7 x 20 = 140, 140 − 16 = 124, 124 ÷ 4 = 31, 31 + 12 = 43

Intermediate
53 + 78 = 131, 131 x 2 = 262, 262 − 77 = 185, 185 ÷ 5 = 37, 37 + 73 = 110, 110 + 22 (20% of 110) = 132, 132 ÷ 3 = 44

Advanced
112 ÷ 14 x 5 = 40, 40^3 = 64000, 64000 x 0.375 = 24000, 24000 − 8667 = 15333, 15333 ÷ 3 x 2 = 10222, 10222 ÷ 2 = 5111, 5111 + 965 = 6076

High-Speed Crossword

H	A	S		A	R	E			
O	T	T		P	O	X		B	R	O
W	R	O	T	E	U	P		R	A	P
L	I	P	O			N	O	J	O	K	E
S	A	P	P	E	D		A	K	I	N
	E	S	T	A		W	E	N	T
A	D	D		C	N	N		N	G	O
R	I	C	K		D	E	A	R
M	A	L	E		R	E	S	E	N	T
A	L	O	N	Z	O		I	C	E	E
D	E	C		O	U	R	T	O	W	N
A	R	K		O	N	E		R	E	D
		T	D	S		D	R	S

Codeword Conundrum

B	O	Y	C	O	T	T	S		Z	E	N	I	T	H
	V		O		R		T	O	O		O			A
C	A	P	Y	B	A	R	A		O	T	T	E	R	S
	L		P		W		F		E		N			
O		Q	U	A	L	I	F	I	E	R		C	U	R
V		U		V		M		C		M		O		E
E	J	A	C	U	L	A	T	E		A	B	U	T	S
R		D		N		G		B		G		N		T
L	Y	R	I	C		I	N	E	X	A	C	T	L	Y
A		U		U	S		R		N		E			L
Y	A	P		L	I	T	I	G	A	T	O	R		
	L		A		N		G		C		A			
W	H	E	R	R	Y		S	M	O	O	T	H	L	Y
A		U		E	K	E		R		E		S		
N	E	W	E	S	T		T	R	A	C	T	I	O	N

Double Fun Sudoku
Tasty Teaser

4	6	7	2	9	5	8	3	1
8	3	5	1	4	7	6	2	9
1	2	9	6	3	8	4	5	7
3	4	2	5	7	1	9	8	6
7	1	6	9	8	2	3	4	5
5	9	8	3	6	4	1	7	2
6	8	1	7	5	3	2	9	4
2	5	4	8	1	9	7	6	3
9	7	3	4	2	6	5	1	8

Brain Buster

7	1	2	5	3	9	4	8	6
4	6	9	2	8	1	3	5	7
8	5	3	4	7	6	1	9	2
6	4	1	7	5	8	2	3	9
5	2	7	1	9	3	6	4	8
9	3	8	6	4	2	7	1	5
1	7	4	8	2	5	9	6	3
2	9	5	3	6	4	8	7	1
3	8	6	9	1	7	5	2	4

Spidoku

Page 69

High-Speed Crossword

C	L	A	S	S		K	R	A	F	T
H	A	D	T	O		L	E	M	O	N
A	M	M	A	N		E	B	E	R	T
D	A	I	L	Y	B	E	A	S	T	
		R	E	S	E	N	T			
C	H	A	R		N	E	E	D	E	D
A	O	L		T	E	X		E	V	E
B	E	S	T	O	F		S	C	A	M
			A	N	I	M	A	L		
V	A	N	I	T	Y	F	A	I	R	
R	I	D	G	E		B	A	R	R	E
O	V	A	L	S		A	R	E	A	S
M	A	M	E	T		D	I	D	N	T

Wordsearch Workout

T	S	H	A	V	I	N	G	F	O	A	M	R
S	I	S	H	O	W	E	R	G	E	L	H	E
R	M	U	X	Z	W	R	K	Y	I	R	R	Y
E	U	R	R	X	L	E	N	N	A	L	F	E
P	I	B	U	T	H	T	A	B	I	H	C	S
P	U	H	B	P	A	T	T	O	H	S	I	M
I	I	T	G	E	J	Y	T	F	L	U	S	H
L	S	O	B	I	R	A	D	H	G	R	T	A
C	G	O	I	I	M	D	H	O	P	B	E	N
L	U	T	R	H	D	L	V	A	Q	L	R	D
I	L	A	T	O	O	E	T	C	W	I	N	T
A	P	A	F	O	Z	D	T	E	K	A	U	O
N	B	O	F	U	L	A	K	T	X	N	U	W
V	N	A	G	O	S	A	R	Y	V	R	W	E
Y	H	Q	C	O	S	M	E	T	I	C	S	L

Double Fun Sudoku
Tasty Teaser

7	1	5	9	4	3	8	2	6
2	8	9	7	1	6	3	5	4
4	6	3	8	2	5	7	1	9
8	2	1	3	6	9	5	4	7
6	9	7	4	5	2	1	3	8
3	5	4	1	8	7	6	9	2
5	7	2	6	9	1	4	8	3
9	3	8	5	7	4	2	6	1
1	4	6	2	3	8	9	7	5

Brain Buster

2	6	1	9	3	8	7	5	4
3	9	5	4	7	1	6	8	2
8	4	7	5	6	2	9	1	3
6	5	2	1	8	9	3	4	7
1	8	9	3	4	7	2	6	5
4	7	3	6	2	5	1	9	8
9	1	8	2	5	3	4	7	6
5	2	6	7	1	4	8	3	9
7	3	4	8	9	6	5	2	1

Matchstick Magic

The matchsticks which have been removed are outlined.

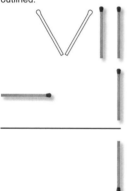

Brain Teaser

D – It goes anti-clockwise from outer to inner, the others going clockwise from outer to inner.

Simple as A, B, C

B	C	A	C	A	B
C	A	B	C	B	A
A	C	B	A	C	B
A	B	C	A	B	C
B	A	C	B	C	A
C	B	A	B	A	C

Page 70

Codeword Conundrum

```
_ A L K A L O I D _ D _ B _ N
H _ I _ N _ C A M E R A _ _ A
I N F L A T I N G _ I _ D _ M
K _ O _ U _ R O S E T T E _ _
E N U M E R A T E _ I _ I _ S
R _ E _ G _ E K E _ M _ A _ _
_ J E T T I S O N _ S P E A K
P _ R _ C _ R _ V _ U _ E _ _
A I M E D _ S C R I B B L E _
R _ A _ A R C _ R _ E _ B _ _
A _ G _ Z _ E X Q U I S I T E
D E N I Z E N _ L _ C _ R _ _
I _ I _ L _ T E L E M E T R Y
G I F T E D _ W _ N _ N _ L _
M _ Y _ D _ T E E T O T A L _
```

Double Fun Sudoku

Tasty Teaser

7	4	6	9	3	8	1	2	5
3	2	1	7	5	4	6	9	8
9	5	8	6	2	1	4	7	3
2	6	9	1	7	5	8	3	4
5	1	4	3	8	2	7	6	9
8	3	7	4	6	9	5	1	2
1	7	2	5	4	3	9	8	6
6	8	5	2	9	7	3	4	1
4	9	3	8	1	6	2	5	7

Brain Buster

4	1	2	5	6	7	3	9	8
7	3	9	2	4	8	1	5	6
5	8	6	9	3	1	7	4	2
8	4	7	1	9	5	6	2	3
2	9	5	6	8	3	4	1	7
1	6	3	4	7	2	5	8	9
3	5	8	7	1	9	2	6	4
9	2	4	3	5	6	8	7	1
6	7	1	8	2	4	9	3	5

Pyramid Plus

A=66, B=61, C=67, D=100, E=135, F=127, G=128, H=167, I=235, J=255, K=295, L=402, M=550, N=697, O=1247.

High-Speed Crossword

```
L I L _ A B E _ _ _
O N A _ B O N _ F A B
S T U _ B A D C A L L
T O N E R S _ I S L E
I N D Y _ T A H O E _
T E R R I F Y _ I T D
_ _ Y E S O R N O _ _
M C C _ T R O U N C E
Y A H O O _ I S L A _
G R U B _ G O T H O T
O N T O P O F _ O S E
D E E _ E L F _ O E R
_ A D S _ T R Y _ _ _
```

1 Minute Number Crunch

Beginner
20% of 40 = 8, 8 x 3 = 24, 24 − 4 = 20, 20 x 5 = 100, 100 − 17 = 83, 83 x 2 = 166, 166 − 40 = 126

Intermediate
120 − 12 (10% of 120) = 108, 108 ÷ 9 x 5 = 60, 60 + 24 (40% of 60) = 84, 84 ÷ 6 x 5 = 70, 70 ÷ 10 x 9 = 63, 63 x 5 = 315, 315 ÷ 9 = 35

Advanced
292 + 219 (292 ÷ 4 x 3) = 511, 511 x 9 = 4599, 4599 x 2 = 9198, 9198 ÷ 18 x 7 = 3577, 3577 − 698 = 2879, 2879 − 1993 = 886, 886 x 5 = 4430

Page 71

High-Speed Crossword

```
S W A M P _ B A B A R
A R B O R _ A M O L E
S I L V E R S P O O N
S T Y E _ H A L T E D
_ _ S L Y L Y _ _ _ _
G O B O O M _ Y U P _
O R A N G E C R U S H
B E G _ T H E M E D _
_ _ C H I P S _ _ _ _
S A L A A M _ P L E A
P U R P L E H E A R T
A D O R E _ A C T I I
M I N I S _ S T E N T
```

Battleship Bout

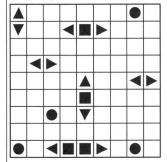

Wordsearch Workout

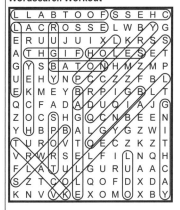

Double Fun Sudoku

Tasty Teaser

3	2	7	6	1	5	9	4	8
5	6	8	4	9	3	1	2	7
1	9	4	7	8	2	3	5	6
4	3	6	8	2	9	7	1	5
7	8	1	5	3	6	2	9	4
9	5	2	1	4	7	6	8	3
6	4	5	2	7	1	8	3	9
2	7	9	3	5	8	4	6	1
8	1	3	9	6	4	5	7	2

Brain Buster

5	1	6	9	2	8	4	7	3
8	4	9	5	7	3	6	1	2
3	2	7	4	1	6	9	8	5
9	8	5	1	6	2	3	4	7
4	7	3	8	9	5	1	2	6
1	6	2	7	3	4	5	9	8
7	9	8	6	5	1	2	3	4
2	5	1	3	4	7	8	6	9
6	3	4	2	8	9	7	5	1

Whatever Next?

7 – Each of the lower numbers is the square root of the higher number in the opposite point of the star.

Brain Teaser

24
6 x 8 = 48/2

Page 72

Mind Over Matter

The sum total of the values of the top two squares is equal to the square of the value of the central square, as is the sum total of the values of the bottom two squares. Thus the missing value is 3, so the missing letter is C.

Double Fun Sudoku

Tasty Teaser

2	6	7	3	8	1	4	9	5
1	9	5	4	7	6	2	8	3
4	3	8	2	9	5	1	6	7
9	1	6	5	3	2	8	7	4
5	7	2	8	1	4	9	3	6
3	8	4	9	6	7	5	1	2
8	5	3	6	2	9	7	4	1
6	2	1	7	4	8	3	5	9
7	4	9	1	5	3	6	2	8

Brain Buster

9	4	2	3	5	8	6	1	7
5	7	3	6	1	9	4	8	2
8	6	1	7	2	4	3	9	5
6	5	9	1	4	7	8	2	3
4	1	8	2	9	3	7	5	6
3	2	7	5	8	6	9	4	1
7	8	5	4	6	2	1	3	9
1	9	6	8	3	5	2	7	4
2	3	4	9	7	1	5	6	8

Codeword Conundrum

S	Q	U	A	W	K		E	M	P	H	A	T	I	C
I		N		H		L		O		R			A	
D	I	F	F	I	C	U	L	T		U	N	I	O	N
E		R		M		D		A		R		C		O
D	R	O	P	P	E	D		R	H	I	Z	O	M	E
		C		E		E		O			R			
J	O	K	E	R		R	E	T	I	C	E	N	C	E
A			E		E			A						L
B	L	I	N	D	F	O	L	D		F	R	A	N	K
		R			Z		R			E		X		
V	E	R	T	I	G	O		O	U	T	L	I	N	E
O		U		S		N		O		E		L		N
L	U	P	U	S		E	M	P	U	R	P	L	E	D
E		T		U		A		I		A		I		U
S	I	S	T	E	R	L	Y		G	A	M	E	T	E

High-Speed Crossword

M	I	T			B	A	D		
O	R	R			A	L	E		B	B	C
P	O	I			B	I	P	O	L	A	R
E	N	E	M	Y			P	L	A	T	O
D	I	D	A			E	C	H	O		
S	C	A	L	E	N	E			K	E	N
			N	I	G	E	R	I	A		
R	I	D		G	A	R	D	N	E	R	
A	R	T	S				E	D	N	A	
C	A	R	P	S		H	A	B	I	T	
E	Q	U	A	L	T	O		L	G	E	
D	I	E		A	A	A		U	M	D	
		P	O	X		E	A	R			

1 Minute Number Crunch

Beginner
50% of 86 = 43, 43 + 17 = 60, 60 x 2 = 120, 120 ÷ 12 = 10, 10 x 20 = 200, 200 ÷ 5 = 40, 40 + 99 = 139

Intermediate
62 x 2 = 124, 124 ÷ 4 x 3 = 93, 93 x 3 = 279, 279 ÷ 9 x 5 = 155, 155 − 69 = 86, 86 x 3 = 258, 258 + 168 = 426

Advanced
72^2 = 5184, 5184 ÷ 9 = 576, 576 ÷ 8 x 5 = 360, 360 x 7 = 2520, 2520 ÷ 40 x 7 = 441, 441 ÷ 9 x 5 = 245, 245 − 76 = 169

Page 73

Domino Placement

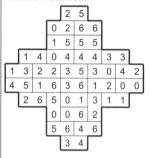

High-Speed Crossword

B	I	S	O	N		L	A	V	E	R
O	N	C	U	E		I	R	E	N	E
T	H	A	T	S	A	F	I	R	S	T
T	A	R		T	N	T		S	U	I
O	L	E		S	O	S		E	R	E
M	E	S	S		N	U	R	S	E	S
			S	K	Y	P	E			
E	S	T	E	E	M		V	A	T	S
L	E	O		N	O	S		S	E	W
I	D	S		Y	U	M		L	E	E
J	U	S	T	A	S	E	C	O	N	D
A	C	E	I	N		L	A	P	S	E
H	E	R	O	S		T	R	E	Y	S

Wordwheel

The nine-letter word is: ORCHESTRA

Wordsearch Workout

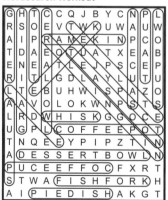

Double Fun Sudoku

Tasty Teaser

2	9	4	1	3	7	5	6	8
3	7	6	8	2	5	4	1	9
1	8	5	9	4	6	3	7	2
5	2	8	3	7	9	1	4	6
7	3	9	6	1	4	8	2	5
6	4	1	5	8	2	9	3	7
4	6	3	7	9	8	2	5	1
8	1	7	2	5	3	6	9	4
9	5	2	4	6	1	7	8	3

Brain Buster

7	5	4	2	9	3	1	6	8
9	1	6	7	8	5	3	2	4
2	8	3	6	4	1	5	7	9
3	4	7	5	6	8	2	9	1
5	6	2	1	7	9	8	4	3
1	9	8	3	2	4	7	5	6
4	2	5	8	1	6	9	3	7
6	7	1	9	3	2	4	8	5
8	3	9	4	5	7	6	1	2

Sum Circle

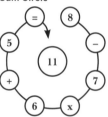

Page 74

1 Minute Number Crunch

Beginner
89 + 47 = 136, 136 ÷ 4 = 34, 50% of 34 = 17, 17 x 6 = 102, 102 − 15 = 87, 87 ÷ 3 = 29, 29 + 39 = 68

Intermediate
261 x 2 = 522, 522 ÷ 9 = 58, 250% of 58 = 145, 145 ÷ 5 x 3 = 87, 87 ÷ 3 = 29, 29 x 7 = 203, 203 − 45 = 158

Advanced
247 ÷ 13 x 3 = 57, 57 ÷ 19 x 5 = 15, 15 x 35 = 525, 525 ÷ 21 x 5 = 125, cube root of 125 = 5, 5 x 1.4 = 7, 7 x 45 = 315

High-Speed Crossword

C	I	D	E	R		R	E	B	U	S
A	D	U	L	T		E	R	U	P	T
N	E	C	K	S		S	I	C	K	O
Y	A	K	S		B	E	C	K	E	R
O	L	D		P	E	T		B	E	E
U	S	U	R	E	R		P	U	P	S
		C	E	R	A	M	I	C		
I	C	K	Y		T	A	C	K	L	E
N	O	G		B	E	D		M	A	X
L	O	O	T	E	D		F	O	R	T
A	L	O	H	A		C	L	O	S	E
W	I	S	E	R		B	I	S	O	N
S	T	E	M	S		S	P	E	N	D

Codeword Conundrum

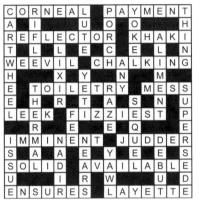

C	O	R	N	E	A	L		P	A	Y	M	E	N	T
A		I		U		O		O		H				
R	E	F	L	E	C	T	O	R		K	H	A	K	I
T		L		L		E		C		E		L		N
W	E	E	V	I	L		C	H	A	L	K	I	N	G
H				X		Y		N				M		
E		T	O	I	L	E	T	R	Y		M	E	S	S
E		H		R		T		A		S		N		U
L	E	E	K		F	I	Z	Z	I	E	S	T		P
		R		E		E		E		Q				E
I	M	M	I	N	E	N	T		J	U	D	D	E	R
S		A		A		E		Y		E		E		S
S	O	L	I	D		A	V	A	I	L	A	B	L	E
U				I		R		W				U		D
E	N	S	U	R	E	S		L	A	Y	E	T	T	E

Double Fun Sudoku

Tasty Teaser

8	5	3	1	6	2	4	7	9
6	1	9	7	4	5	8	2	3
4	2	7	3	8	9	5	6	1
1	8	6	9	5	7	3	4	2
3	9	2	8	1	4	7	5	6
5	7	4	6	2	3	9	1	8
9	6	1	5	7	8	2	3	4
2	3	5	4	9	6	1	8	7
7	4	8	2	3	1	6	9	5

Brain Buster

7	4	1	9	8	6	2	3	5
8	2	9	5	3	4	7	1	6
5	3	6	2	1	7	9	8	4
1	5	2	4	6	8	3	9	7
9	8	7	1	5	3	4	6	2
3	6	4	7	9	2	8	5	1
4	1	3	8	7	5	6	2	9
2	9	8	6	4	1	5	7	3
6	7	5	3	2	9	1	4	8

Spidoku

Page 75

High-Speed Crossword

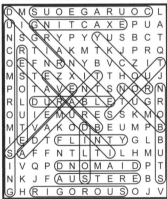

R	E	N	A	L		P	E	P	S	I
A	R	E	N	A		A	R	R	I	D
Z	I	G	G	Y		R	I	O	T	S
Z	E	A	L		R	I	C	O		
		T	E	X	A	S		F	O	G
P	A	I	R	E	D		P	H	O	
L	I	V		S	I	P		O	N	E
O	D	E		C	E	N	S	O	R	
Y	E	N		H	A	N	O	I		
	A	W	O	L		U	T	A	H	
L	I	N	E	R		A	G	I	L	E
I	N	C	A	S		S	A	V	O	R
P	A	Y	N	E		S	T	E	E	R

Wordsearch Workout

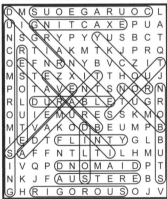

Double Fun Sudoku

Tasty Teaser

5	7	9	2	1	6	8	4	3
1	8	3	7	5	4	9	2	6
2	4	6	8	9	3	1	7	5
9	6	8	3	4	2	5	1	7
7	2	1	5	8	9	3	6	4
4	3	5	1	6	7	2	8	9
3	9	2	4	7	8	6	5	1
6	5	7	9	2	1	4	3	8
8	1	4	6	3	5	7	9	2

Brain Buster

7	6	3	1	5	4	8	2	9
9	8	1	2	7	6	5	3	4
2	4	5	9	8	3	6	1	7
8	3	9	6	2	1	7	4	5
1	2	6	5	4	7	9	8	3
4	5	7	3	9	8	1	6	2
6	1	2	7	3	9	4	5	8
5	7	4	8	6	2	3	9	1
3	9	8	4	1	5	2	7	6

Matchstick Magic

The matchsticks which have been moved are outlined.

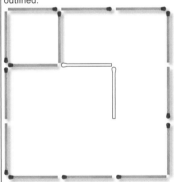

Brain Teaser

B

Domino Placement

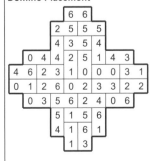

Page 76

Codeword Conundrum

M	O	L	E	S	T		A	C	O	L	Y	T	E	S
O		A		T		U		O		A		H		T
D	U	N	C	E		S	U	P	E	R	H	E	R	O
I		C		E	V	E		R		C		I		O
C	H	E	A	P		D	E	A	T	H	T	R	A	P
U			E		L		W					P		
M	A	J	O	R	I	T	Y		E	F	F	O	R	T
	R		B		N		S		A		A		O	
Z	O	D	I	A	C		I	N	K	S	T	A	N	D
	M			U		A			Q			I		
J	A	B	B	E	R	I	N	G		U	N	P	I	N
U		A		X		N		E	R	A		R		A
D	I	S	A	P	P	E	A	R		R	U	I	N	S
G		I		E		P		M		E		M		T
E	S	C	A	L	A	T	E		I	D	I	O	C	Y

Double Fun Sudoku

Tasty Teaser

5	9	2	6	4	3	1	8	7
3	7	4	1	8	9	5	2	6
8	6	1	2	5	7	9	4	3
7	1	5	9	2	8	3	6	4
9	3	6	4	7	1	8	5	2
4	2	8	3	6	5	7	9	1
6	8	3	5	1	2	4	7	9
2	5	9	7	3	4	6	1	8
1	4	7	8	9	6	2	3	5

Brain Buster

7	3	1	2	6	4	9	8	5
5	2	8	1	3	9	7	4	6
9	4	6	7	5	8	3	2	1
2	5	9	4	1	6	8	3	7
1	8	4	3	2	7	5	6	9
3	6	7	8	9	5	4	1	2
6	7	3	9	4	2	1	5	8
8	1	5	6	7	3	2	9	4
4	9	2	5	8	1	6	7	3

Pyramid Plus

A=53, B=135, C=80, D=10, E=118, F=188, G=215, H=90, I=128, J=403, K=305, L=218, M=708, N=523, O=1231.

High-Speed Crossword

P	C	S		M	S	G				
A	H	A		A	L	L		P	O	D
J	O	H	N	D	O	E		A	N	A
A	R	A	B		B	E	A	C	O	N
M	U	R	A	L		L	I	F	T	
A	S	A		O	K	E	E	F	F	E
	D	A	V	I	N	C	I			
P	R	E	T	E	N	D		C	B	S
L	O	S	T		S	P	O	R	E	
A	M	E	N	D	S		E	C	O	N
T	A	R		U	P	T	R	E	N	D
A	N	T		M	A	R		A	C	E
			P	R	Y		N	O	R	

1 Minute Number Crunch

Beginner
6 + 8 = 14, 14 ÷ 7 = 2, 2 + 47 = 49, 49 ÷ 7 = 7, 7 + 2 = 9, 9 ÷ 3 = 3, 3 + 68 = 71

Intermediate
20% of 135 = 27, 27 x 6 = 162, 162 ÷ 9 x 5 = 90, 90 − 18 (20% of 90) = 72, 72 + 79 = 151, 151 − 126 = 25, 25 + 15 (25 ÷ 5 x 3) = 40

Advanced
558 − 310 (558 ÷ 9 x 5) = 248, 248 x 0.375 = 93, 93 x 7 = 651, 651 + 434 (651 ÷ 3 x 2) = 1085, 1085 ÷ 5 x 2 = 434, 434 ÷ 7 x 3 = 186, 186 x 7 = 1302

Page 77

High-Speed Crossword

M	A	P		A	B	C		A	D	S
O	F	A		L	E	O		V	I	E
W	I	L	L	I	A	M	T	E	L	L
E	R	I	E		B	A	N	A	L	
D	E	N	A	D	A		C	U	T	E
		V	E	R	A		E	E	R	
	S	T	E	V	E	J	O	B	S	
M	I	A		O	N	A	N			
E	Z	R	A		A	R	L	I	S	S
D	E	B	T	S		O	N	T	O	
I	S	A	A	C	N	E	W	T	O	N
C	U	B		A	B	E		O	R	G
S	P	Y		M	A	L		W	E	S

1 Minute Number Crunch

Beginner
15 x 3 = 45, 45 ÷ 9 = 5, 5 + 49 = 54, 54 ÷ 9 = 6, 6^2 = 36, 36 + 20 = 56, 56 ÷ 4 = 14

Intermediate
26 x 8 = 208, 208 ÷ 4 x 3 = 156, 156 ÷ 3 = 52, 52 x 12 = 624, 624 ÷ 8 x 5 = 390, 390 ÷ 10 x 3 = 117, 117 ÷ 9 = 13

Advanced
Square root of 1369 = 37, 37 x 11 = 407, 407 + 2047 = 2454, 2454 ÷ 2 = 1227, 1227 + 818 (1227 ÷ 3 x 2) = 2045, 2045 ÷ 5 x 3 = 1227, 1227 ÷ 3 = 409

Wordsearch Workout

Double Fun Sudoku

Tasty Teaser

8	7	3	2	4	1	9	6	5
1	9	2	5	8	6	7	3	4
4	5	6	7	3	9	8	2	1
2	1	7	3	9	8	5	4	6
5	3	8	6	7	4	1	9	2
6	4	9	1	5	2	3	8	7
3	2	1	9	6	5	4	7	8
7	8	5	4	2	3	6	1	9
9	6	4	8	1	7	2	5	3

Brain Buster

9	2	4	6	5	8	3	1	7
3	1	6	4	7	2	9	5	8
7	5	8	9	1	3	6	2	4
6	9	1	7	8	4	2	3	5
2	4	7	5	3	9	8	6	1
5	8	3	2	6	1	7	4	9
4	7	2	3	9	5	1	8	6
8	3	9	1	4	6	5	7	2
1	6	5	8	2	7	4	9	3

Whatever Next?

896 – Assign a number to each letter according to its place in the alphabet, so A=1, B=2, C=3, etc. Multiply this by the number in the same point of the star and then by the central figure, to give the number in the opposite point of the star. P(16)x8=128x7=896.

Brain Teaser

2

54+16=70÷(18+17)=2   90+9=99÷(19+14)=3
55+35=90÷(26+19)=2

Page 78

Mind Over Matter

The sum total of the values of the letter in the right squares is subtracted from the sum total of the values of the letters in the left squares to give the value of the letter in the central square. Thus the missing value is 26, so the missing letter is Z.

Double Fun Sudoku

Tasty Teaser

7	3	1	8	4	2	5	6	9
8	2	4	9	5	6	3	7	1
5	6	9	7	1	3	8	4	2
6	9	3	4	7	1	2	5	8
2	1	5	6	9	8	4	3	7
4	7	8	3	2	5	1	9	6
1	5	6	2	3	9	7	8	4
9	4	2	5	8	7	6	1	3
3	8	7	1	6	4	9	2	5

Brain Buster

9	1	3	8	6	5	2	7	4
2	7	5	9	4	3	8	1	6
6	4	8	7	2	1	3	9	5
3	9	1	5	7	2	4	6	8
4	8	6	1	3	9	7	5	2
5	2	7	4	8	6	1	3	9
8	3	9	2	5	7	6	4	1
1	6	2	3	9	4	5	8	7
7	5	4	6	1	8	9	2	3

Codeword Conundrum

M	A	P	P	E	D		E	L	D	R	I	T	C	H
U		H		O		U		E		U				O
C	A	T	A	C	L	Y	S	M		F		T		M
U		N		P		A	P	P	L	A	U	S	E	
S	L	I	T		H	U	G		E				G	
	E		O		I		O	N	Y	X		J		R
S	T	A	M	I	N	A		O		I	M	A	G	O
A		Q		N		B	A	R		V		Z		W
F	L	U	K	E		E		M	U	E	Z	Z	I	N
E		A		F	E	T	A		N		E		R	
G		F				L	I	T		O	A	K	S	
U	P	H	E	A	V	A	L		R		L		I	
A		I		B		L	Y	R	I	C	I	S	T	S
R		S		L		O			E		T		A	
D	I	S	H	E	V	E	L		D	I	E	S	E	L

High-Speed Crossword

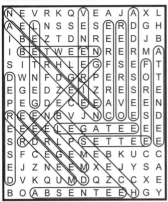

1 Minute Number Crunch

Beginner
39 ÷ 3 = 13, 13 x 2 = 26, 26 + 36 = 62, 62 ÷ 2 = 31, 31 − 7 = 24, 24 ÷ 3 = 8, 8 x 10 = 80

Intermediate
494 − 39 = 455, 455 ÷ 5 = 91, 91 + 66 = 157, 157 x 2 = 314, 314 − 88 = 226, 226 ÷ 2 = 113, 113 x 6 = 678

Advanced
572 x 2 = 1144, 1144 − 143 (1144 x 0.125) = 1001, 1001 x 11 = 11011, 11011 − 7477 = 3534, 3534 ÷ 2 = 1767, 1767 ÷ 3 x 2 = 1178, 1178 ÷ 19 x 5 = 310

Page 79

Battleship Bout

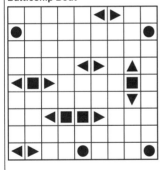

High-Speed Crossword

J	A	I	M	E		E	B	A	Y
A	S	P	E	N	S		B	I	L	E
W	H	O	S	T	H	E	B	O	S	S
			A	R	A	B				
N	E	W	S	Y		O	D	O	R	
A	T	E			I	N	A	R	O	W
W	H	A	T	S	M	Y	N	A	M	E
S	E	R	I	E	S		L	E	S	
	L	Y	N	N		R	O	B	O	T
			S	P	A	R				
W	H	E	R	E	S	W	A	L	D	O
E	U	R	O		S	E	T	O	U	T
S	T	A	Y		R	E	A	D	S	

Wordwheel

The nine-letter word is: PARAMEDIC

Wordsearch Workout

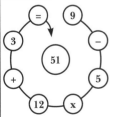

Double Fun Sudoku

Tasty Teaser

5	8	4	2	7	9	3	6	1
9	7	3	1	5	6	2	4	8
6	2	1	3	8	4	7	5	9
3	4	5	6	1	7	9	8	2
7	9	2	8	3	5	6	1	4
8	1	6	9	4	2	5	7	3
4	3	9	7	6	8	1	2	5
2	6	8	5	9	1	4	3	7
1	5	7	4	2	3	8	9	6

Brain Buster

9	5	3	7	8	4	1	2	6
1	4	7	2	9	6	5	3	8
8	6	2	3	1	5	7	9	4
3	8	4	9	5	2	6	1	7
7	1	9	8	6	3	4	5	2
5	2	6	1	4	7	9	8	3
6	7	8	5	3	9	2	4	1
2	9	1	4	7	8	3	6	5
4	3	5	6	2	1	8	7	9

Sum Circle

Page 80

1 Minute Number Crunch

Beginner
45 − 10 = 35, 35 ÷ 7 = 5, 5 + 28 = 33, 33 ÷ 3 = 11, 11 − 7 = 4, 4 x 6 = 24, 24 − 15 = 9

Intermediate
265 ÷ 5 = 53, 53 x 8 = 424, 424 − 176 = 248, 248 ÷ 8 = 31, 31 + 79 = 110, 110 ÷ 11 x 4 = 40, 40 x 9.5 = 380

Advanced
161 ÷ 7 x 3 = 69, 69 + 115 = 184, 184 x 5 = 920, 920 ÷ 8 x 5 = 575, 575 − 492 = 83, 83² = 6889, 6889 − 5971 = 918

High-Speed Crossword

F	I	L	A	S		T	U	S	K	S
E	R	A	S	E		A	F	O	O	T
M	O	T	H	E	R	G	O	O	S	E
U	N	I		N	E	T		T	H	E
R	I	N		A	C	E		H	E	R
S	C	A	R		L	A	K	E	R	S
		P	R	I	M	O				
B	U	S	M	A	N		S	A	F	E
E	N	T		D	I	G		C	O	X
A	M	A		I	N	N		A	R	E
T	A	K	E	A	G	A	N	D	E	R
I	D	E	A	L		W	A	I	S	T
T	E	S	T	S		S	W	A	T	S

Codeword Conundrum

C	O		R	E	L	U	C	T	A	N	T	L	Y
R	A	B	B	I		A		U		E		E	
A		J		G	A	Z	E	B	O		W	O	M	B
F	R	E	S	H		Y		R		E		O	
T		C		T		W	A	D	D	L	I	N	G
	T		F	L	E	A		A		N		E	
A	D	I	E	U		X		I		A	F	A	R
C		V		L	A	P	W	I	N	G		R	M
R	E	E	F		B		O			O	B	E	Y	S
I		L		B		R	O	A	R		Q		
D	A	Y	B	R	E	A	K		G		U		X
	L		A		S		T		E	L	E	G	Y
B	A	S	S		S	T	E	R	E	O		N	L
	R		T		E		I		U	N	C	L	E
I	M	P	E	C	U	N	I	O	U	S		Y	M

Double Fun Sudoku

Tasty Teaser

8	9	5	4	1	2	7	6	3
2	1	3	6	7	8	5	4	9
4	7	6	5	9	3	2	8	1
3	2	9	8	6	1	4	7	5
1	4	8	7	3	5	6	9	2
6	5	7	2	4	9	3	1	8
9	6	1	3	5	7	8	2	4
5	8	4	9	2	6	1	3	7
7	3	2	1	8	4	9	5	6

Brain Buster

7	9	5	6	2	4	1	8	3
2	8	6	9	1	3	4	5	7
4	1	3	8	5	7	9	6	2
3	2	4	1	8	5	7	9	6
9	6	8	7	3	2	5	4	1
5	7	1	4	6	9	3	2	8
6	4	9	2	7	1	8	3	5
1	5	2	3	9	8	6	7	4
8	3	7	5	4	6	2	1	9

Spidoku

Page 81

High-Speed Crossword

D	O	H	S		I	R	I	S	H
S	A	R	A	H		M	E	D	I	A
A	L	A	M	O		I	C	O	N	S
P	I	L	L	O	W	T	A	L	K	
		E	T	H	A	N			
N	E	W	T		A	T	T	E	N	D
O	W	E		A	T	E		M	O	O
R	E	B	O	R	N		N	U	D	E
		B	R	O	K	E			
	S	H	E	E	T	M	U	S	I	C
J	O	E	Y	S		A	T	O	N	E
I	M	S	E	T		R	E	S	I	N
B	E	A	D	S		T	R	O	T	

Wordsearch Workout

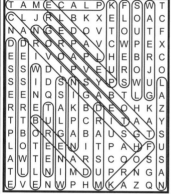

Double Fun Sudoku

Tasty Teaser

4	8	2	3	5	9	7	1	6
3	7	1	2	8	6	9	4	5
6	5	9	1	4	7	2	3	8
9	6	5	8	3	4	1	7	2
7	2	3	6	1	5	8	9	4
1	4	8	7	9	2	5	6	3
2	1	7	4	6	8	3	5	9
8	9	4	5	7	3	6	2	1
5	3	6	9	2	1	4	8	7

Brain Buster

5	1	7	4	8	2	6	3	9
6	3	2	9	5	1	8	7	4
4	8	9	7	3	6	1	2	5
3	5	6	1	9	7	2	4	8
2	4	8	3	6	5	9	1	7
9	7	1	2	4	8	3	5	6
1	9	5	6	7	3	4	8	2
7	2	4	8	1	9	5	6	3
8	6	3	5	2	4	7	9	1

Matchstick Magic

The matchsticks which have been moved are outlined.

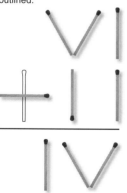

Brain Teaser

12 – In the 1st hexagon opposite numbers add up to 36. In the 2nd hexagon opposite numbers add up to 43. In the 3rd hexagon opposite numbers add up to 32.

1 Minute Number Crunch

Beginner

37 – 8 = 29, 29 x 3 = 87, 87 + 35 = 122, 50% of 122 = 61, 61 – 11 = 50, 50 x 3 = 150, 150 ÷ 5 = 30

Intermediate

457 + 754 = 1211, 1211 – 666 = 545, 545 ÷ 5 = 109, 109 x 7 = 763, 763 + 89 = 852, 852 ÷ 3 x 2 = 568, 568 ÷ 8 x 5 = 355

Advanced

161 + 115 (161 ÷ 7 x 5) = 276, 276 + 184 (276 ÷ 3 x 2) = 460, 460 + 92 (20% of 460) = 552, 552 – 398 = 154, 154 x 4 = 616, 616 x 1.875 = 1155, 1155 + 462 (1155 ÷ 5 x 2) = 1617

Page 82

Codeword Conundrum

K	N	I	C	K	E	R	S		W	I	C	K	E	T
	E		O		N		U	S	E		O		O	
E	X	A	M	I	N	E	S		D	O	N	J	O	N
	T		M		U		H		B		A			
Z		P	A	C	I	F	I	E	R	S		I	M	P
I		U		A		I		M		C		L		A
P	A	P	E	R	C	L	I	P		E	T	H	E	R
P		T		C		O		N		O		S		S
E	M	E	E	R		H	A	R	L	E	Q	U	I	N
R		T		I		E		I		S		S		I
S	U	E		D	I	S	M	A	N	T	L	E		P
	E		G		A		E		U		I			
V	E	R	V	E	T		G	R	E	E	N	E	R	Y
I			A		E	L	M		D		A		I	
E	L	A	T	E	D		A	B	S	T	R	U	S	E

Double Fun Sudoku

Tasty Teaser

4	7	3	9	6	2	5	8	1
9	1	5	7	3	8	6	2	4
6	2	8	1	4	5	3	9	7
8	3	9	5	1	4	7	6	2
2	6	7	8	9	3	1	4	5
5	4	1	6	2	7	9	3	8
1	9	2	4	5	6	8	7	3
3	8	6	2	7	1	4	5	9
7	5	4	3	8	9	2	1	6

Brain Buster

2	6	7	4	3	1	5	9	8
8	5	4	7	2	9	1	6	3
3	1	9	8	6	5	7	2	4
1	7	2	6	5	8	3	4	9
5	8	6	3	9	4	2	7	1
9	4	3	1	7	2	6	8	5
4	3	1	2	8	6	9	5	7
7	2	5	9	4	3	8	1	6
6	9	8	5	1	7	4	3	2

Pyramid Plus

A=1, B=132, C=29, D=90, E=19, F=133, G=161, H=119, I=109, J=294, K=280, L=228, M=574, N=508, O=1082.

High-Speed Crossword

S	T	E	P		M	A	S	C	O	T
O	R	A	L		A	R	C	A	D	E
L	I	S	A		N	E	A	T	E	N
D	O	T	S		C	A	N			
		E	T	C	H		S	C	A	M
V	A	R	I	O	U	S		A	L	A
E	R	E	C	T		C	A	N	O	N
R	I	G		S	P	A	N	D	E	X
B	A	G	S		A	R	T	Y		
		H	I	S		E	C	H	O	
A	S	S	E	S	S		D	A	U	B
N	E	E	D	L	E		U	N	T	O
T	E	A	S	E	D		P	E	T	E

1 Minute Number Crunch

Beginner

47 + 27 = 74, 74 ÷ 2 = 37, 37 – 16 = 21, 21 ÷ 3 = 7, 7 x 15 = 105, 105 ÷ 5 = 21, 21 ÷ 3 = 7

Intermediate

41 + 92 = 133, 133 x 4 = 532, 532 ÷ 4 x 3 = 399, 399 + 266 (399 ÷ 3 x 2) = 665, 665 + 85 = 750, 750 x 1.3 = 975, 975 – 489 = 486

Advanced

59 x 6 = 354, 354 + 236 (354 ÷ 3 x 2) = 590, 590 ÷ 10 x 3 = 177, 177 ÷ 3 x 2 = 118, 118 x 4 = 472, 472 – 319 = 153, 153 + 119 (153 ÷ 9 x 7) = 272

Page 83

High-Speed Crossword

O	A	K	S		K	A	R	A	T	S
D	R	E	W		I	T	A	L	I	A
D	I	N	E		M	E	T	A	L	S
S	A	K	E		K	I	S	S	E	S
		E	T	H	A	N				
Y	E	S	S	I	R		K	E	A	
A	R	E		P	D	A		I	N	K
P	R	Y		A	M	A	N	D	A	
		O	S	I	N	G				
I	M	P	I	S	H		E	K	E	S
M	A	I	T	A	I		M	O	L	E
O	R	T	E	G	A		I	N	S	T
N	E	T	M	E	N		A	G	E	S

Domino Placement

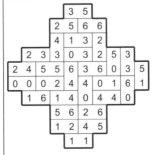

Wordsearch Workout

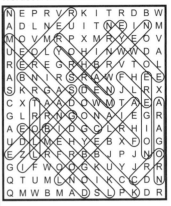

Double Fun Sudoku

Tasty Teaser

6	5	7	3	8	4	1	2	9
8	4	9	2	1	6	5	7	3
1	2	3	7	9	5	8	4	6
2	7	5	1	3	9	6	8	4
9	1	4	6	7	8	2	3	5
3	8	6	5	4	2	9	1	7
4	3	8	9	6	1	7	5	2
7	6	2	8	5	3	4	9	1
5	9	1	4	2	7	3	6	8

Brain Buster

2	6	4	9	1	7	3	8	5
9	7	8	3	5	6	4	2	1
3	5	1	2	8	4	9	7	6
7	4	5	6	9	2	8	1	3
1	3	9	4	7	8	6	5	2
6	8	2	1	3	5	7	4	9
5	2	7	8	6	9	1	3	4
8	1	6	5	4	3	2	9	7
4	9	3	7	2	1	5	6	8

Whatever Next?

T – Start at the top and move forwards in the alphabet first 2 places, then 3, then 2, then 3, then 2 (to T), then 3 to W.

Brain Teaser

F

Page 84

Mind Over Matter

The value of the letter in the central square is half that of the sum total of the values of the letters in the other squares. Thus the missing value is 19, so the missing letter is S.

Double Fun Sudoku

Tasty Teaser

8	9	6	1	4	5	3	7	2
1	2	5	3	9	7	4	8	6
4	3	7	8	2	6	9	1	5
7	5	9	4	6	1	8	2	3
6	8	1	7	3	2	5	9	4
2	4	3	9	5	8	1	6	7
9	7	4	6	8	3	2	5	1
5	6	8	2	1	4	7	3	9
3	1	2	5	7	9	6	4	8

Brain Buster

3	9	1	7	6	2	8	5	4
5	7	6	4	8	9	3	1	2
4	2	8	3	1	5	7	6	9
2	8	7	9	5	1	4	3	6
1	6	5	2	4	3	9	7	8
9	3	4	6	7	8	5	2	1
8	5	3	1	2	4	6	9	7
7	1	9	8	3	6	2	4	5
6	4	2	5	9	7	1	8	3

Codeword Conundrum

D	I	S	A	F	F	E	C	T		S	C	A	L	P
E		U		O		X		R		Q		C		I
F	A	B	L	E		C	R	O	Q	U	E	T		E
E		J		T		E		D		E		E		C
R	E	U	S	A	B	L	E		S	L	U	D	G	E
		G		L		D		C						M
I	M	A	M		P	O	W	E	R	H	O	U	S	E
N		T		F		V		L		Y		N		A
C	H	E	E	R	F	U	L	L	Y		I	D	O	L
U			E		M			F		E				
M	O	C	K	E	D		B	U	L	L	F	R	O	G
B		O		Z		L		N		A		T		L
E		B	R	I	G	A	N	D		B	R	A	V	O
N		R		N		V		U		B		K		B
T	W	A	N	G		A	C	E	T	Y	L	E	N	E

High-Speed Crossword

M	E	T		B	U	S			
A	N	A		E	T	A		T	I	C
N	A	M	E	T	A	G		E	D	U
I	M	P	S		H	A	M	M	E	R
L	E	A	P	S		I	P	A	D	
A	L	F		A	M	S	T	E	L	S
		L	O	R	E	T	T	A		
S	P	O	K	A	N	E		R	I	M
E	U	R	O		P	R	I	C	E	
T	R	I	K	E	S		I	Z	O	D
T	E	D		T	H	E	P	O	N	D
O	R	A		C	O	W		N	I	L
			H	E	E		A	C	E	

1 Minute Number Crunch

Beginner
$12 \div 6 = 2$, $2 + 20 = 22$, $22 \times 2 = 44$, $44 - 30 = 14$, $14 \div 7 = 2$, $2 + 66 = 68$, 25% of $68 = 17$

Intermediate
$61 - 15 = 46$, $46 \times 3 = 138$, $138 \times 1.5 = 207$, $207 \div 9 = 23$, $23 + 57 = 80$, $80 \div 10 \times 7 = 56$, $56 \times 11 = 616$

Advanced
$117 \div 9 \times 5 = 65$, $65 \div 13 \times 8 = 40$, $40 \div 2.5 = 16$, $16^2 = 256$, $256 + 160 (256 \times 0.625) = 416$, $416 \div 16 \times 5 = 130$, $130 - 91 (130 \div 10 \times 7) = 39$

Page 85

1 Minute Number Crunch

Beginner
$35 \times 3 = 105$, $105 + 81 = 186$, $186 \div 6 = 31$, $31 \times 9 = 279$, $279 - 42 = 237$, $237 + 3 = 240$, $240 \div 12 \times 5 = 100$

Intermediate
$89 + 98 = 187$, $187 \times 2 = 374$, $374 \times 1.5 = 561$, $561 \div 3 = 187$, $187 - 78 = 109$, $109 \times 4 = 436$, $436 + 47 = 483$

Advanced
$11 \times 33 = 363$, $363 - 121 (363 \div 3) = 242$, $242 \times 9 = 2178$, $2178 \div 18 \times 11 = 1331$, $1331 + 11$ (cube root of 1331) $= 1342$, $1342 \div 2 = 671$, $671 \times 4 = 2684$

High-Speed Crossword

H	O	S	E	D		E	R	A	S	E
A	N	K	L	E		M	A	R	E	S
S	T	U	M	P		I	N	C	A	S
P	A	L		O	W	L		A	L	A
S	P	L	A	S	H	Y		D	A	Y
			R	I	O		T	I	N	S
	W	H	A	T	S	W	H	A	T	
C	R	A	B		W	O	O			
H	E	S		T	H	R	U	S	T	S
A	S	H		A	O	K		C	A	P
S	T	O	O	P		S	C	A	R	E
E	L	U	D	E		U	P	B	O	W
D	E	T	E	R		P	A	S	T	S

Wordwheel

The nine-letter word is: CONDIMENT

Wordsearch Workout

U	F	O	D	I	E	Y	P	Z	K	W	L	J
T	H	E	P	A	S	T	H	X	R	I	B	P
Z	Z	E	L	A	W	S	D	W	O	R	C	Y
M	Z	O	T	B	A	T	H	E	W	I	F	E
Y	G	N	I	K	N	I	S	W	H	G	S	L
N	A	S	N	E	I	L	A	T	U	N	N	O
F	Y	F	A	C	M	N	T	Y	A	I	I	M
G	A	C	A	U	A	E	F	K	L	N	F	E
N	S	H	N	Q	L	S	E	L	Z	O	F	A
I	P	A	R	P	S	D	T	K	Y	R	O	T
L	M	S	E	B	N	E	I	L	Y	I	C	I
I	N	E	M	E	M	O	R	I	E	S	N	N
A	H	S	W	C	K	Z	S	H	S	W	G	
S	S	S	H	T	H	E	F	U	T	U	R	E
D	A	F	O	O	T	B	A	L	L	A	G	T

Double Fun Sudoku

Tasty Teaser

4	5	8	7	2	6	3	1	9
7	6	9	1	5	3	4	2	8
1	3	2	4	9	8	6	7	5
8	2	5	6	1	9	7	4	3
3	7	6	2	8	4	9	5	1
9	4	1	3	7	5	2	8	6
6	1	7	5	3	2	8	9	4
2	8	3	9	4	1	5	6	7
5	9	4	8	6	7	1	3	2

Brain Buster

3	4	5	2	7	8	1	9	6
7	1	6	5	9	4	3	8	2
9	8	2	6	3	1	4	5	7
5	6	1	8	2	9	7	3	4
8	3	9	4	6	7	5	2	1
4	2	7	1	5	3	9	6	8
1	9	3	7	8	2	6	4	5
6	7	8	3	4	5	2	1	9
2	5	4	9	1	6	8	7	3

Sum Circle

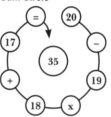

Page 86

1 Minute Number Crunch

Beginner
$37 \times 3 = 111$, $111 - 3 = 108$, $108 \div 4 = 27$, $27 \times 3 = 81$, $81 \div 9 = 9$, $9 + 26 = 35$, $35 \div 5 = 7$

Intermediate
$237 + 732 = 969$, $969 \div 3 \times 2 = 646$, $646 \div 2 = 323$, $323 + 98 = 421$, $421 \times 3 = 1263$, $1263 - 845 = 418$, $418 \times 2 = 836$

Advanced
$996 \div 4 = 249$, $249 \div 3 \times 2 = 166$, $166 - 98 = 68$, $68 \div 0.8 = 85$, $85 \div 17 \times 14 = 70$, $70 \div 0.7 = 100$, $100^3 = 1000000$

High-Speed Crossword

I	M	P	S			C	O	O	P	S
R	A	R	E		L	A	D	D	E	R
I	R	O	N		O	R	D	E	R	S
S	C	H	E	D	U	L	E			
		O	C	T		O	S	C	A	R
L	U	C	A	S		S	T	O	L	I
A	S	K						N	A	B
S	E	E	D	S		S	C	A	N	S
T	R	Y	I	T		E	R	R		
			P	R	I	C	E	T	A	G
P	U	P	P	E	T		D	I	L	L
A	S	S	E	S	S		O	S	L	O
L	A	I	R	S			S	T	A	B

Codeword Conundrum

P	E	D	O	M	E	T	E	R		J	I	V	E	D
O		E		I		H		O		E		I		E
W	A	L	T	Z		A	Q	U	E	O	U	S		F
E		I		Z		N		X		P		I		E
R	E	C	H	E	C	K	S		F	A	L	T	E	R
		I		N			A		R					E
B	O	O	M		C	U	R	M	U	D	G	E	O	N
Y		U		F		N		E		Y		R		C
S	U	S	P	I	C	I	O	N	S		B	A	B	E
T			N		T			T		H		D		
A	P	P	E	A	L		S	T	R	A	T	I	F	Y
N		A		L		I		H		R		C		I
D		S	P	I	T	T	L	E		A	B	A	S	E
E		T		S		C		R		S		T		L
R	O	A	S	T		H	O	M	E	S	T	E	A	D

Double Fun Sudoku

Tasty Teaser

4	8	6	2	1	7	5	3	9
9	1	5	3	6	8	4	2	7
3	7	2	9	5	4	8	1	6
1	5	4	7	9	3	2	6	8
8	9	3	1	2	6	7	4	5
2	6	7	4	8	5	1	9	3
6	2	1	5	7	9	3	8	4
7	3	8	6	4	1	9	5	2
5	4	9	8	3	2	6	7	1

Brain Buster

8	9	3	4	1	5	2	6	7
6	7	2	9	3	8	1	5	4
5	4	1	7	2	6	3	8	9
1	6	4	8	7	2	9	3	5
2	8	7	5	9	3	4	1	6
3	5	9	6	4	1	7	2	8
9	1	5	2	6	4	8	7	3
7	3	8	1	5	9	6	4	2
4	2	6	3	8	7	5	9	1

Spidoku

Page 87

High-Speed Crossword

P	E	A	C	E		A	I	D	E	S
A	L	L	A	N		C	R	O	U	P
S	P	A	R	E	C	H	A	N	G	E
T	A	S		M	A	E		K	E	N
A	S	K		I	N	D		E	N	D
S	O	A	K	E	D		A	Y	E	S
		A	S	Y	E	T				
P	S	S	T		C	A	L	A	I	S
I	O	N		C	A	T		S	N	L
G	O	O		U	N	I		T	H	E
S	T	R	I	K	E	T	H	R	E	E
T	H	E	R	E		U	B	O	A	T
Y	E	S	E	S		P	O	S	T	S

Wordsearch Workout

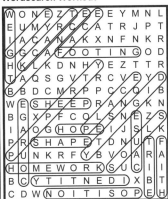

Double Fun Sudoku

Tasty Teaser

9	5	3	7	2	1	4	8	6
4	7	6	9	5	8	2	3	1
1	2	8	4	3	6	5	7	9
5	8	7	1	9	4	3	6	2
2	3	9	5	6	7	1	4	8
6	1	4	3	8	2	7	9	5
8	9	5	2	7	3	6	1	4
3	4	2	6	1	9	8	5	7
7	6	1	8	4	5	9	2	3

Brain Buster

2	5	8	7	6	1	3	9	4
9	3	6	4	2	5	8	1	7
1	4	7	9	3	8	2	5	6
8	9	2	5	4	6	7	3	1
7	1	4	8	9	3	5	6	2
3	6	5	2	1	7	9	4	8
6	2	1	3	7	9	4	8	5
5	7	9	1	8	4	6	2	3
4	8	3	6	5	2	1	7	9

Matchstick Magic

The matchsticks which have been moved are outlined.

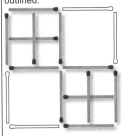

Brain Teaser

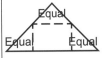

Simple as A, B, C

C	A	B	B	C	A
B	A	C	C	A	B
C	C	B	B	A	A
A	B	C	A	B	C
A	C	A	C	B	B
B	B	A	A	C	C

Page 88

Codeword Conundrum

Double Fun Sudoku

Tasty Teaser

7	6	4	9	1	8	2	5	3
1	9	3	4	2	5	7	8	6
5	8	2	3	7	6	9	4	1
8	7	5	6	9	1	4	3	2
4	2	6	5	8	3	1	9	7
3	1	9	7	4	2	8	6	5
9	5	1	2	3	4	6	7	8
6	4	8	1	5	7	3	2	9
2	3	7	8	6	9	5	1	4

Brain Buster

1	2	5	9	7	6	8	4	3
7	8	6	3	1	4	9	2	5
4	3	9	5	2	8	6	1	7
8	1	3	7	4	5	2	6	9
6	9	2	1	8	3	5	7	4
5	7	4	2	6	9	1	3	8
2	6	8	4	5	7	3	9	1
3	5	7	6	9	1	4	8	2
9	4	1	8	3	2	7	5	6

Pyramid Plus

A=117, B=78, C=61, D=50, E=34, F=195, G=139, H=111, I=84, J=334, K=250, L=195, M=584, N=445, O=1029.

High-Speed Crossword

A	M	P		A	H	S			
C	A	R		L	E	O		T	M	S
O	N	E	S	E	L	F		H	I	P
R	U	T	H		M	A	K	E	M	E
N	A	T	E	S		A	L	I	A	
S	L	Y		H	A	T	R	A	C	K
			I	C	E	C	O	L	D	
P	E	N	A	L	T	Y		Y	E	W
U	M	P	S		S	H	I	N	E	
R	A	I	S	E	S		I	N	C	A
S	I	N		G	U	M	D	R	O	P
E	L	K		A	R	E		E	R	O
		D	E	X		D	E	N		

1 Minute Number Crunch

Beginner
51 ÷ 3 = 17, 17 + 22 = 39, 39 ÷ 3 = 13, 13 x 4 = 52, 52 ÷ 13 = 4, 4^2 = 16, 16 + 9 = 25

Intermediate
127 x 3 = 381, 381 + 69 = 450, 450 x 1.2 = 540, 540 ÷ 9 x 7 = 420, 420 + 21 = 441, square root of 441 = 21, 21 + 6 (21 ÷ 7 x 2) = 27

Advanced
256 ÷ 0.5 = 512, cube root of 512 = 8, 8 x 1.75 = 14, 14 x 2.5 = 35, 35^2 = 1225, 1225 ÷ 49 x 6 = 150, 68% of 150 = 102

Page 89

High-Speed Crossword

E	B	B		P	A	D			
S	E	A		B	R	A		S	K	I
C	A	B	A	R	E	T		H	A	T
O	N	Y	X		S	E	N	O	R	A
R	I	C	E	S		O	P	A	L	
T	E	A		A	C	C	E	P	T	S
		R	A	V	I	O	L	I		
S	U	R	R	E	A	L		N	B	A
U	N	I	T		A	N	G	E	L	
A	G	A	S	S	I		U	C	L	A
V	E	G		M	O	R	T	A	L	S
E	R	E		O	W	E		R	O	K
		G	A	P		T	W	A		

1 Minute Number Crunch

Beginner
47 + 61 = 108, 108 ÷ 6 = 18, 18 + 12 = 30, 30 x 6 = 180, 180 − 6 = 174, 174 ÷ 2 = 87, 87 ÷ 3 = 29

Intermediate
42 + 19 = 61, 61 x 9 = 549, 549 ÷ 3 x 2 = 366, 366 ÷ 3 = 122, 122 + 11 = 133, 133 ÷ 7 x 4 = 76, 76 x 4 = 304

Advanced
62 ÷ 0.5 = 124, 124 x 8 = 992, 992 ÷ 16 x 11 = 682, 682 x 3 = 2046, 2046 ÷ 6 x 5 = 1705, 80% of 1705 = 1364, 1364 x 0.25 = 341

Wordsearch Workout

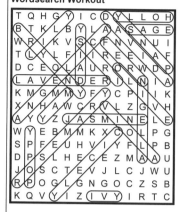

Double Fun Sudoku

Tasty Teaser

7	9	6	2	1	5	8	4	3
4	2	3	8	9	7	1	5	6
1	8	5	4	6	3	2	7	9
9	4	7	1	3	6	5	8	2
8	3	1	9	5	2	7	6	4
5	6	2	7	8	4	3	9	1
2	1	9	5	4	8	6	3	7
3	7	8	6	2	9	4	1	5
6	5	4	3	7	1	9	2	8

Brain Buster

2	4	8	1	6	7	9	3	5
7	3	9	5	4	8	2	1	6
1	5	6	9	2	3	7	8	4
5	7	4	8	1	2	6	9	3
6	9	3	7	5	4	1	2	8
8	1	2	3	9	6	5	4	7
9	6	7	4	3	1	8	5	2
3	8	1	2	7	5	4	6	9
4	2	5	6	8	9	3	7	1

Whatever Next?

64 – The numbers in the outer points of the star are the cubes of the adjacent numbers in the central hexagon.

Brain Teaser

(21 x 14) − 3 − 3 = 288

Page 90

Mind Over Matter

The value of the letter in the central square is one quarter of the sum total of the value of the letters in the outer four squares. Thus the missing value is 12, so the missing letter is L.

Double Fun Sudoku

Tasty Teaser

6	5	4	7	1	8	2	9	3
8	7	2	3	6	9	5	1	4
1	3	9	5	4	2	6	7	8
7	1	5	2	3	4	9	8	6
9	6	3	1	8	7	4	2	5
2	4	8	9	5	6	7	3	1
3	8	7	6	2	5	1	4	9
5	9	1	4	7	3	8	6	2
4	2	6	8	9	1	3	5	7

Brain Buster

9	7	4	6	3	2	5	8	1
3	6	1	8	5	4	9	2	7
2	5	8	9	1	7	4	3	6
8	3	6	4	7	5	2	1	9
7	9	5	2	8	1	3	6	4
1	4	2	3	6	9	7	5	8
5	1	3	7	9	6	8	4	2
4	8	7	1	2	3	6	9	5
6	2	9	5	4	8	1	7	3

Codeword Conundrum

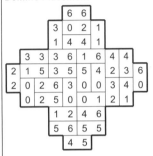

High-Speed Crossword

S	O	L		P	O	E			
T	H	O		A	L	L		B	A	T
E	D	W	A	R	D	S		E	D	U
L	E	E	S		S	E	N	D	I	N
L	A	S	S	O		A	R	E	A	
A	R	T		F	U	R	I	O	U	S
		B	U	F	F	A	L	O		
G	R	I	S	S	O	M		M	A	H
R	O	D	E			P	A	S	T	A
A	D	D	S	U	P		B	U	R	T
D	D	E		G	L	A	C	I	E	R
S	Y	R		L	E	I		T	S	E
			Y	A	M		E	T	D	

1 Minute Number Crunch

Beginner
91 + 25 = 116, 116 ÷ 2 = 58, 58 ÷ 2 = 29, 29 + 17 = 46, 46 ÷ 2 = 23, 23 + 17 = 40, 25% of 40 = 10

Intermediate
47 x 3 = 141, 141 − 75 = 66, 66 x 2 = 132, 132 ÷ 6 x 5 = 110, 110 x 0.8 = 88, 88 ÷ 4 x 3 = 66, 66 x 4 = 264

Advanced
39^2 = 1521, 1521 ÷ 9 x 7 = 1183, 1183 ÷ 7 x 5 = 845, 845 x 7 = 5915, 5915 − 4738 = 1177, 1177 x 4 = 4708, 4708 + 9929 = 14637

Page 91

Domino Placement

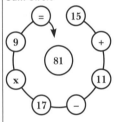

High-Speed Crossword

S	E	N	T	U	P			T	H	U	D
E	V	E	N	S	O			W	I	S	E
M	A	I	T	A	I			O	P	E	N
I	N	N	S			N	F	S			
					T	O	T	A	L		
A	C	E	S		A	R	E	N	A	S	
H	U	N	T	A	N	D	P	E	C	K	
A	B	O	A	R	D		S	W	A	Y	
	A	S	P	I	C						
		L	D	L		P	O	E	M		
J	I	B	E		I	C	E	A	X	E	
O	V	E	R		C	H	A	F	E	S	
E	Y	E	S		K	I	T	S	C	H	

Wordwheel

The nine-letter word is: PRESUMING

Wordsearch Workout

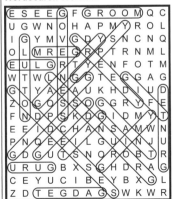

Double Fun Sudoku

Tasty Teaser

1	6	4	9	5	7	8	3	2
3	7	9	1	8	2	5	6	4
2	8	5	4	6	3	1	7	9
8	4	2	7	9	5	3	1	6
5	9	7	3	1	6	2	4	8
6	1	3	8	2	4	7	9	5
7	5	1	2	4	9	6	8	3
9	2	8	6	3	1	4	5	7
4	3	6	5	7	8	9	2	1

Brain Buster

8	7	5	9	2	1	3	6	4
1	6	4	8	3	7	2	5	9
3	9	2	4	6	5	1	8	7
7	3	6	1	5	9	4	2	8
5	2	1	3	8	4	9	7	6
9	4	8	6	7	2	5	3	1
4	8	7	5	9	3	6	1	2
6	5	9	2	1	8	7	4	3
2	1	3	7	4	6	8	9	5

Sum Circle

= → 15
9   81   +
x   11
17   −

Page 92

1 Minute Number Crunch

Beginner
189 − 37 = 152, 152 ÷ 2 = 76, 76 + 6 = 82, 82 ÷ 2 = 41, 41 + 22 = 63, 63 ÷ 9 x 2 = 14, 14 x 3 = 42

Intermediate
17^2 = 289, 289 x 2 = 578, 578 + 125 = 703, 703 x 3 = 2109, 2109 − 1617 = 492, 492 + 164 (492 ÷ 3) = 656, 656 − 497 = 159

Advanced
234 ÷ 13 x 10 = 180, 180 − 169 (square of 13) = 11, 11^2 = 121, 121 + 683 = 804, 804 ÷ 0.4 = 2010, 2010 ÷ 67 x 2 = 60, 60 ÷ 1.25 = 48

Spidoku

Page 93

---

142 Fun Puzzles

High-Speed Crossword

S	A	L	■	E	R	R	■	P	O	D
U	S	A	■	W	O	E	■	A	H	A
D	I	S	P	E	L	S	■	S	I	R
S	A	V	E	■	L	E	S	S	O	N
■	■	■	E	L	B	O	W	S	■	■
E	D	G	E	O	F	■	E	G	A	D
L	E	A	■	A	T	M	■	O	W	E
M	E	S	A	■	H	E	R	O	E	S
■	■	■	C	H	E	W	E	D	■	■
J	O	L	T	E	D	■	S	L	A	M
A	P	E	■	M	I	X	T	U	R	E
K	E	N	■	I	C	Y	■	C	I	A
E	N	D	■	N	E	Z	■	K	A	T

Codeword Conundrum

C	O	A	X	E	D	■	S	W	I	F	T	E	S	T
O	■	T	■	X	■	A	■	O	■	D	■	■	■	R
M	A	L	A	I	S	E	■	P	■	R	A	I	S	E
M	■	A	■	L	■	V	Y	I	N	G	■	F	■	N
A	U	S	T	E	R	E	■	T	■	I	L	I	A	C
N	■	■	O	■	E	N	S	I	G	N	■	C	■	H
D	E	G	R	E	E	■	Q	■	O	G	R	E	S	■
O	■	■	S	■	K	N	U	R	L	■	E	■	■	T
■	S	C	O	P	E	■	I	■	D	E	A	R	L	Y
A	■	U	■	E	D	I	B	L	E	■	N	■	■	■
L	A	S	E	R	■	N	■	A	N	E	M	O	N	E
K	■	H	■	J	E	L	L	Y	■	N	■	Z	■	C
A	D	I	E	U	■	A	■	S	A	R	C	O	M	A
L	■	O	■	R	■	N	■	■	O	■	N	■	■	S
I	N	N	U	E	N	D	O	■	F	L	U	E	N	T

Double Fun Sudoku

Tasty Teaser

1	9	7	8	4	2	5	3	6
8	4	3	6	5	9	2	1	7
2	5	6	7	1	3	8	4	9
3	6	5	9	8	1	4	7	2
4	2	9	3	7	5	6	8	1
7	8	1	4	2	6	3	9	5
9	7	4	2	6	8	1	5	3
6	1	8	5	3	7	9	2	4
5	3	2	1	9	4	7	6	8

Brain Buster

5	1	7	9	8	3	2	4	6
8	2	9	5	6	4	3	1	7
3	4	6	7	1	2	5	9	8
4	6	5	3	2	7	9	8	1
7	3	2	1	9	8	6	5	4
1	9	8	6	4	5	7	2	3
9	8	1	2	7	6	4	3	5
2	7	3	4	5	1	8	6	9
6	5	4	8	3	9	1	7	2

Spidoku

Page 93

High-Speed Crossword

S	C	A	M	P	I	■	E	R	M	A
P	O	P	A	R	T	■	G	O	O	N
Y	O	U	L	O	O	K	G	O	O	D
■	■	E	B	O	N	■	M	R	S	■
P	A	S	S	E	■	I	B	M	■	■
A	S	P	■	A	F	L	A	M	E	■
T	H	A	T	S	B	E	T	T	E	R
H	E	R	O	I	C	■	E	M	O	■
■	■	K	E	G	■	A	S	S	E	S
P	E	P	■	N	A	S	A	■	■	■
I	L	L	D	O	M	Y	B	E	S	T
B	L	U	E	■	P	E	E	W	E	E
B	A	G	S	■	S	T	R	E	A	M

Wordsearch Workout

(see grid)

Double Fun Sudoku

Tasty Teaser

4	1	8	6	2	3	9	7	5
6	9	7	5	1	4	8	2	3
2	5	3	7	8	9	6	4	1
7	3	9	8	6	2	5	1	4
1	4	6	3	5	7	2	8	9
8	2	5	9	4	1	3	6	7
3	8	2	1	7	5	4	9	6
5	6	1	4	9	8	7	3	2
9	7	4	2	3	6	1	5	8

Brain Buster

5	9	4	7	8	3	2	1	6
7	3	2	1	9	6	8	4	5
8	6	1	4	2	5	9	7	3
9	2	3	5	4	8	7	6	1
4	7	6	3	1	2	5	8	9
1	8	5	6	7	9	3	2	4
2	5	9	8	6	1	4	3	7
3	1	7	2	5	4	6	9	8
6	4	8	9	3	7	1	5	2

Matchstick Magic

The matchsticks which have been moved are outlined.

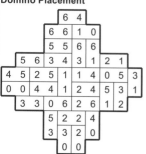

Brain Teaser

Black

Domino Placement

(see grid)

Page 94

Codeword Conundrum

W	A	T	E	R		S	Q	U	E	A	M	I	S	H
I		U		E		K		N		F				O
S	U	B	J	A	C	E	N	T		R	I	V	E	T
T		E		G		W		R		A		A		E
F	I	R	M	E	R		Z	O	D	I	A	C	A	L
U			N		I		U		D		U			
L	I	G	H	T		N	I	B	S		T	O	S	S
L		R		S		E		L		P		U		E
Y	O	Y	O		A	X	L	E		A	R	S	O	N
		P		E		O		D		G				T
E	P	H	E	M	E	R	A		W	A	P	I	T	I
T		O		B		A		T		N		N		M
H	E	N	N	A		B	A	R	R	I	C	A	D	E
I				L		L		O		S		P		N
C	R	E	A	M	I	E	S	T		M	O	T	E	T

Double Fun Sudoku

Tasty Teaser

2	7	6	9	8	4	1	3	5
1	8	4	5	6	3	9	2	7
9	5	3	1	2	7	8	6	4
5	2	7	8	3	6	4	9	1
3	1	8	2	4	9	7	5	6
6	4	9	7	1	5	3	8	2
7	3	1	6	9	2	5	4	8
8	9	2	4	5	1	6	7	3
4	6	5	3	7	8	2	1	9

Brain Buster

3	9	6	4	2	5	8	1	7
4	7	5	6	8	1	2	9	3
8	2	1	7	3	9	5	4	6
2	1	4	5	6	8	3	7	9
9	3	7	1	4	2	6	5	8
6	5	8	9	7	3	4	2	1
1	6	9	3	5	4	7	8	2
5	8	3	2	1	7	9	6	4
7	4	2	8	9	6	1	3	5

Pyramid Plus

A=76, B=66, C=103, D=144, E=92, F=142, G=169, H=247, I=236, J=311, K=416, L=483, M=727, N=899, O=1626.

High-Speed Crossword

M	I	N	I	S		H	A	T	C	H
I	N	A	N	E		A	T	E	A	M
S	T	R	A	W		R	E	A	L	M
S	O	C	C	E	R	B	A	L	L	
		A	D	I	O	S				
T	U	R	N		B	R	E	E	Z	E
E	R	A					L	I	D	
A	N	G	E	L	A		D	I	P	S
		M	A	Y	B	E				
H	O	C	K	E	Y	P	U	C	K	
M	E	L	E	E		T	A	L	O	N
O	R	D	E	R		E	R	N	I	E
D	R	E	S	S		S	T	A	L	E

1 Minute Number Crunch

Beginner
27 + 24 = 51, 51 ÷ 3 = 17, 17 + 9 = 26, 50% of 26 = 13, 13 − 4 = 9, 9 x 8 = 72, 72 − 23 = 49

Intermediate
69 x 2 = 138, 138 ÷ 3 x 2 = 92, 92 ÷ 4 = 23, 23 + 137 = 160, 160 ÷ 5 x 2 = 64, square root of 64 = 8, cube root of 8 = 2

Advanced
588 x 2 = 1176, 1176 ÷ 8 x 5 = 735, 735 ÷ 15 x 11 = 539, 539 x 2 = 1078, 1078 − 929 = 149, 149 x 7 = 1043, 1043 + 528 = 1571

Page 95

High-Speed Crossword

W	I	D	E		F	R	I	D	A	Y
I	T	E	M		D	E	N	O	T	E
R	O	B	B	E	R	B	A	R	O	N
E	N	T	E	R			J	A	N	S
			D	R	A	M	A			
A	C	T	S		T	O	M	A	T	O
B	O	O		P	A	W		L	A	W
C	O	P	C	A	R		M	I	N	E
			O	N	I	C	E			
E	D	A	M			A	D	I	E	U
R	U	B	B	E	R	B	A	N	D	S
O	N	B	A	S	E		L	I	N	E
S	K	A	T	E	D		S	T	A	R

1 Minute Number Crunch

Beginner
25 + 93 = 118, 118 ÷ 2 = 59, 59 + 7 = 66, 66 ÷ 11 x 2 = 12, 12 ÷ 3 = 4, 4 + 28 = 32, 32 x 4 = 128

Intermediate
452 ÷ 4 = 113, 113 + 169 = 282, 282 x 1.5 = 423, 423 ÷ 9 x 7 = 329, 329 x 2 = 658, 658 − 479 = 179, 179 x 3 = 537

Advanced
129 ÷ 3 x 2 = 86, 86 x 13 = 1118, 1118 x 2 = 2236, 2236 − 559 (25% of 2236) = 1677, 1677 − 949 = 728, 728 ÷ 14 x 5 = 260, 260 − 104 (260 ÷ 5 x 2) = 156

Wordsearch Workout

Double Fun Sudoku

Tasty Teaser

7	6	8	3	5	1	4	9	2
4	9	3	7	6	2	1	5	8
2	5	1	4	9	8	7	6	3
8	3	4	5	1	9	2	7	6
5	7	9	2	3	6	8	1	4
1	2	6	8	4	7	5	3	9
6	1	2	9	8	5	3	4	7
3	8	5	6	7	4	9	2	1
9	4	7	1	2	3	6	8	5

Brain Buster

5	6	7	2	4	1	8	3	9
1	2	3	6	8	9	4	5	7
8	9	4	3	5	7	2	1	6
3	4	9	8	7	5	6	2	1
6	8	1	4	2	3	7	9	5
2	7	5	9	1	6	3	4	8
7	3	6	1	9	4	5	8	2
4	1	2	5	6	8	9	7	3
9	5	8	7	3	2	1	6	4

Whatever Next?

H − Assign a number to each letter according to its place in the alphabet, then multiply the numbers in opposite points to give the central number.

Brain Teaser

B 27 − Starting top left, the letters progress through the alphabet, omitting two letters each time. The numbers represent the sum of the positions in the alphabet of the missing letters. When the end of the alphabet is reached return to A as if the letters were written in a circle.

Page 96

Mind Over Matter

The value of the letter in the top right is deducted from that in the top left, and the value of the letter in the bottom right is deducted from that in the bottom left, then the result of the bottom sum is taken from that of the top to give the value in the central square. Thus the missing value is 4, so the missing letter is D.

Double Fun Sudoku
Tasty Teaser

4	9	6	7	2	3	1	8	5
2	7	1	5	8	4	9	6	3
8	3	5	9	6	1	4	2	7
7	1	8	3	4	5	2	9	6
5	6	4	2	9	8	3	7	1
3	2	9	6	1	7	5	4	8
6	4	3	1	7	9	8	5	2
9	5	2	8	3	6	7	1	4
1	8	7	4	5	2	6	3	9

Brain Buster

4	8	3	1	9	2	7	6	5
5	2	6	8	7	3	4	9	1
7	9	1	4	5	6	3	8	2
6	5	4	9	2	7	1	3	8
9	3	7	5	8	1	6	2	4
2	1	8	3	6	4	9	5	7
1	6	2	7	3	8	5	4	9
3	4	9	2	1	5	8	7	6
8	7	5	6	4	9	2	1	3

Codeword Conundrum

D	R	A	G	O	N	F	L	Y		L	O	O	S	E
I		M		U		R		E		A		L		P
A	B	B	O	T		A	W	A	R	D	E	D		I
L		I		L		I		R		Y		E		C
S	I	G	N	A	L	L	Y		F	L	A	N	G	E
		U		W			M		I					N
H	O	O	K		S	Q	U	E	A	K	I	E	S	T
E		U		J		U		N		E		X		R
A	B	S	T	E	M	I	O	U	S		A	P	S	E
D				T		Z			F		E			
B	E	R	A	T	E		A	T	T	O	R	N	E	Y
O		O		I		L		H		E		S		O
A	C	A	S	C	A	D	E		T	H	I	N	K	
R		K		O		S		T		U		V		E
D	O	Y	E	N		T	R	A	N	S	C	E	N	D

High-Speed Crossword

M	I	S	S	M		M	E	T	A	L
U	N	I	T	E		E	L	O	P	E
F	O	R	E	S		R	A	I	S	E
F	R	E	E	S	A	M	P	L	E	
			L	I	S	A	S			
E	B	A	Y		S	I	E	S	T	A
L	O	L		B	I	D		K	E	G
S	P	A	C	E	S		C	I	A	O
			R	E	T	R	O			
	R	E	A	L	S	I	M	P	L	E
M	U	L	T	I		S	P	E	A	K
O	L	S	E	N		E	E	R	I	E
D	E	E	R	E		S	L	U	R	S

1 Minute Number Crunch

Beginner

96 − 19 = 77, 77 ÷ 7 = 11, 11^2 = 121, 121 + 14 = 135, 135 ÷ 5 = 27, 27 ÷ 9 = 3, 3 x 16 = 48

Intermediate

17 + 18 = 35, 35 ÷ 7 x 3 = 15, 300% of 15 = 45, 45 ÷ 9 x 5 = 25, 25 x 13 = 325, 120% of 325 = 390, 390 − 39 (10% of 390) = 351

Advanced

387 ÷ 9 x 5 = 215, 215 ÷ 5 x 4 = 172, 172 − 129 (172 ÷ 4 x 3) = 43, 43 x 8 = 344, 344 + 301 (344 ÷ 8 x 7) = 645, 645 ÷ 5 x 3 = 387, 387 ÷ 9 x 7 = 301

ARCTURUS

© 2013 by Arcturus Publishing Limited
Puzzles copyright © 2013 Puzzle Press Ltd

This 2013 edition is published for Barnes & Noble, Inc. by Arcturus Publishing Limited.

ISBN 978-1-4351-4978-6

Manufactured in Malaysia

2 4 6 8 10 9 7 5 3 1